SISTERS AND BROTHERS SING!

Second Edition

edited by

Sharon and Tom Neufer Emswiler

with much help from

Nancy Chinuge Carroll, design editor and artist

Linda Muhleman, music advisor

J. Sheppard Crumrine, guitar advisor

Cheryl Munn, photographer

The Daily Pantagraph—photographs
Bloomington, Illinois

Vicki Cheek, artist

Gerald Myrow, notographer

Anne Paxton, typist

and many other friends

published by

The Wesley Foundation Campus Ministry
211 N. School Street
Normal, Illinois 61761

Price: $3.50 plus 50¢ postage and handling.
10 copies for $25 plus $2.00 postage and handling.

TABLE OF CONTENTS

Note: We hope you will make up other indexes for your own use. The Table of Contents
is a topical index of songs. You may want to expand this to include all parts of th
Church year and other topics useful to you.
All songs in this hymnal which are copyrighted may not be reproduced again with
permission from the copyright holder. If you wish to reproduce any of these son
write to us and we will be glad to send you the addresses of the copyright holders
Enclose a self-addressed, stamped envelope.

INTRODUCTION

We believe that the songs we sing help to shape our thinking about life. It is therefore imperative that these songs actually reflect what we affirm as the truth about life. The music in this hymnal consciously recognizes the *whole* people of God—sisters and brothers together. It also refuses to allow us to box God into narrow sexual identifications. Instead we are challenged to expand our consciousness of who God is and how we are called to relate and respond to God. Thus, the songs chosen to appear in this hymnal all use *inclusive* language when speaking of people, (sons and daughters, persons, folk, sisters and brothers, etc.) instead of the all too common masculine terms "men," "brothers," etc. We have also chosen songs which generally refer to God, Christ, and the Holy Spirit in non-sexual ways. In the few cases where sexual references to God have been allowed, we have kept them in careful balance. To allow God to be over-identified with either male or female ways of speaking is to limit our concept of who God is and how we can relate to this God.

It is our hope that you will truly make this hymnal your own by adding songs to it that are meaningful to your own Christian community. We have three-hole punched it for that very reason. Our hope is that you will get some kind of loose-leaf binder in which to put your hymnal. You can then add new songs and worship resources to the back either by categories as the present hymnal is organized or by any other system you wish. Costs of such binders are expensive. However, if you purchase a quantity of them, you should be able to get a substantially cheaper price. If you have trouble finding a source for your binders, write us and we'll give you our most current information. We believe that the loose-leaf style reflects an emerging insight in liberation theology which recognizes the need for each person and each faith community to develop their own unique, ever changing expressions of faith.

This hymnal is a reality through the good graces of a great many persons. Some of their names appear on the title page. Others appear as credits at various places in the book. Still others are not specifically named though their ideas and spirit have helped add quality to our efforts. Several of the contributors gave us special reprint rates or allowed us to reproduce their music free. Without these generous gifts it would have been impossible for us to make this size of book available to you as inexpensively as we have. Others have helped by doing music copying, art work, and by giving constructive suggestions and encouragement. We have also received great cooperation and many invaluable suggestions from Bill LaBounty of Illinois State University Printing Services and Kent Deffenbaugh of Illinois Graphics. To all who helped on this project we say thanks.

This is the second edition of our hymnal. It is greatly expanded and changed. It has been a joy to see how enthusiastically our first edition sold out. We learned much from it which we have tried to incorporate into this edition. We still have much to learn. We hope you'll help us in this process by filling out the feedback sheet we've enclosed in this book and returning it to us.

We hope that you find this hymnal an exciting beginning point for a whole panorama of creative worship.

Sharon and Tom Neufer Emswiler
Co-editors

ADDING MUSIC AND RESOURCES TO YOUR HYMNAL ♪

This hymnal is organized according to specific categories. Admittedly no categorization is totally satisfactory. Many hymns and other worship resources overlap and should go several places. We have tried to remedy this problem somewhat through our indexes. We believe that the categories into which the hymns are divided are helpful in giving a basic outline of the hymnal. We also believe they can be valuable when it comes to adding new music and other resources. You may want to continue these categories as you add new material to your hymnal. One major source of new non-sexist music is our own hymnal supplement described on page iii of this book. It will come out annually and provide a beginning of fresh new worship resources.

There are two basic sources for additional music for your hymnal. One is already published music in other books or in sheet music form. The second is new original compositions not yet published which have perhaps come from persons in your own community.

You must receive permission to reprint any music already published and under copyright or even unpublished works that are copyrighted. This is true even if you are only going to be using this music with your own congregation. Publishers have a wide variety of policies concerning permission for reprinting. We have found most to be quite cooperative, allowing reprinting at reasonable rates, 2¢ per copy or less. When writing for permission to reprint a song, we suggest that you enclose a self-addressed stamped envelope for the copyright holder's convenience in replying.

If you want to print music that has not been copyrighted, you should encourage the individual to copyright that music.* You should then list that copyright notation along with the words "reprinted by permission" on your master copy for reprints.

The same procedure is required to reprint other worship resources. However, you may not want to go to all the trouble of copyrighting new materials especially if you want such resources to be shared freely with other congregations.

If you want to encourage creativity within your local community of faith, we suggest that you consider having a workshop with your local group where interested persons can discuss issues such as the importance of non-sexist language in worship, methods of creativity, etc. Out of such a workshop, various creative expressions may well grow.

---

*A copyright notation can be listed even before the music has been registered with the copyright office. Such a notation records the intention of the copyright owner to record the copyright as soon as possible. Form "E" should be used for registering copyrights on individual pieces of music. These forms can be obtained from the Registrar of Copyrights, Library of Congress, Washington, D.C. 20559. There is a small fee involved for each copyright registration.

HYMNAL SUPPLEMENTS

Creativity is not something that freezes with a printer's ink. It is an on-going process that is never completed. One of the ways to plug into this continuous stream of creativity is by subscribing to our annual <u>Sisters and Brothers</u>, <u>Sing</u>! <u>Hymnal Supplement</u>. Scheduled to come out each September, this booklet will contain at least twelve new non-sexist hymns plus other new worship resources. It comes in both a quantity and an individual price and you can buy permission to reprint only those songs you want from it for your own congregation. This supplement replaces our Add-A-Hymn program which we had in our first edition. We found that sending hymns several times a year increased our costs considerably and we had to pass this on to you. Also, the supplement will be bound and three-hole punched so that it will fit conveniently with your hymnal, second edition, in a loose-leaf binder, or it can be used separately. If either you or someone you know writes music and would like to submit some of it for consideration for our supplements, simply send it to us along with a self-addressed stamped envelope. We are always delighted to receive new material as this helps to expand the circle of creativity of which this hymnal is a part.

PLEASE SEND ME _____ copies of the hymnal supplement at $2.50 per copy including postage and handling or $2.00 per copy when ten or more copies are ordered at once.

_____ I want the reprint license which allows me to reprint songs from the supplement for use with my own congregation. Cost, $20 per supplement.

I am enclosing a check made out to The Wesley Foundation for _____

_____ Please bill me (We must add a 25¢ charge for billing)

NAME_____ Phone_____

ADDRESS_____

Send to: The Wesley Foundation, 211 N. School St., Normal, Illinois 61761

FEEDBACK SHEET

Because the experience of putting together a hymnal is an on-going process (see our Hymnal Supplements article on the other side of this page), we value your comments about our hymnal. We want to know your reactions to the general design of our hymnal and to the specific songs and other worship resources we have included. We ask that you spend a few minutes filling out this feedback sheet and that you then send it to us. In this way future editions of the hymnal and our supplements can benefit from your suggestions.

1. How do you like our overall design for the hymnal?
   It's size? ____just right, ____too small, ____too big
   The art work? ____just right, ____not enough, ____too much
   Do you have some favorites in the art work of the hymnal?
       (Please describe and put page number)

   Do you see some places where you feel the art work is not good?
       (Please describe and put page number)

   The other worship resources? Are these typed and positioned in the most usable way or do you have suggestions for improvement here?

   The arrangement of the music into sections? Is this helpful or confusing? Do you have alternative suggestions?

   The indexes? Are they sufficient? Would you suggest others?

2. How do you rate the music in the hymnal?
   The overall quality of the music is ____excellent, ____good ____poor.
   Are there particular songs which you have found especially useful?
   (Please list them by page number and title if more than one song appears on a page)

   Are there particular songs which you feel should be left out of subsequent editions of the hymnal? (Please list them by page number and title if more than one song appears on a page)

3. How do you rate the Other Worship Resources in the hymnal?
   The overall quality of these resources is ____excellent, ____good, ____poor.
   Are there any resources you feel are especially poor? (Please list by number)

   Are there any resources you feel are especially good? (Please list by number)

4. Other comments about the hymnal you would like to make:

PRAISE AND PRAYER

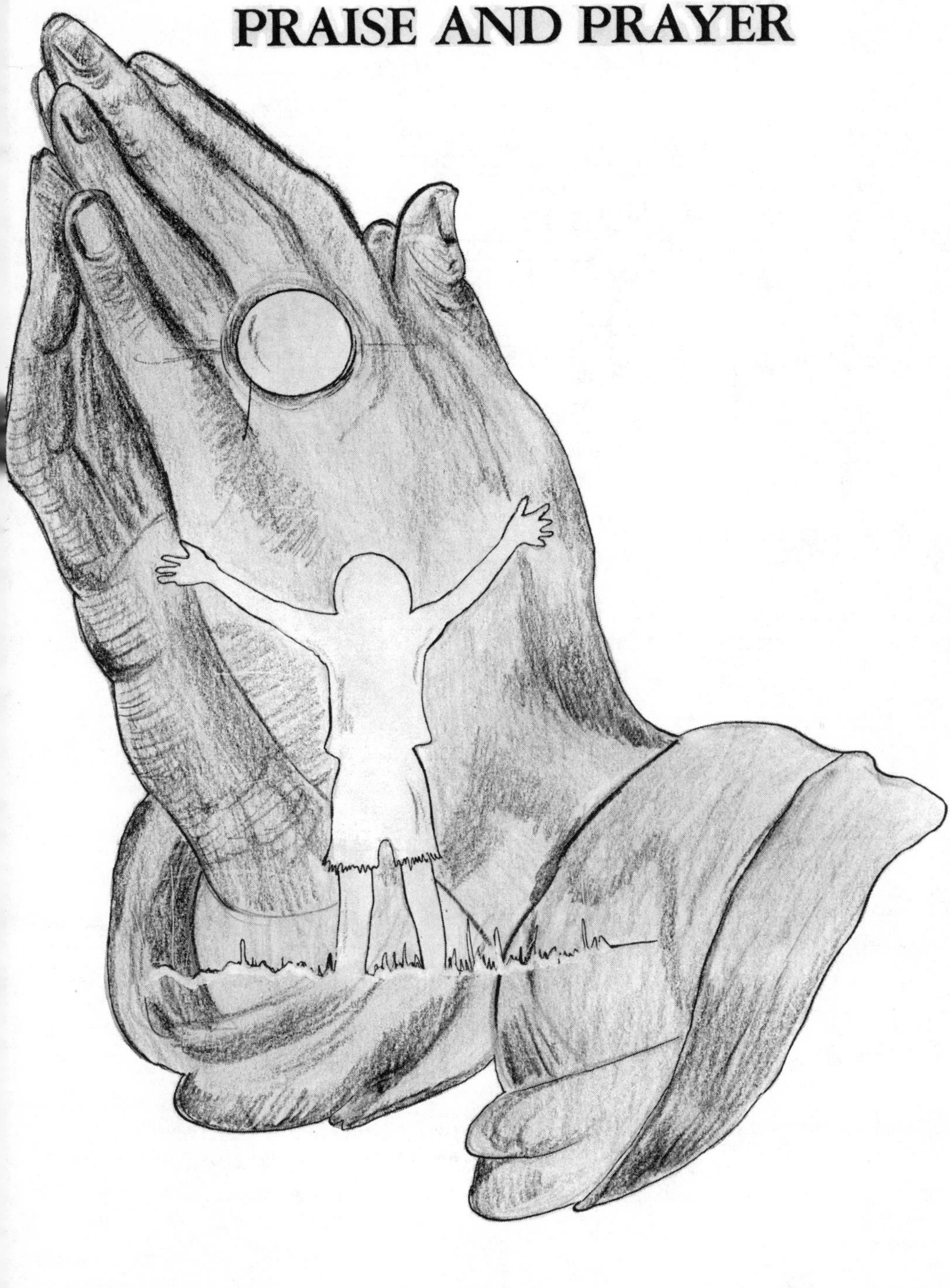

All God's Children

Words and Music by RUTH DUCK

(VERSE)
1. Let us en-ter God's tem - ple; Let us of-fer God's prais - es!

In each coun-try and lang - uage one great sound the world rais - es!

(CHORUS) And it's too late, too late, to leave out the hopes_ of_ an-y land, and it

can't wait, can't wait, We're all God's chil-dren in the

hea-ven-ly band, yes, we're all God's chil-dren in the hea-ven-ly band. _____

2. See the children come running,
    Hearts and eyes full of laughter.
    Slow but sure in their coming,
    Folk with canes follow after,
    And it's too late, too late,
    To leave out the young or ignore the old,
    And it can't wait, can't wait,
    We're all God's children with a heavenly goal.
    (Repeat last line)

3. I will enter with singing.
    My guitar softly playing,
    I will sing of God's goodness,
    While the people are praying,
    And it's too late, too late,
    To keep your senses and lose your soul.
    And it can't wait, can't wait,
    We're all God's children and we want to be whole.
    (Repeat last line)

4. See! the Spirit is moving,
    Speaking through your young women,
    Dreaming dreams in your old men,
    Teaching peace through your children,
    And it's too late, too late,
    To leave out the gifts of woman or man,
    And it can't wait, can't wait,
    We're all God's children in the heavenly plan.
    (Repeat last line)

5. Look inside – see the faces,
    Lined with life and with longing,
    Poor and rich, calm and troubled,
    Seeking hope and belonging.
    And it's too late, too late,
    To wait for heaven on a faraway shore.
    And it can't wait, can't wait,
    We're all God's children forevermore.
    (Repeat last line twice)

The Daily Pantagraph

HEARTS FULL OF LAUGHTER

O Happy Day

Words by Philip Doddridge
Tune by Edward F. Rimbault
Musical Setting by John F. Wilson

Let's Sing and Dance

Words and Music by
Tom Neufer Emswiler

WITH SPIRIT

1. We give thanks to God for the great gifts of love and
2. When we're tired and drained and feel-ing low, God's love still

care and hope. ___ Where-ev-er we go, what-ev-er we
comes to us. ___ Where-ev-er we go, what-ev-er we

do, God's gifts can help us cope. ___ (CHORUS) So let's sing ___ and
do, this is a love we trust. ___

dance, al-le-lu-ia! ___ Let us sing ___ and

dance, ___ al-le lu-ia.
3. Sun-shine warms our souls and
4. In a hu-man touch, a

stars beam bright, the world sings out its praise. ___ Where-
hand held out, we sense that God is here. ___ Where-

ev-er we go, what-ev-er we do, God's love can fill our
ev-er we go, what-ev-er we do, God's love can come so

days. ___ So let's sing ___ and dance al-le-lu-ia! ___ Let us
clear. ___

sing ___ and dance, ___ al-le-lu-ia. ___

5

God's Golden Sunshine
Words and Music by CAROLYN McDADE
(VERSE)
C
1. I've got God's gold-en sun-shine a- shin-ing in my win-dow, I've got
warm sum-mer breez-es a- blow-ing in my win-dow; I've got
G7 C
God's gold-en sun-shine in my soul. —— I've got God's gold-en
warm sum-mer breez-es in my soul. —— I've got warm sum-mer
C AMI
sun-shine a- shin-ing in my win-dow, God's gold-en sun-shine is
breez-es a- blow-ing in my win-dow; Warm sum-mer breez-es are
F G7 C (CHORUS) 𝄋 G7 F C
shin-ing in my soul. —— Sing-ing Hal-le- lu - Hal-le- lu-jah,
blow-ing in my soul. ——
F G7 C G7 F C
Hal-le- lu- jah. —— Sing-ing Hal-le- lu - Hal-le-lu-jah,
F G7 1. C 2. C (VERSE) C
Hal-le- lu - jah. —— 2. I've got jah. —— 3. I've got the love of
C
free-dom, of free-dom in my spir-it, I've got the love of free-dom in my
G7 C
soul. —— I've got the love of free-dom, of free- dom in my
C AMI F G7 C (D.S. AL CODA)
spir-it, I've got the love of free-dom in my soul. —— Sing-ing
© 1972 Carolyn McDade, used by permission. From Sing a Womansong, available from: The Ecumenical Women's Centers, 1653 W. School St., Chicago, Illinois 60657

God's Golden Sunshine

CODA
VERSE
C
jah. 4. Gon- na stand and sing life's prais-es, life's
C
prais-es in my spir-it; Gon-na stand and sing life's prais-es in my
G7 C
soul. Gon-na stand and sing life's prais-es, life's prais-es in my
C AMI F G7 C CHORUS
spir-it; Gon-na stand and sing life's prais-es in my soul. Sing-ing
G7 F C F G7 C
Hal-le-lu- Hal-le-lu-jah, Hal-le-lu-jah,
C G7 F C F
Sing-ing Hal-le-lu- Hal-le-lu-jah, Hal-le-
G7 C FINE LAST TIME VERSE C
lu- jah. 5. I've got a long-ing for peace, for
C
peace in my spir-it. Got a long-ing for peace in my
G7 C
soul. I've got a long-ing for peace, for peace in my spir-it,
AMI F G7 C
Got a long-ing for peace in my soul. Sing-ing

8

Rise Up, O People of God

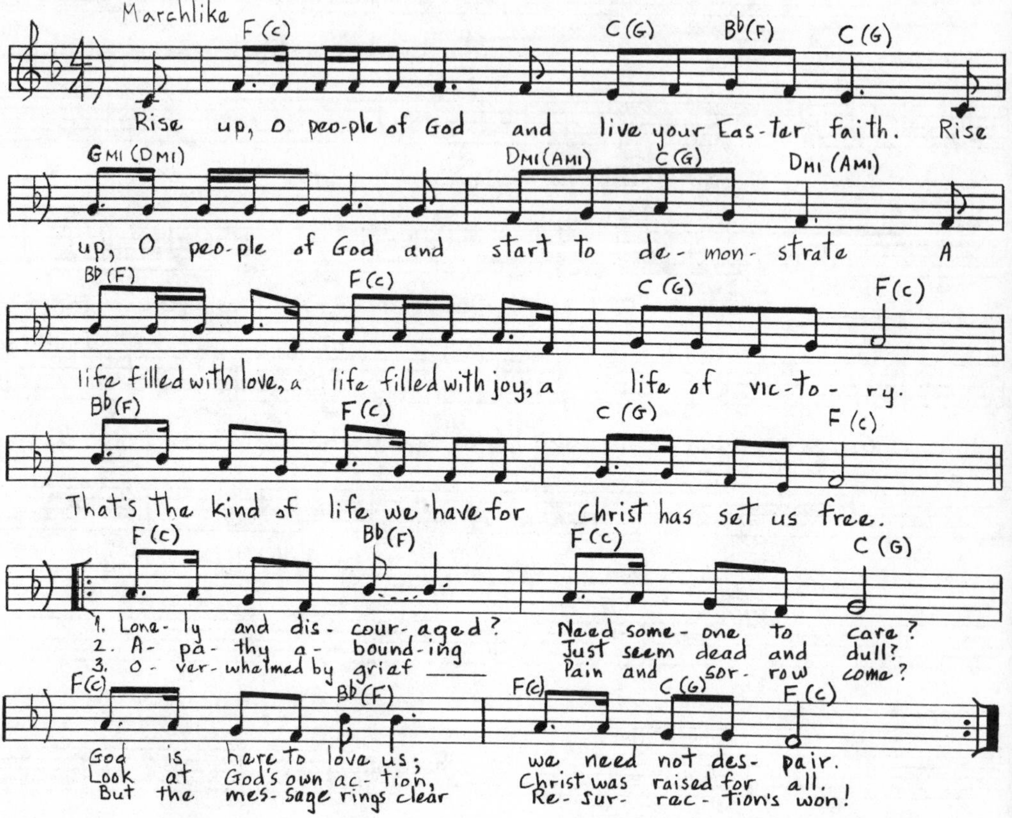

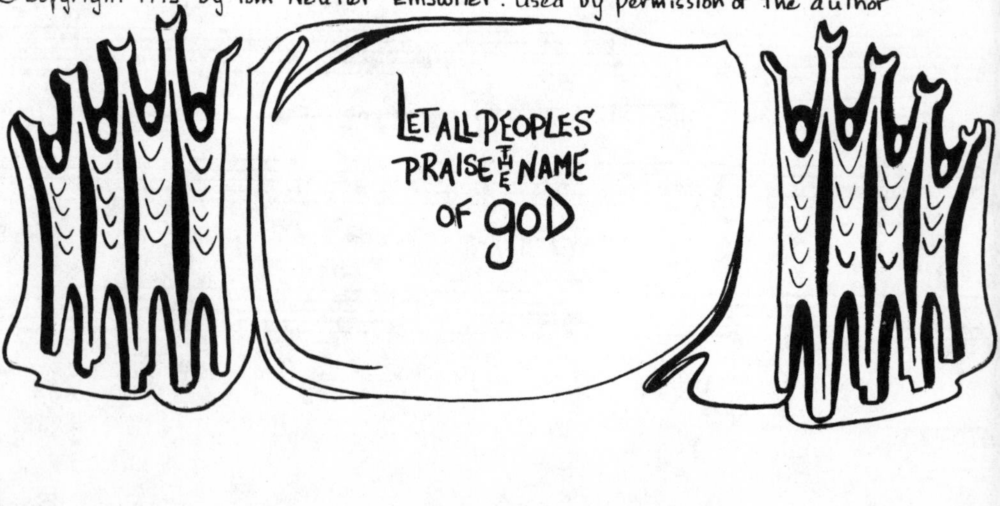

Acts 3:6
Source Unknown

Sil - ver and gold have I none, But such as I have give I thee. In the name of Je - sus Christ Of Naz - ar - eth, rise up and walk. Walk - ing and leap - ing and prais - ing God, Walk - ing and leap - ing and prais - ing God - in the name of Je - sus Christ of Naz - ar - eth, rise up and walk!

to be is to do

Glory, Glory
Traditional

Glo - ry glo - ry, _____ Hal - le - lu - jah. _____ Since I
No more sad - ness, _____ No more sor - row _____ Since I
I feel bet - ter, _____ So much bet - ter _____ Since I

laid _____ my bur - dens down. Glo - ry, glo - ry, ___ Hal - le-
laid _____ my bur - dens down. There's a bright - er _____ day to-
laid _____ my bur - dens down. There's a bright - er _____ day to-

lu - jah, since I laid _____ my bur - dens down. _____
mor - row since I laid _____ my bur - dens down. _____
mor - row since I laid _____ my bur - dens down. _____

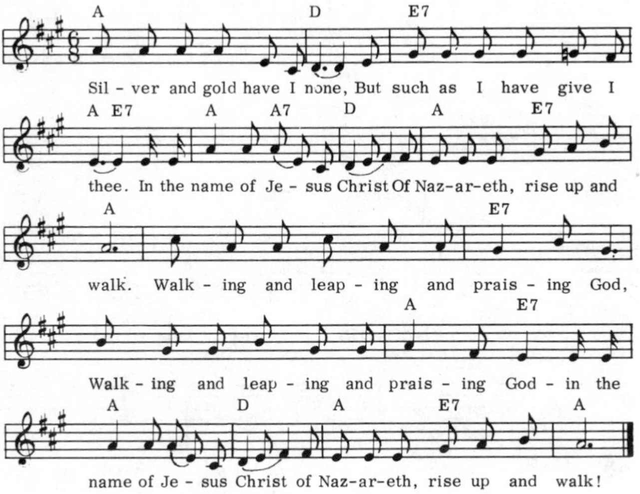

Three Cheers

Words and Music by ART ALLEN

All praise to our God who has giv-en us life. O-pen your heart and re-joice! For all of our bless-ings we give God the praise: so sing al-le-lu-ia to-day. Stand on the moun-tain and tell all the world: "Three cheers for God's lov-ing way!" Go spread the news as you walk day by day: soon the whole world will know. The love God has shown us is more than we hope for it fills us with love, peace and joy. And though we may stum-ble God quick-ly for-gives. The love of God nev-er dies.

Three Cheers

ENTHUSIASM IS
ONE OF THE MOST IMPORTANT FACTORS

No load too heav-y,— no road too wind-ing, no riv-er too deep to cross: __ God shares our bur-dens and shares our joys. Praise God __ ev-er- more! __ Stand on __ the moun-tain and tell all __ the world: "Three cheers for God's lov-ing way!" __ Go spread the news as you walk day by day: soon the whole world will sing: __ "All praise to __ our God who __ has giv-en __ us life. O-pen your heart and re-joice! __ For all of our bless-ings __ we give God the praise: so sing al-le-lu-ia to- day. __ All day. __ So sing al-le-lu-ia to-day."

TOWARD MAKING A PERSON CREATIVE

12

We Are Gathered

Words and Music by Dorie Ellzey

(TO BE SUNG RESPECTFULLY SLOW)

We are ga-thered here to-ge-ther, (1) in the pre-sence of the spir-it, the
(2) with our dus-ty feet and bo-dies, we're
(3) we are stran-gers in a strange land,
(4) just to cel-a-brate the un-ion, the

spir-it that keeps break-ing in our lives.____ Well, we don't have all the
tired and sore and rest-less and we don't know how we feel.___ Well, we wash each oth-ers
no-mads in the de-sert, we are ex-iles meant to roam.___ We have left the past be-
Com-ing to-ge-ther of our souls in time and space.___ Well, we know God's reign is

an-swers but we sure do have the ques-tions; we know that to cre-ate is to sur-
san-dals and a-noint our heads with wa-ter, and some-where in the pain there is a
hind us and the ones who called us "chil-dren" we're search-in' out a new fron-tier, A
Com-in' and we know it don't come ea-sy; but still we trust our vi-sion of the

vive.
space that starts to heal.___ We're trav-'lin' ___ on a road we've nev-er seen be-fore.___
place to call our home.___
smile on fu-ture's face.___

And oh, it's ___ hard to know which ___ way to go, _____ but

some-where there's a prom-ise 'bout some ___ dis-tant shore that

those who seek _____ will some-day know. ___

(FINE ENDING)

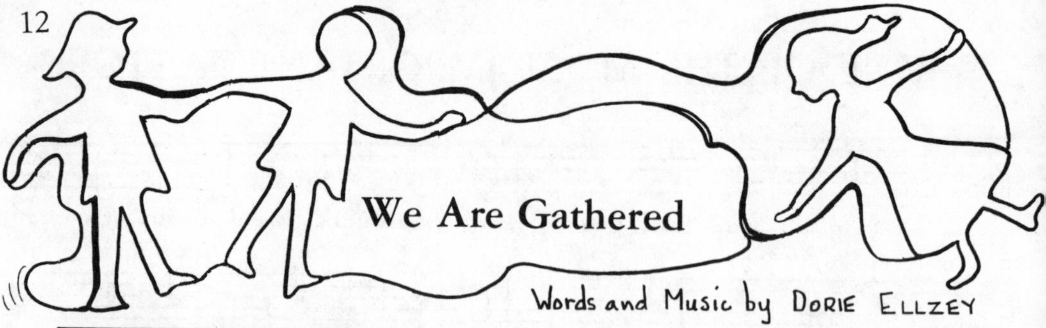

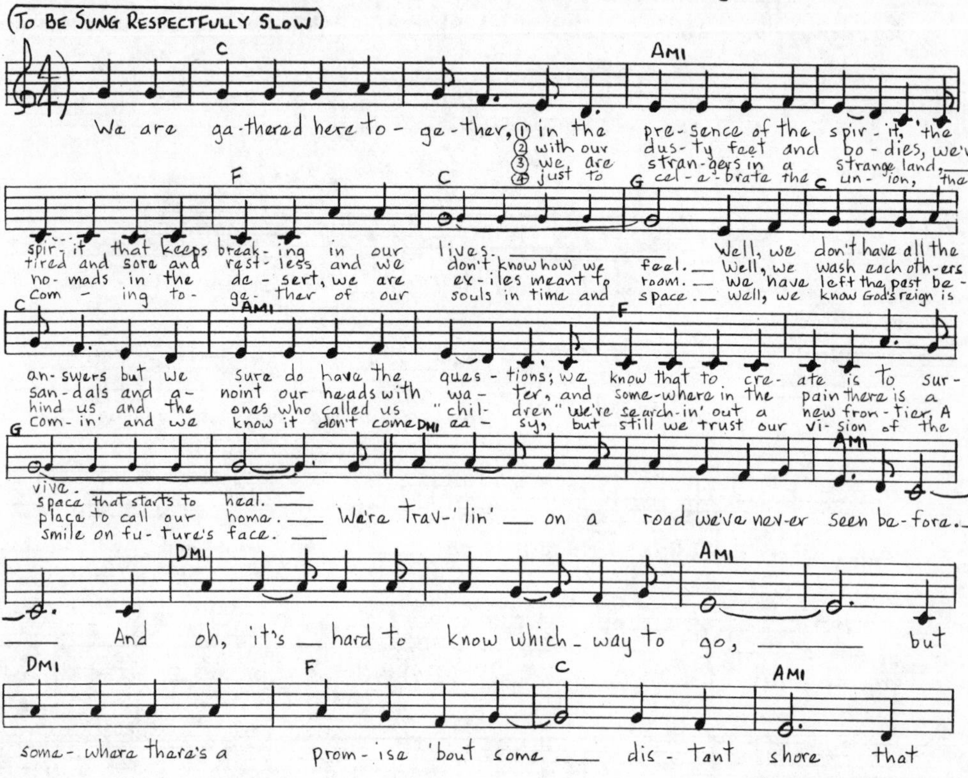

Male and Female

Dedicated to Barbara and Jim Tilton

Donald Marsh
Richard Avery

FEMALE
In God's image
MALE

Bb   **Ab**   **Bb**

Male and fe-male, God cre--a--ted: Man and wo---man,
Male and fe-male, so God made us, Free to choose our
Male and fe-male, God cre--a--ted, Then God said, "Ah,
Male and fe-male, in God's i-mage: Ho---ly my--st'ry!

F7   **Ebma7**   **Dm**

by God's love. Boy and girl, Girl and boy...
work and way. Boy and girl, Girl and boy...
yes, that's good!" Boy and girl, Girl and boy...
Won-drous joy! Boy and girl, Girl and boy...

Cm7   **Dm7**

Sin--gle or to--ge--ther, E---qual and shar-ing,
Bear-ing all the work and Shar--ing the glo--ry.
Diff'-rent but u--nit--ed, Prais-ing each o--ther,
Ten--ors and so--pra-nos, Al--tos and bass--es,

Ebma7   **F7**

Bold-ly de--clar-ing, This is who we are:
This is our sto--ry, This is who we are:
Sis-ter and bro-ther, This is who we are:
Na-tions and ra--ces, This is who we are:

Bb   **F**

WE ARE ALL THE CHILD-REN OF GOD! HAL-LE-LU-JAH!

Eb   **F**   **F7**   **Bb**

FREE TO BE LOVED AND E-QUAL, WE ARE ALL THE CHILD-REN OF

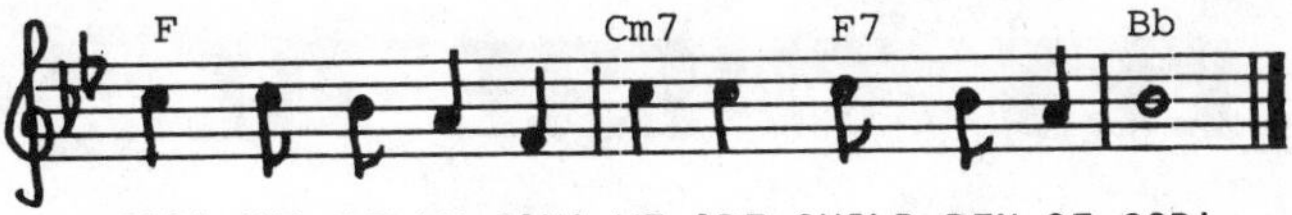
F   **Cm7**   **F7**   **Bb**

GOD! HAL-LE-LU-JAH! WE ARE CHILD-REN OF GOD!

Thank God

Deuteronomy 32:18

Words and Music by ART ALLEN

Thank God,_____ God is mar-ve-lous. Thank God,_____ who gave us birth. Thank God,_____ we are the chil-dren of God. Sing God's* praise for all you're worth!

1. From the dawn-ing of cre — a-tion, to the hope which lies a — head. We can see the love of God — pra-vail from be-gin-ning to the — end.

2. Thanks to God for cleans-ing — wa-ter, for the cup and bread of — life; for the liv-ing word that sets — us — free for this faith com-mun-i — ty.

3. Raise your voice in cel-e — bra-tion, beat the drums to lead the — way. Strum gui-tars to make a joy — ful — noise, as we sing God's praise to-day.

* If you feel awkward singing nouns all the time, substitute "her" at this point in the chorus. (We do not usually credit a "he" with giving birth.)

© Copyright 1975 by Art Allen. Used by permission.

LET THERE BE JOY!

Faith is saying YES to God

Yes I Am!

Words and Music by
KEN MEDEMA

*1. Gonna do a lit-tle sing-ing,_____ yes I am!

Gonna do a lit-tle sing-ing,_____ yes I am!

_____ Gonna do a lit-tle sing-ing,_____ yes I am!

_____ Yes I am, yes I am, yes I am!_____

37710
*2. Gonna do a little praying
 3. Gonna sing about Jesus

Amen

16

SURPRISED BY JOY

Amazing Grace

JOHN NEWTON, 1725-1807   American melody from Carrell and Clayton
"Virginia Harmony" 1831

1. A-maz-ing grace! How sweet the sound, That saved a wretch like me! I once was lost, but now I am found, Was blind, but now I see.

2. 'Twas grace that taught my heart to fear, And grace my fears re-lieved; How pre-cious did that grace ap-pear The hour I first be-lieved.

3. Thro' many dangers, toils, and snares,
   I have already come;
   'Tis grace hath bro't me safe thus far,
   And grace will lead me home.

4. When we've been there ten thousand years,
   Bright shining as the sun,
   We've no less days to sing God's praise
   Than when we'd first begun.

Child of Earth and Sky

Richard Avery
Donald Marsh

In honor of a person and a place:
Jim Hall and Ghost Ranch, Abiquiu, New Mexico
(and the United Presbyterian Conference Center
he directs)

I, a child of the earth,   From the dust I had my
I, a child of the sky,   Born with Spi-rit-wings to
God of earth, God of sky,   O Great Spi-rit, who am

birth,   In earth's beau-ty grew to stand, Walk in
fly,   Winds and vis-ions make me strong, Sun and
I?   Who am I that I should know All this

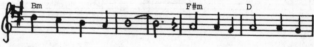

peace up---on the land.   And when I die in the
moon both hear my song.   And when I die may my
glo---ry where I go?   Here till I die, till my

ground my heart will lie.   I love the
Spi---rit rise up high.   I love the
days and nights pass by,   I lift my

Soar with the Spirit

```
C#m          D  C#m
```

earth like the jump-ing deer,   Like the
sky   like the soar-ing dove,   Like a
praise for the world I love,   Of---fer

```
Bm7.                    E
```

pine tree on the hill, Like the bi--son on the
storm cloud in the wind, Like an ea--gle fly-ing
mu------sic of my heart, Care for ev-'ry-thing I

```
E           F#m
```

plain And my feet dance with the splash-ing rain.
far   And my heart sings with the morn--ing star.
see: Ho--ly mount--ain, ea----gle, deer and tree.

```
F#m   B        F#m         B
```

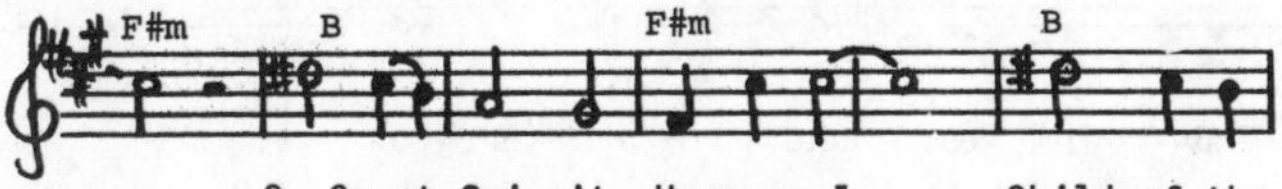

O Great Spi-rit, Here am I,   Child of the

```
B        F#m
```

Coda after
3rd stanza:

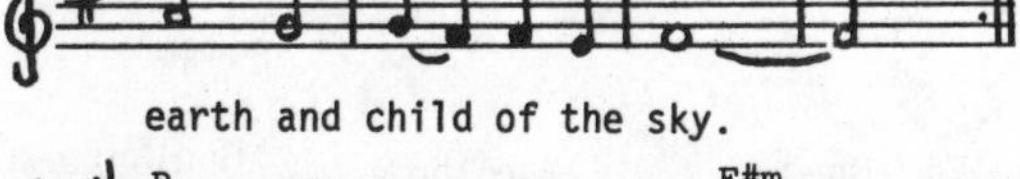

earth and child of the sky.

```
B              F#m
```

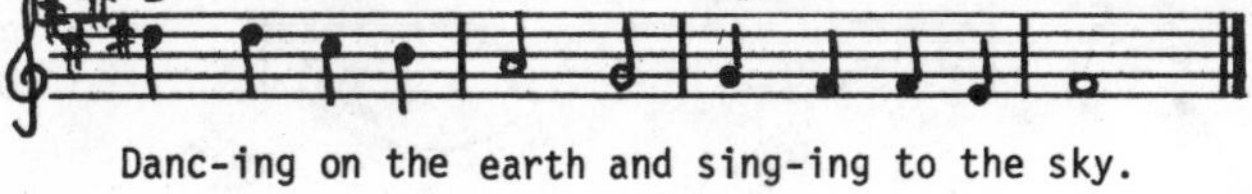

Danc-ing on the earth and sing-ing to the sky.

You Fill the Day

Capo 3(C)

Joe Wise, Arr. Saul Striks

REFRAIN

You fill the day with your glo-ry and your pow-er.

You fill the night with your qui-et and your deep love.

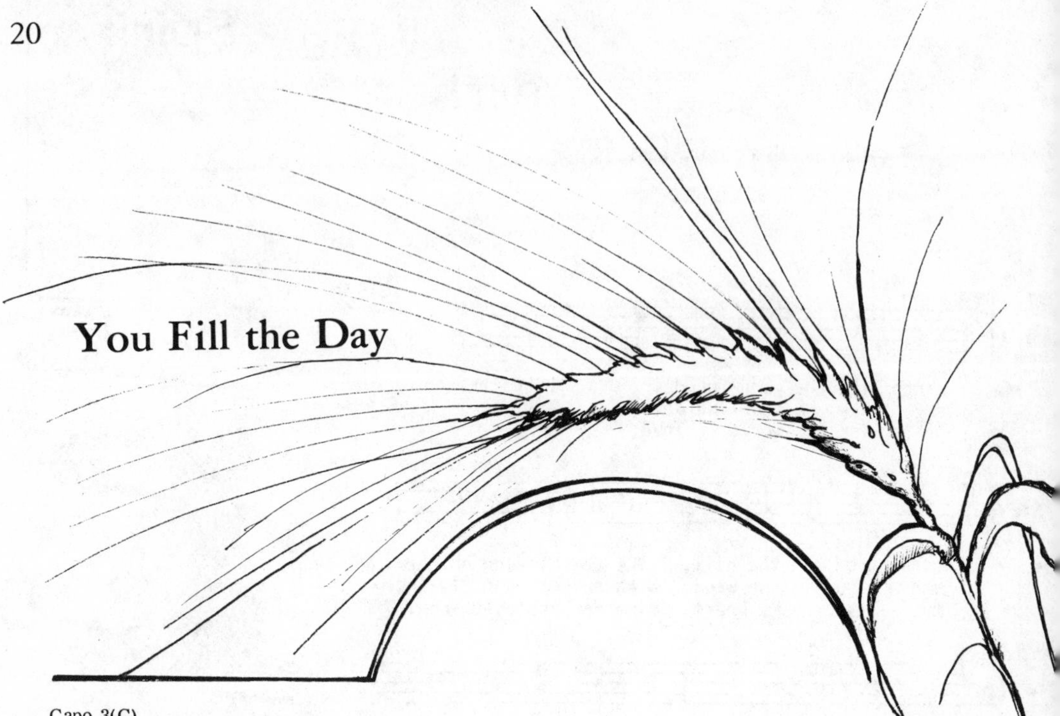

VERSES

1. Run with your head up in the wind, run with your head up in the
2. Stand with your face up in the sun, stand with your face up in the
3. Lay with your face up in the rain, lay with your face up in the
4. Walk hand in hand with one you love, walk hand in hand with one you

1. wind, the wind: Your ___ head held high, your ___ soul an o-pen door, And
2. sun, the sun: Your ___ head held high, your ___ soul an o-pen door, And
3. rain, the rain: Your ___ head held high, your ___ soul an o-pen door, And
4. love, you love: Your ___ head held high, your ___ soul an o-pen door, And

1. breathe the wind that makes you free, _____ and
2. feel the warmth that makes you free, _____ and
3. drink the rain that makes you free, _____ and
4. hold the hand that makes you free, _____ and

1. breathe the wind that makes you free.
2. feel the warmth that makes you free.
3. drink the rain that makes you free.
4. hold the hand that makes you free.

22

Then It Dawns on Me

Joe Wise

very freely

Dm   **C**

Oh the night looks ne - ver end - ing; oh, my

(2nd,3rd) And the night looks ne - ver end - ing; and the

Dm   **C**   *a tempo*   **C**

night looks ne - ver end - ing. And then it dawns on

night seems ne - ver end - ing.

F   **C**

me your word is light. Your love is stron-ger than the

Am   **Dm**   **Dm7**

night and then the dark-ness in my soul packs up its

Dm   **Dm7**   **C**

bags and has to go, your love is Light.

Am   **Dm**

The morn-ing's come, and you come stream-in' 'cross my

Dm7   **Dm**   **Dm7**

face and put the sha - dows all to chase, your love is

C   **Am**

Light, your love is Light.

very freely

1. But I get all cloud-ed up, fill my life with me
2. But I get all cloud-ed up, watch my life fog in

1. and my, do my work and read my pa-per leave no
2. the race, won-der why I can't be still e-nough to

1. room for you or why I tram-ple o-ver
2. look you in the face. I build my towers of

1. peo-ple and ac-quire my pre-cious things. I
2. Ba-bel and lock us all in tight and

1. no-tice on-ly man-sions and the way a ti-tle
2. ne-ver seem to no-tice that our lan-guage turns to

1. rings, I sel-dom watch the sun-set, I'm still em-
2. night. I think I'd like to learn to love, be as

1. bar-assed by a tear, and I'm so a-fraid
2. reck-less as the wind, yet I'm so a-fraid

1. this game I've played is the brain-child of my fear.
2. to let me out and let you come all in.

Your love is Light.

Watch With Me

Joe Wise
(ASCAP)

Friendship

divides

our

grief ÷

and

doubles

our

x joy / joy

Watch one hour with me. Stay just a

way by my side. When my al - le - lu - ia

days streak in - to blues and grays, be my

guide. Stay a - while. Watch with me.

1. I won't ask you to be strong with me, I won't
2. And in hard times I will look for you, want you
3. And when death comes I'll reach for your hand, feel our

1. ask you to be kind, I won't ask you to stay
2. gen-tle by my side, and in soft eyes tell me
3. love flow in your breath, in your eyes I'll find a

1. long with me;   just   help me find my   mind;
2. one more time,   no   need to run and   hide;
3. way to stand   and   see more life than   death;

1.   stay with   me.
2.   stay with   me.
3.   stay with   me.

**Nothing
is
so
strong
as
gentleness;
nothing
is
so
gentle
as
real
strength.**

The Daily Pantagraph

Let there be such oneness between you that when

one cries the other will taste salt.

26

Love Divine

BEECHER 87.87.D.

CHARLES WESLEY, 1707-1788

JOHN ZUNDEL, 1815-1882

Capo 3, PLAY IN G

1. Love di - vine, all loves ex - cell - ing, Joy of heav'n, to
2. Breathe, O breathe thy lov - ing - spir - it In - to ev - 'ry

earth come down; Fix in us thy hum - ble _ dwell - ing;
trou - bled breast! Let us all in thee in - her - it;

All thy faith-ful mer - cies crown! Je - sus, thou art
Let us find that sec - ond rest. Take a - way our

all, com - pas - sion, Pure un - bound - ed love thou _ art; _ Vis - it us with
bent to _ sin - ning; Al - pha and O - me - ga _ be; _ End of faith as

LOVE DIVINE, ALL LOVES EXCELLING

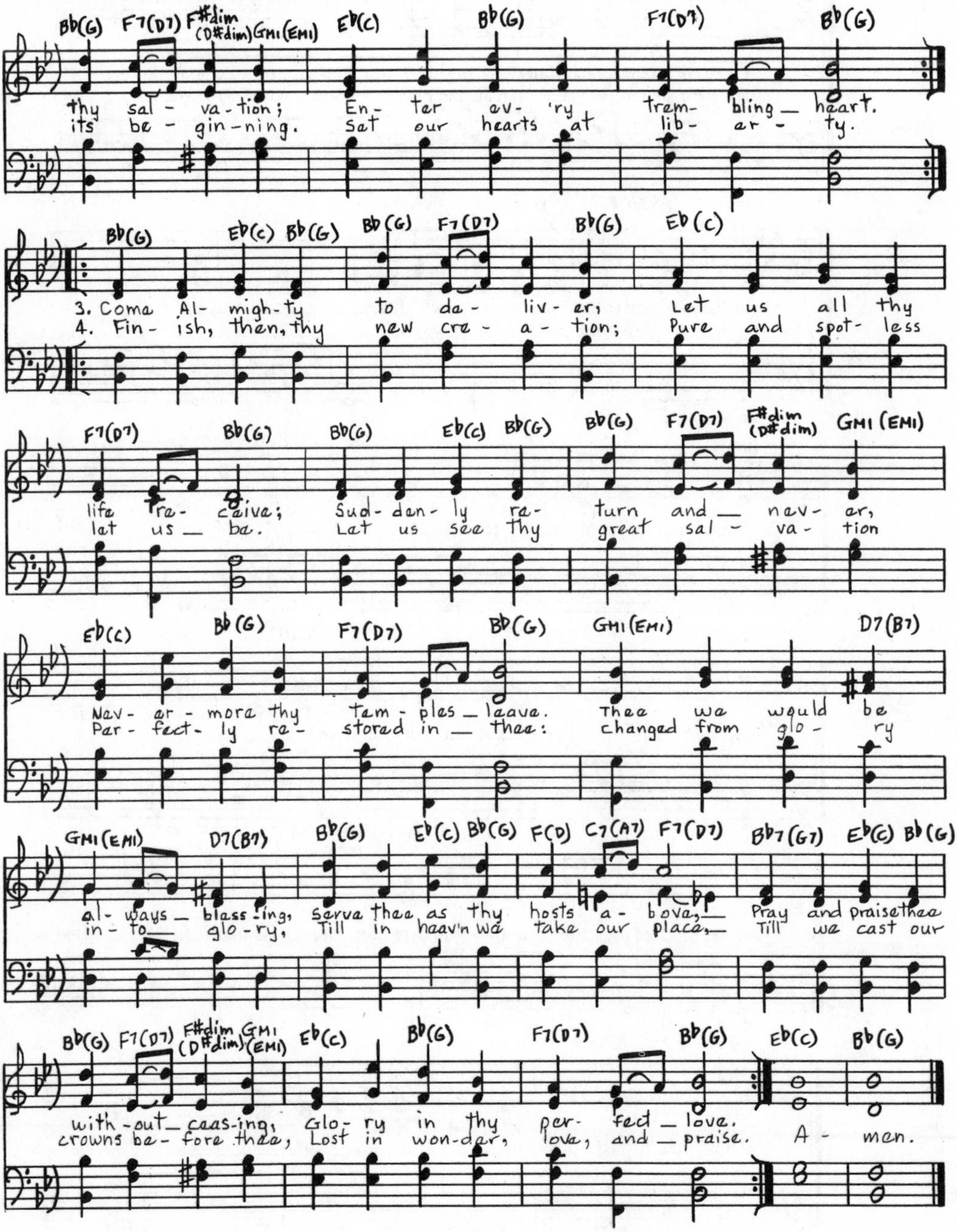

Friendship

Words and Music by
SONNY SALSBURY

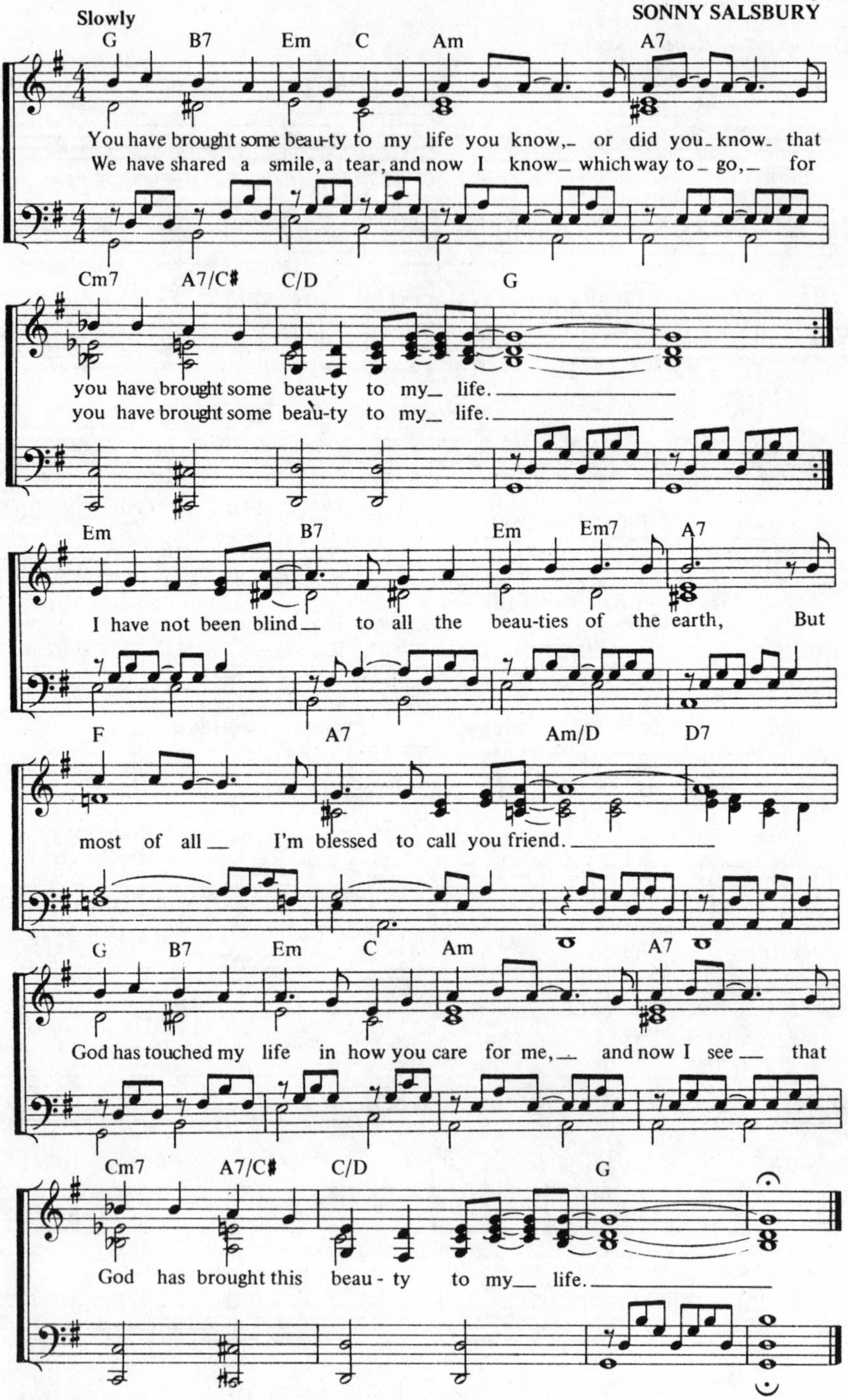

A Lifetime

Words and Music by CHRIS INSERRA

D DMA7 CMA7 D D DMA7 CMA7

1. A life- time is such a long, long
2. — Hill- sides, val- leys and flow- ing
3. — You're the ones who make life so
4. I can't be- gin to ex- press the

D DMA7 CMA7 D DMA7

time; So man- y things — to do and see. There's so — much that
streams make up this world — in which we live. We're on- ly such a
great. You have so much — to give the world. You're not a- fraid to
mean- ing that you have add- — ed to my life. You've giv- en me the

CMA7 D EMI A D

needs to be learned; — So man- y goals to reach.
small part of it. It's being is be- yond our reach.
give of your- selves; — you make — life — real.
great- est — gift by giv- — ing your- selves.

AMA7 DMA7 AMA7 D6

1,2,3. But it's peo- ple who make liv- ing worth- while It's
4. And it's you — who make me want to smile. It's

AMA7 DMA7 AMA7 D6

peo- ple who make — me want to smile.
you — who make — my liv- ing worth- while.

There's so much that needs to be learned

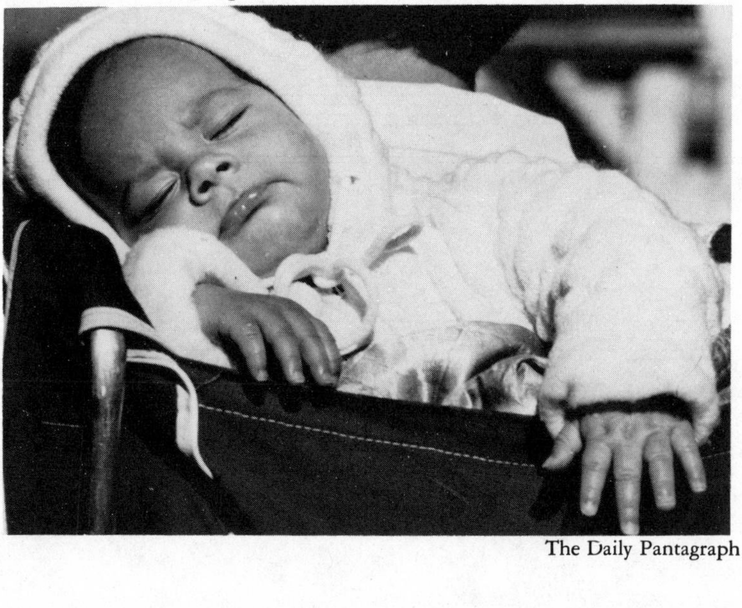

The Daily Pantagraph

Easy Like Mountains

Ray Repp

Kind of ____ eas - y ____ like moun - tains ____

melt - ing in ____ the rain, your hand ____ smooth - in'! ____ (3x) I'll try

all the rug - ged edg - es, ____ know - in' with - out ____ words

____ how to soft - en ____ the pain. _____ Kind of ____

last time to

eas - y ____ like moun - tains ____ melt - ing in ____ the rain. _____

VERSES

1) And when the words I speak are not my
2) And ev - 'ry time I hid be - hind my
3) What's that I see be - hind those wear - y

own _____ and my man - ner is quite un -
door _____ from the things that I cared not to
eyes _____ where your smile _____ used to _____

true, _____ You are ____ there _____ with the gen - tle -
see _____ You were ___ there _____ and you lift - ed my
be? _____ Lean on ____ me _____ for a - while, and I'll

ness of your smile, lead - ing me to some - thing
bur - den of fear, help - ing me to be more
of - fer you all that _____ you have shared with

new. _____ But
free. _____ But melt - ing in ____ the rain,
me. _____

Kind of _____ eas - y like moun - tains melt - ing

in the rain.

The road to a friend's house
is never long.

Song of the Wounded

Words and Music
by **JOE WISE**

REFRAIN

CAPO 4

Love is gen - tle, love is kind,

gives the room and takes the time,

plays the soft - est mel - o - dy,

'til you find your har - mo - ny.

Love is gen - tle, love is kind,

walks a - round in - side your mind,

o - pens doors and leaves the key,

finds the why of you and me. *(to verse; 3rd time to CODA)*

SONG OF THE WOUNDED, cont. (2)

VERSE

1. Take it slow with me.___ Just let me
1. grow and___ be free, and I'll shoot a thou-sand ten-drils up to
1. touch your morn-in' sky.

2. Take your sweet
2. Don't be so

1. time with me;___ come make a rhyme___ with me.___ Watch me
2. sure of me;___ don't make a cure___ of me.___ Bless my

1. flow, and let me wash you when I cry. *(Refrain)*
2. wings, then let me find my piece of sky. *(Refrain)*

CODA

Walk me a-

round and hear the sound you know I've got to give.

flute or other melodic instrument

Song of the Wounded

Though the song speaks for itself, we thought it might be elucidating to know that it was a joint work of Joe Wise and John Pell for a movie on the life of Jean Vanier, who has devoted himself to working with adults with mental handicaps — or, as he names them, 'the wounded.'

**"I can make the dandelion blow
but what makes the wind blow?"**

Our Song

Words and Music by JANE WELLS

1. The wind whis-pers soft-ly through the trees in the night. __ The
   sun sends its warmth to me __ with its gen-tle rays. __

clouds send their mes-sag-es a-cross a per-fect sky. __ A bird tells his
Fire warms the cold of night with em-bers glow-ing strong. __ The chill of my

se-cret to me with his hap-py song. But you can talk to me with your
lone-li-ness may come but nev-er stays, For you can warm my soul with your

eyes. 2. The song. 3. I can see a hap-pi-ness in a small child's face.

I have found a look of doubt as oth-ers ask me why. But I have learned to

trust, my friend, and feel your mind's em-brace. __ And I can see the love in your

eyes, Yes, I can see the love in your eyes.

The Jesus Blues

Capo 1 (C)

Words and Music by LINDA RICH

SING LAUGH CRY

What Makes the Wind Blow?

A SONG FOR PENTECOST
dedicated to Nancy Carter

Donald Marsh
Richard Avery

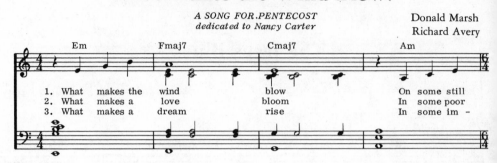

now be – yond com – pare?

love blooms an – y – where.

The Daily Pantagraph

Moto Imeaka

East African folk song
Arr. Betty Pulkingham

Capo 1 (E)

*This song in Swahili is sung throughout East Africa. The literal English translation of the refrain is: 'The fire is burning today, fire is the work of Jesus, the fire is burning today, let us sing Hallelujah, the fire is burning.' The English verse in the musical text has essentially the same meaning. Other suggested verses: 'God's Spirit is burning.....','God's power is burning.....'. The last line may be repeated accumulatively, in reverse order: 'Praise God I've got God's Spirit.....', 'power.....', 'fire.'

Alleluia!

Slowly
(descant optional)

Source Unknown

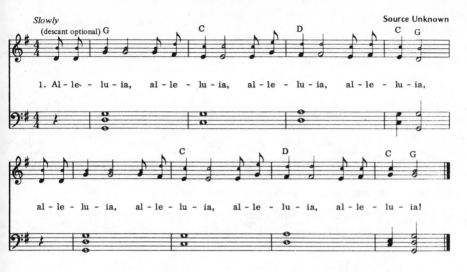

1. Al - le - lu - ia, al - le - lu - ia, al - le - lu - ia, al - le - lu - ia,

al - le - lu - ia, al - le - lu - ia, al - le - lu - ia, al - le - lu - ia!

2. Fill me, Jesus. 3. Hear our prayer now.

Spirit of the Living God

Adapted from "Spirit Of the Living God"
Words and Music by
Daniel Iverson

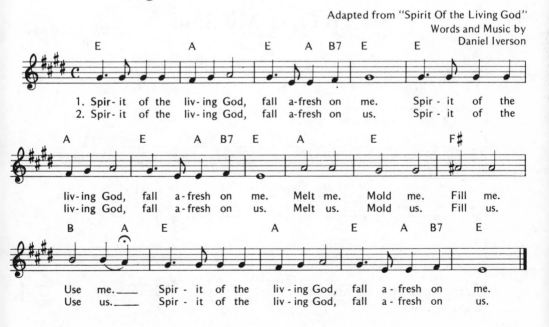

1. Spir - it of the liv - ing God, fall a-fresh on me. Spir - it of the
2. Spir - it of the liv - ing God, fall a-fresh on us. Spir - it of the

liv - ing God, fall a-fresh on me. Melt me. Mold me. Fill me.
liv - ing God, fall a-fresh on us. Melt us. Mold us. Fill us.

Use me.___ Spir - it of the liv - ing God, fall a - fresh on me.
Use us.___ Spir - it of the liv - ing God, fall a - fresh on us.

40

Jesus, Jesus

Source Unknown
(May be sung as a round.)

Je - sus, Je - sus, Can I tell you how I___ feel?

You have giv - en me your___ rich - es, I love you so. so.

True Riches : JOY in the Spirit

Sweep Over My Soul

Words and Music by
Harry D. Clarke

1. Sweep o-ver my soul,___ Sweep o-ver my soul;___
2. Fill my life with *joy,___ Fill my life with *joy,___

Come, gra-cious Spir - it, Sweep o-ver my soul.___
Come, gra-cious Spir - it, Fill my life with *joy.___

*3. love, 4. peace.

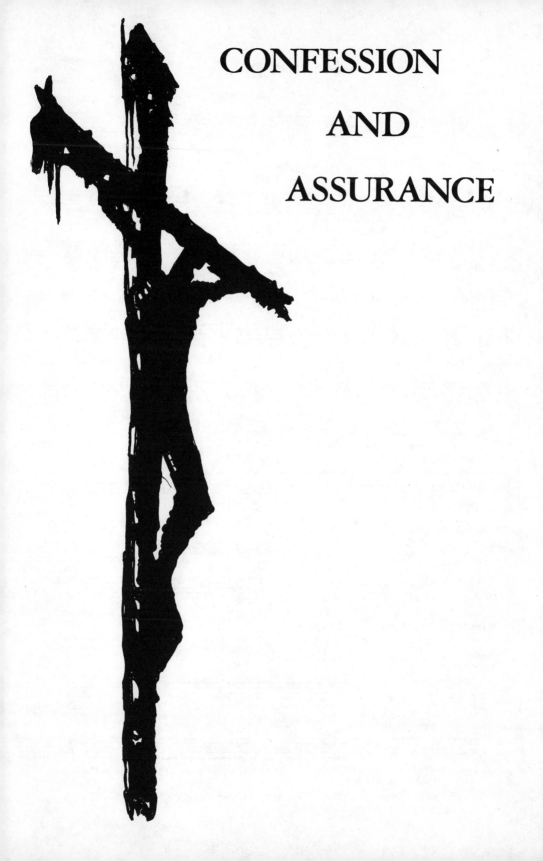

CONFESSION
AND
ASSURANCE

My People

Joe Wise
Arr. Saul Striks

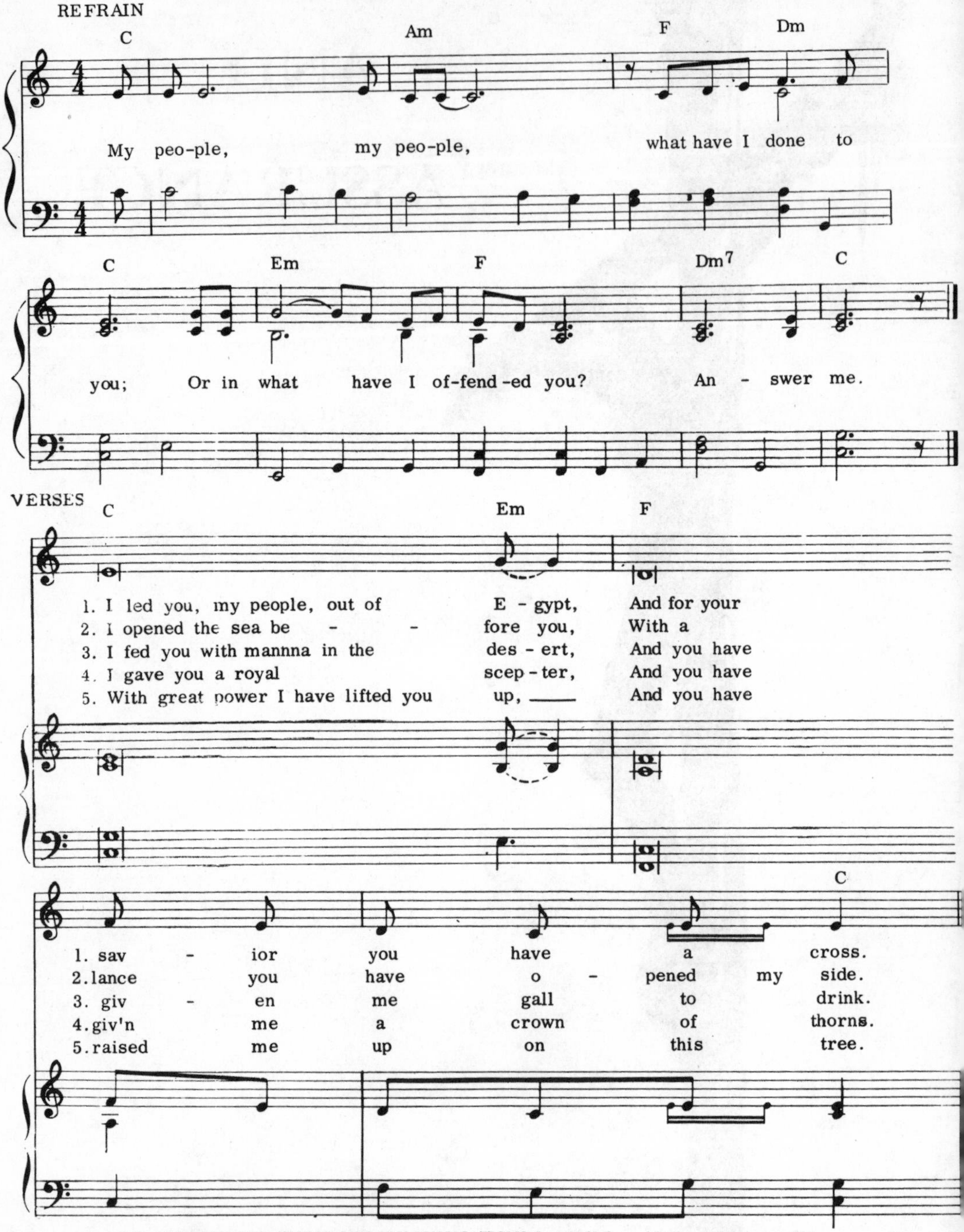

REFRAIN

My peo-ple, my peo-ple, what have I done to you; Or in what have I of-fend-ed you? An - swer me.

VERSES

1. I led you, my people, out of E - gypt, And for your
2. I opened the sea be - - fore you, With a
3. I fed you with mannna in the des - ert, And you have
4. I gave you a royal scep - ter, And you have
5. With great power I have lifted you up, — And you have

1. sav - ior you have a cross.
2. lance you have o - pened my side.
3. giv - en me gall to drink.
4. giv'n me a crown of thorns.
5. raised me up on this tree.

Apple Tree
Capo 5 Play in C
Words and Music by LINDA RICH
F(C) AMI (EMI) B♭(F) C(G)
I loved you like the ap-ple tree that blos-soms in my sight. And I
loved you like the warm spring rains that fall on earth at — night. I
G MI (D MI)
loved you like the ea-gle who tea-ches her young to fly. I
C7 (G7) (FINE)
loved you free-ly but in re-turn I was cru-ci-fied.
You ask of God and I tell you, "God is just like Me". You
speak of hea-vy bur-dens and I prom-ise to make you free. You
say, "What is truth?" And I an-swer, "I'm the light, the Truth, the Way."
(D.S. AL FINE)
Pi-late washed his hands of Me... Will you just walk a-way. I
© 1976 by Inter-Varsity Christian Fellowship of the U.S.A. Used by permission.

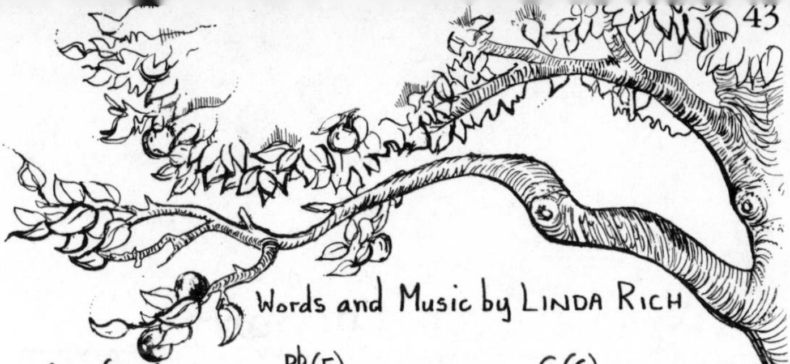

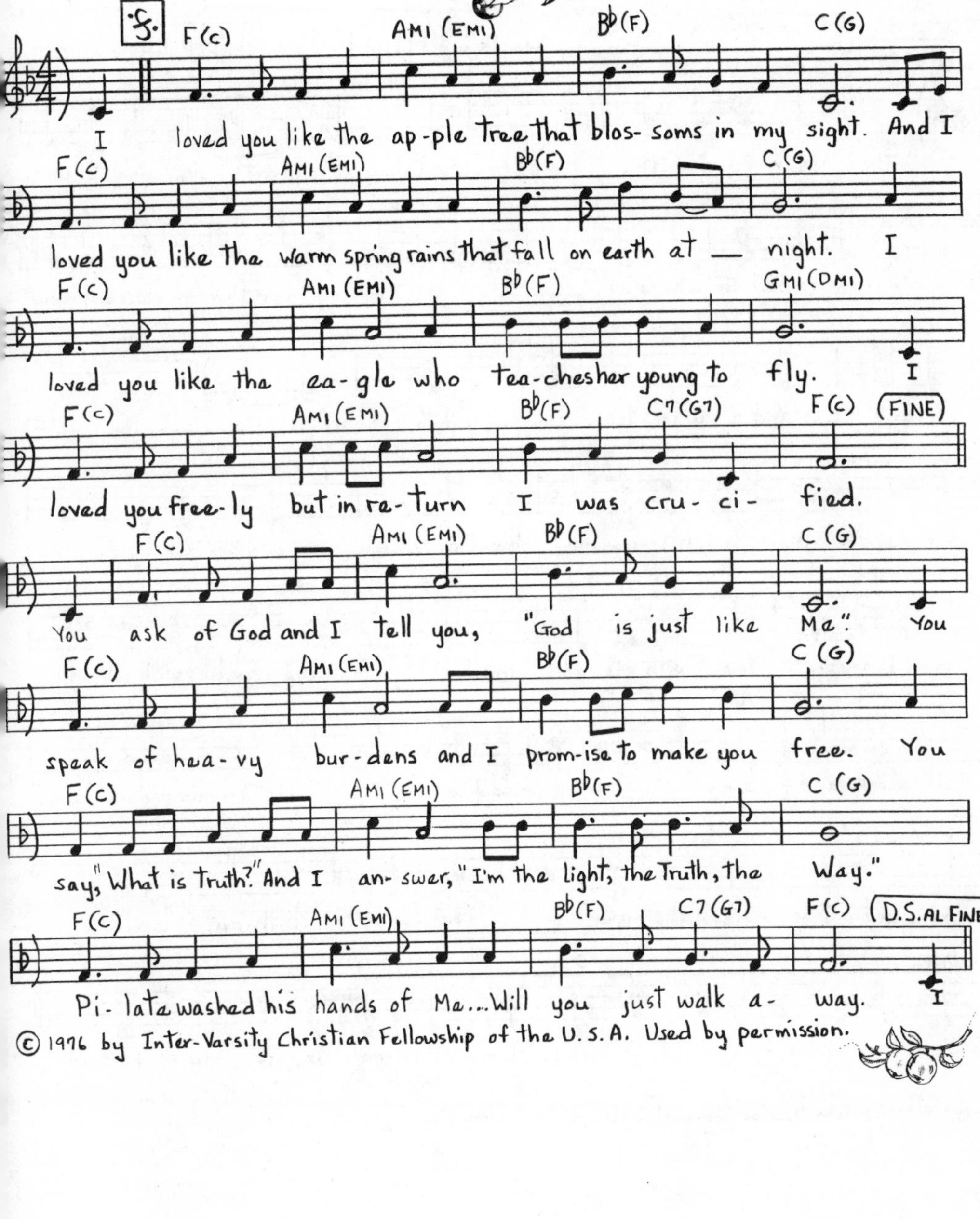

I'm Sorry

Words and Music by Tom Neufer Emswiler

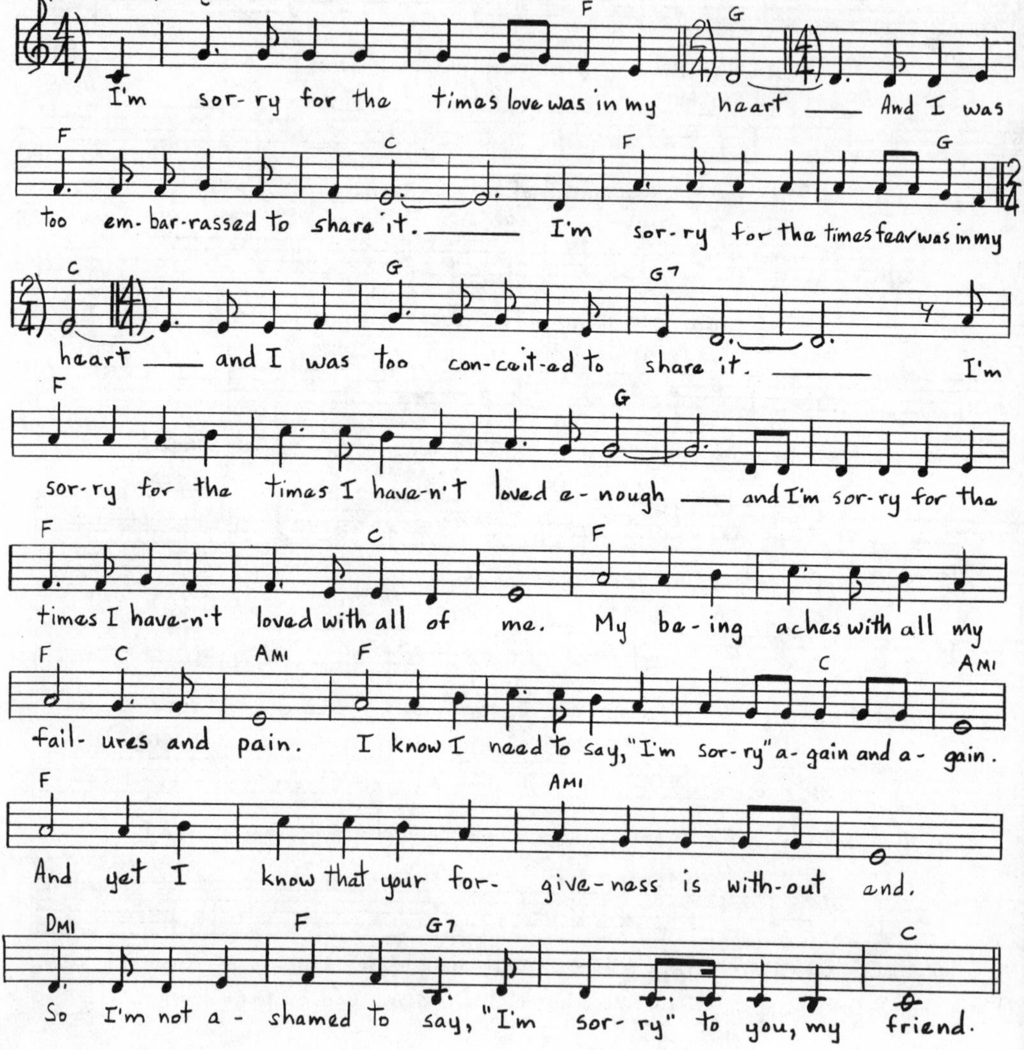

(REFRAIN)

I'm sor-ry for the times love was in my heart ___ And I was too em-bar-rassed to share it. ___ I'm sor-ry for the times fear was in my heart ___ and I was too con-ceit-ed to share it. ___ I'm sor-ry for the times I have-n't loved a-nough ___ and I'm sor-ry for the times I have-n't loved with all of me. My be-ing aches with all my fail-ures and pain. I know I need to say, "I'm sor-ry" a-gain and a-gain. And yet I know that your for-give-ness is with-out and. So I'm not a-shamed to say, "I'm sor-ry" to you, my friend.

I'm Sorry

(VERSES - REPEAT REFRAIN AFTER EACH 2 VERSES)

Dmi   F   G   C

{ Some-one was-n't beau-ti-ful _ and I looked _ a- way. _____
{ Some-one stretched out a hand _ and I said not to- day. _____

{ Some-one need-ed to be held _ but I clung to safe- ty. _____
{ Some-one need-ed to hear truth _ but I feared to dis-a- gree. _____

{ Some-one was hun- gry and cold _ and I ig-nored the need. _____
{ Some-one of-fered me a bribe _ And my heart filled with greed. _____

C   Dmi   G7   Fdim.   C

_ I'm sor- ry, I'm sor- ry. _____

Blessed are

the sorrowful ...

Mt.5:4

Cheryl Munn

There Is a Balm in Gilead

Traditional

There_ is a balm in Gil-e-ad To make the wound-ed whole,_
There is a balm in Gil-e-ad To heal the sin-sick soul.

Fine

1. Some - times I feel dis - cour - aged, And_ think my_ work's in -
2. If you can - not preach like Pe - ter, If you can - not_ pray like_

D.C. al Fine

vain, But_ then the Ho - ly Spir - it Re - vives my soul a - gain._
Paul, You can tell the love of Je - sus, And say, "He died for all!"

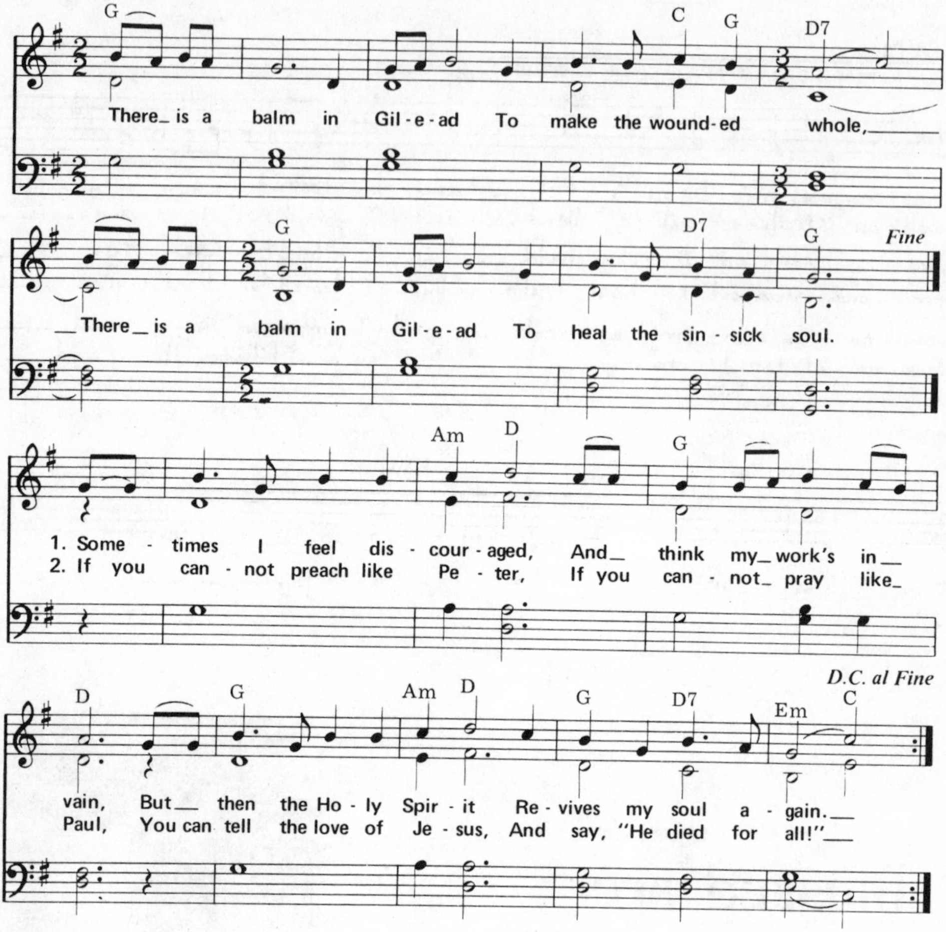

To Talk With God

Words from the Hindi
Music by Martin West

Solo

1. To talk_ with_ God, no breath is_ lost,_____ Talk on, talk on, talk on!_____
2. To walk_ with_ God, no strength is_ lost,_____ Walk on, walk on, walk on!_____
3. To wait_ on_ God, no time is_ lost,_____ Wait on, wait on, wait on!_____

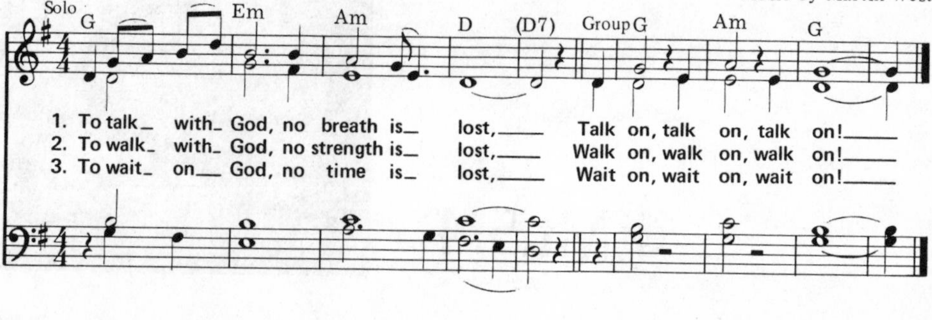

Peace I Am

Barbara Neighbors

Peace I am, peace I am.
Love love
etc. etc.

Qui - et, calm, stead - y, sure, peace I am.
love
etc.

Be Still My Soul

Barbara Neighbors

Be still my soul be still my soul,

Be in per - fect peace. Be still my soul, be

still my soul, Be in per - fect peace.

Be Still And Know That I Am God

Windfall of Love

Words and Music by
JUDITH MAY NEWTON

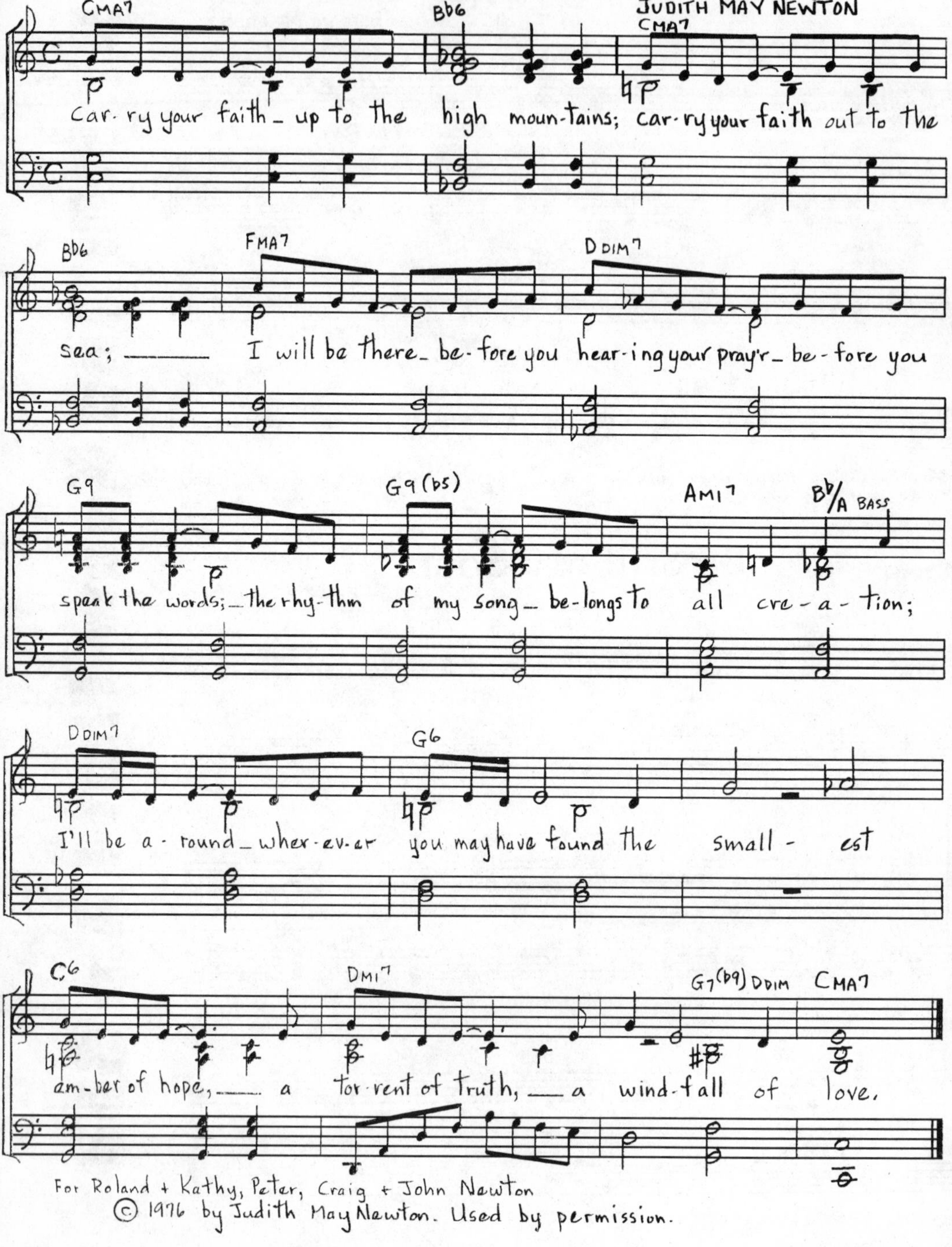

Car-ry your faith up to the high moun-tains; car-ry your faith out to the sea; ___ I will be there be-fore you hear-ing your pray'r be-fore you speak the words; the rhy-thm of my song be-longs to all cre-a-tion; I'll be a-round wher-ev-er you may have found the small - est am-ber of hope, ___ a tor-rent of truth, ___ a wind-fall of love.

For Roland + Kathy, Peter, Craig + John Newton

I Heard the Voice of Jesus Say

JOHN 1:16; MATTHEW 11:28
JOHN 4:14; 8:12
HORATIO BONAR, 1808-1889

VOX DILECTI CMD
JOHN B. DYKES, 1823-1876

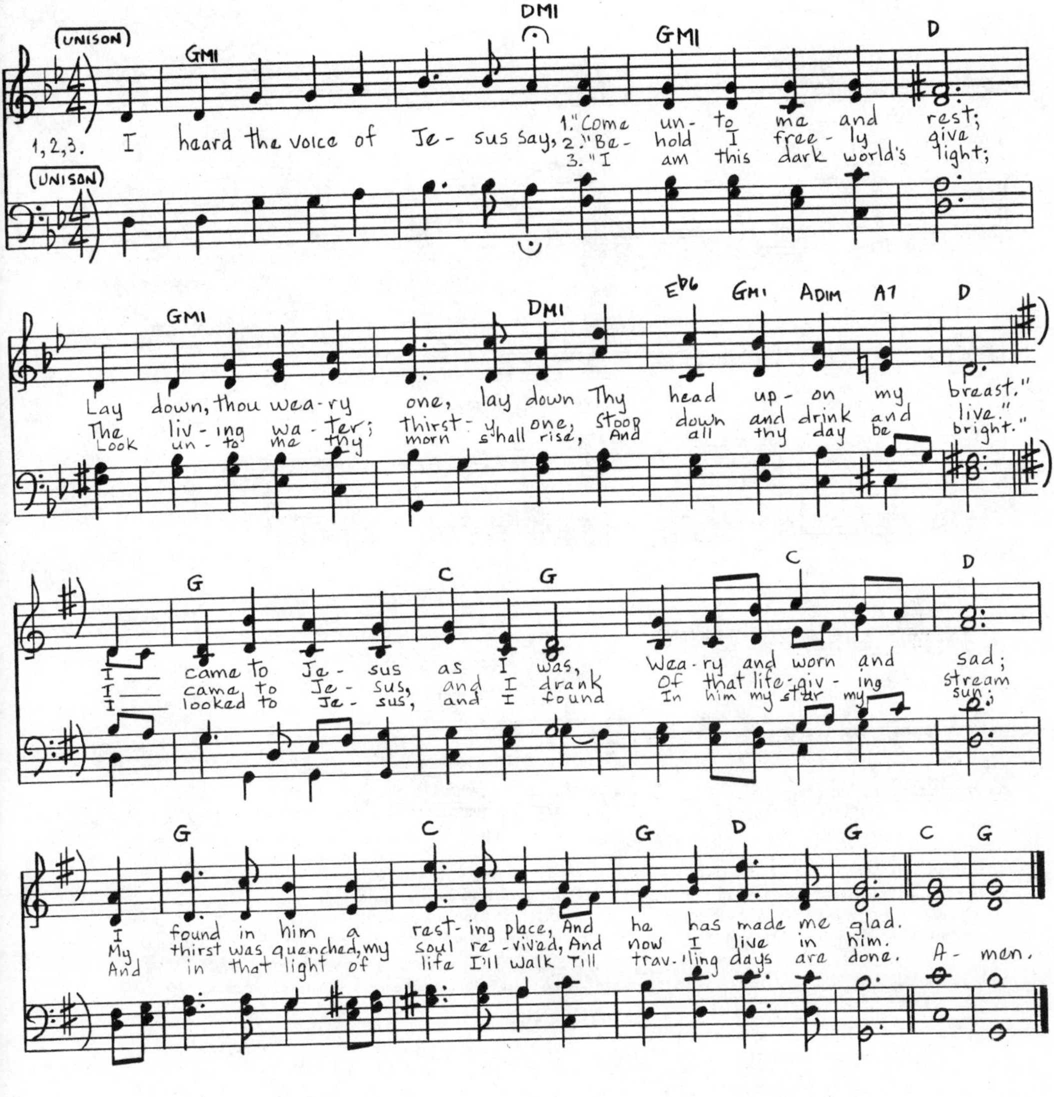

Life Is a River

Barbara Neighbors

1. Life in this world is like a lake,
Water we use and share and take.
What we call death is but the mist
Rising to God in joy and bliss.

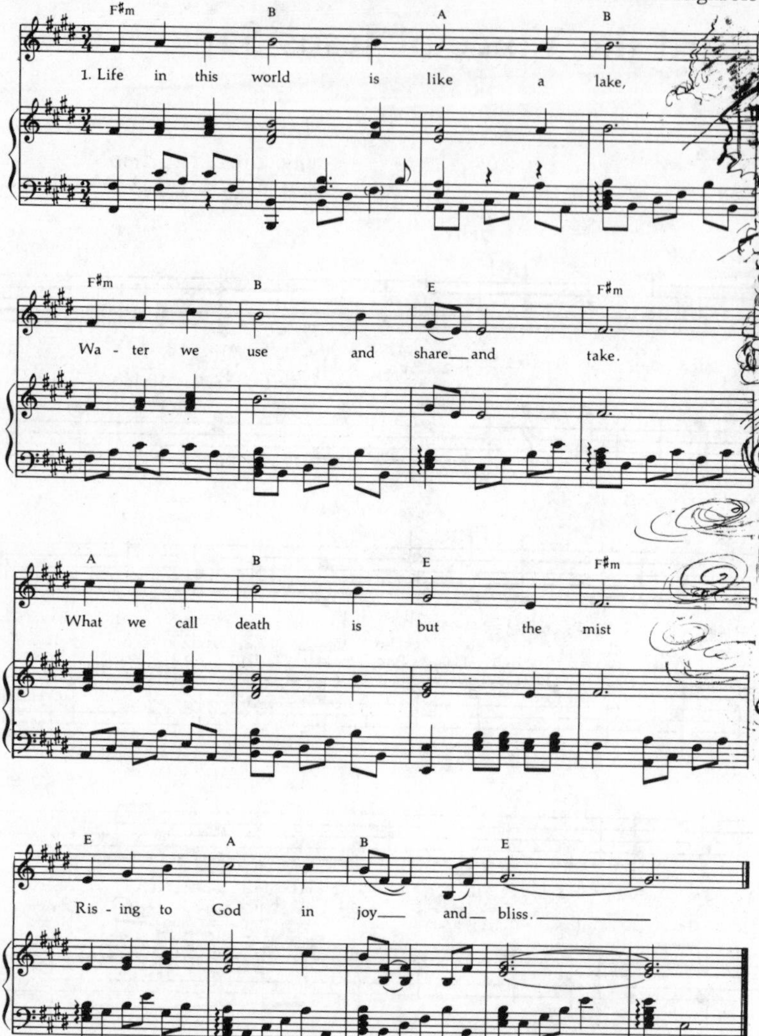

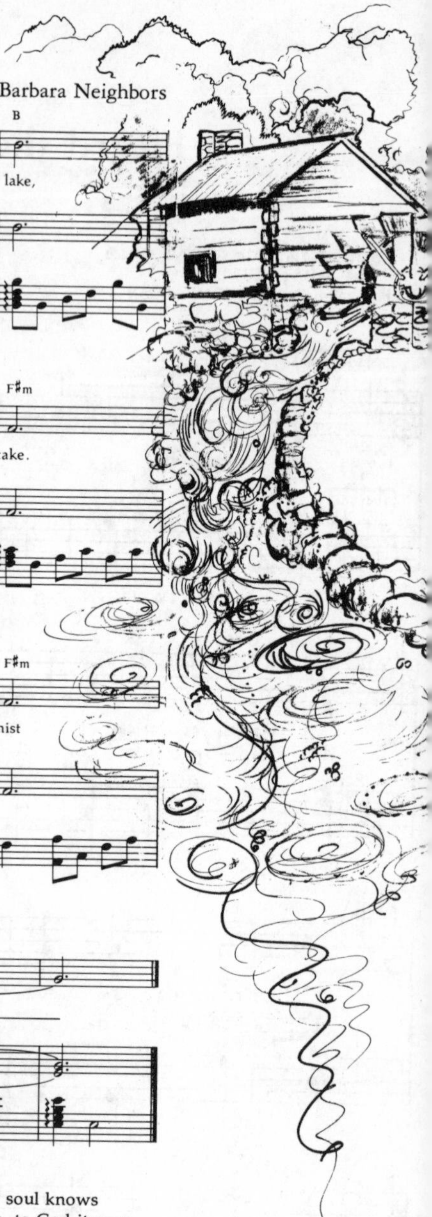

2. Rivers and lakes, streams and rain,
Teardrops and snow, they're all the same.
Oceans rise upward, clouds take form
Return to earth with every storm.

3. Life is a river your soul knows
From God it comes, to God it goes.
God is our life, our breath, our goal,
The river flows, we are made whole. (Repeat Verse 1)

Peace Like a River

Traditional, Arr: Carol Dettoni

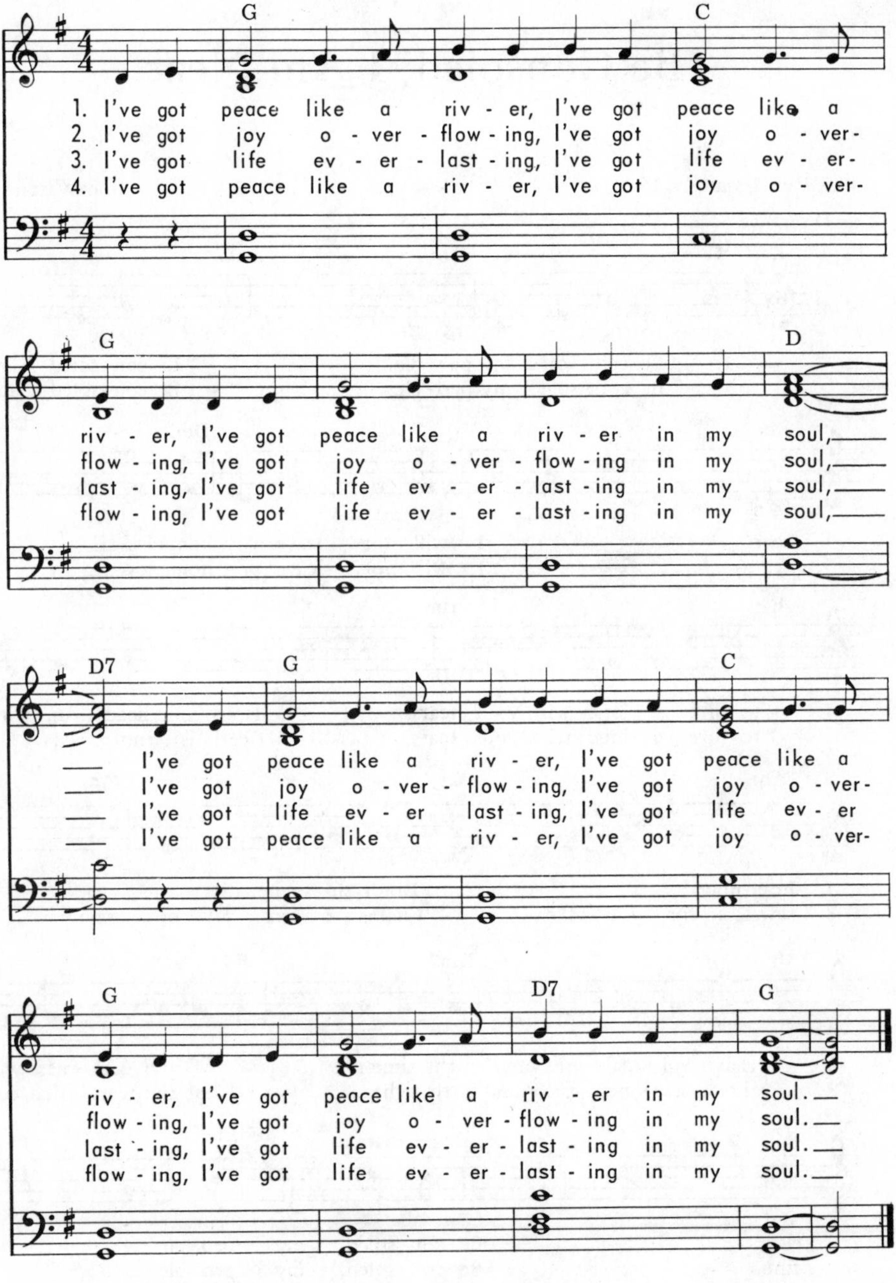

Be Consoled, I Am Near

Based on Isaiah 49:15

Joe Wise

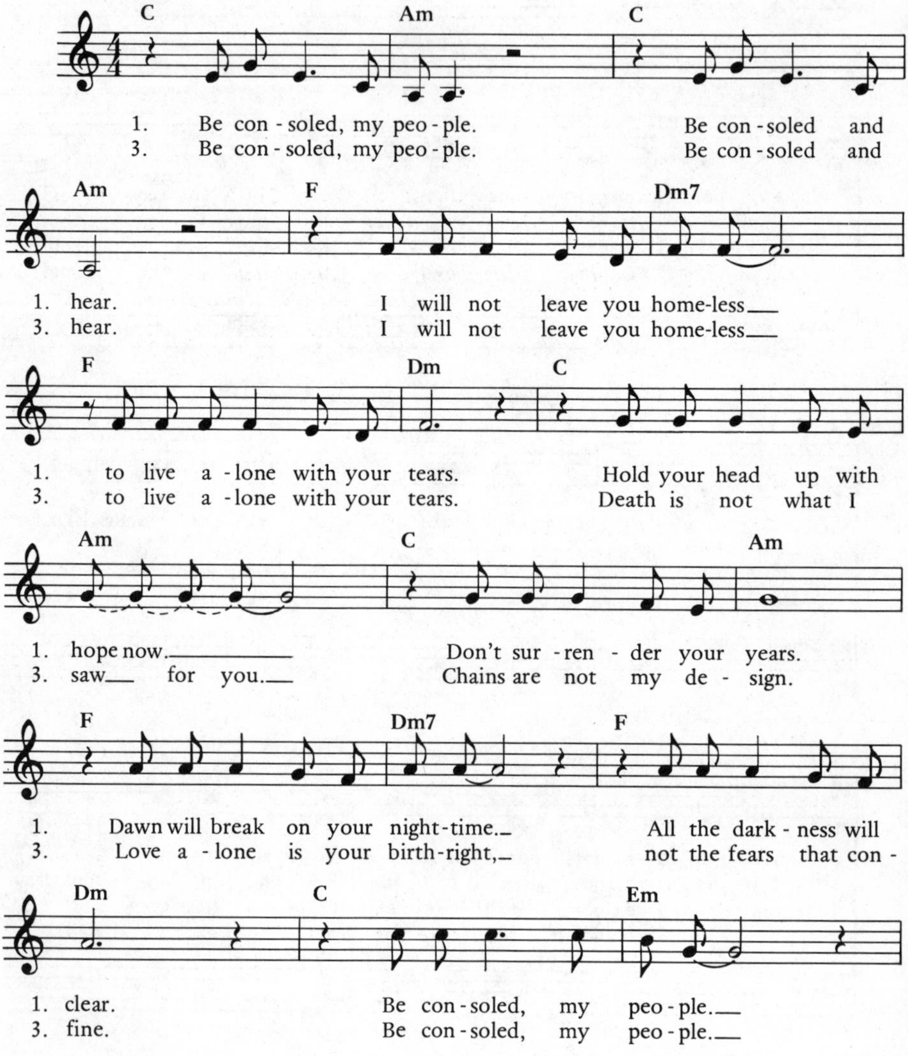

1. Be con-soled, my peo-ple. Be con-soled and
3. Be con-soled, my peo-ple. Be con-soled and

1. hear. I will not leave you home-less
3. hear. I will not leave you home-less

1. to live a-lone with your tears. Hold your head up with
3. to live a-lone with your tears. Death is not what I

1. hope now. Don't sur-ren-der your years.
3. saw for you. Chains are not my de-sign.

1. Dawn will break on your night-time. All the dark-ness will
3. Love a-lone is your birth-right, not the fears that con-

1. clear. Be con-soled, my peo-ple.
3. fine. Be con-soled, my peo-ple.

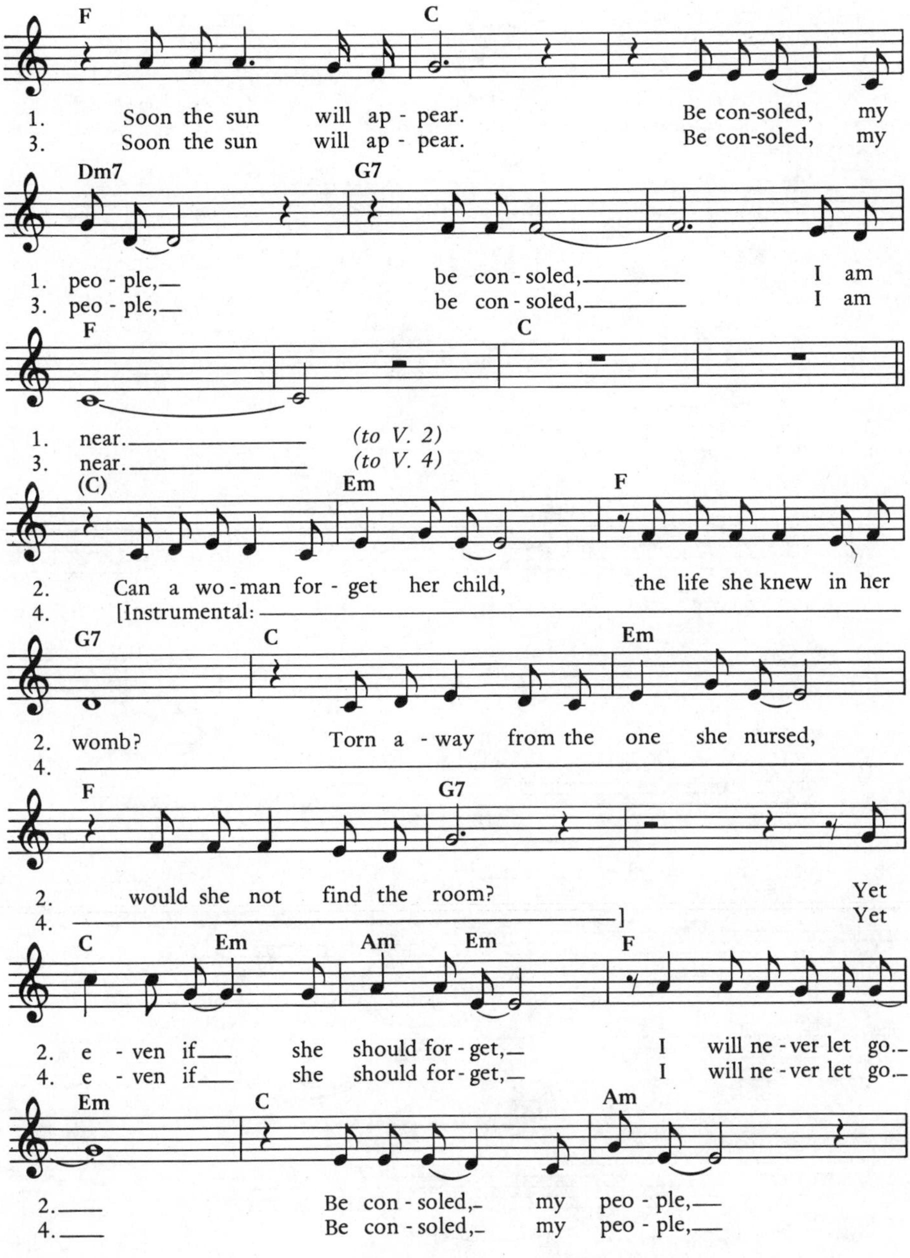

1. Soon the sun will ap - pear. Be con-soled, my
3. Soon the sun will ap - pear. Be con-soled, my

1. peo - ple,— be con - soled,——— I am
3. peo - ple,— be con - soled,——— I am

1. near.——————— *(to V. 2)*
3. near.——————— *(to V. 4)*

2. Can a wo - man for - get her child, the life she knew in her
4. [Instrumental: ———————————

2. womb? Torn a - way from the one she nursed,
4.

2. would she not find the room?] Yet
4. Yet

2. e - ven if__ she should for - get,— I will ne - ver let go._
4. e - ven if__ she should for - get,— I will ne - ver let go._

2.__ Be con - soled,— my peo - ple,—
4.__ Be con - soled,— my peo - ple,—

54

BE CONSOLED, I AM NEAR, cont. (3)

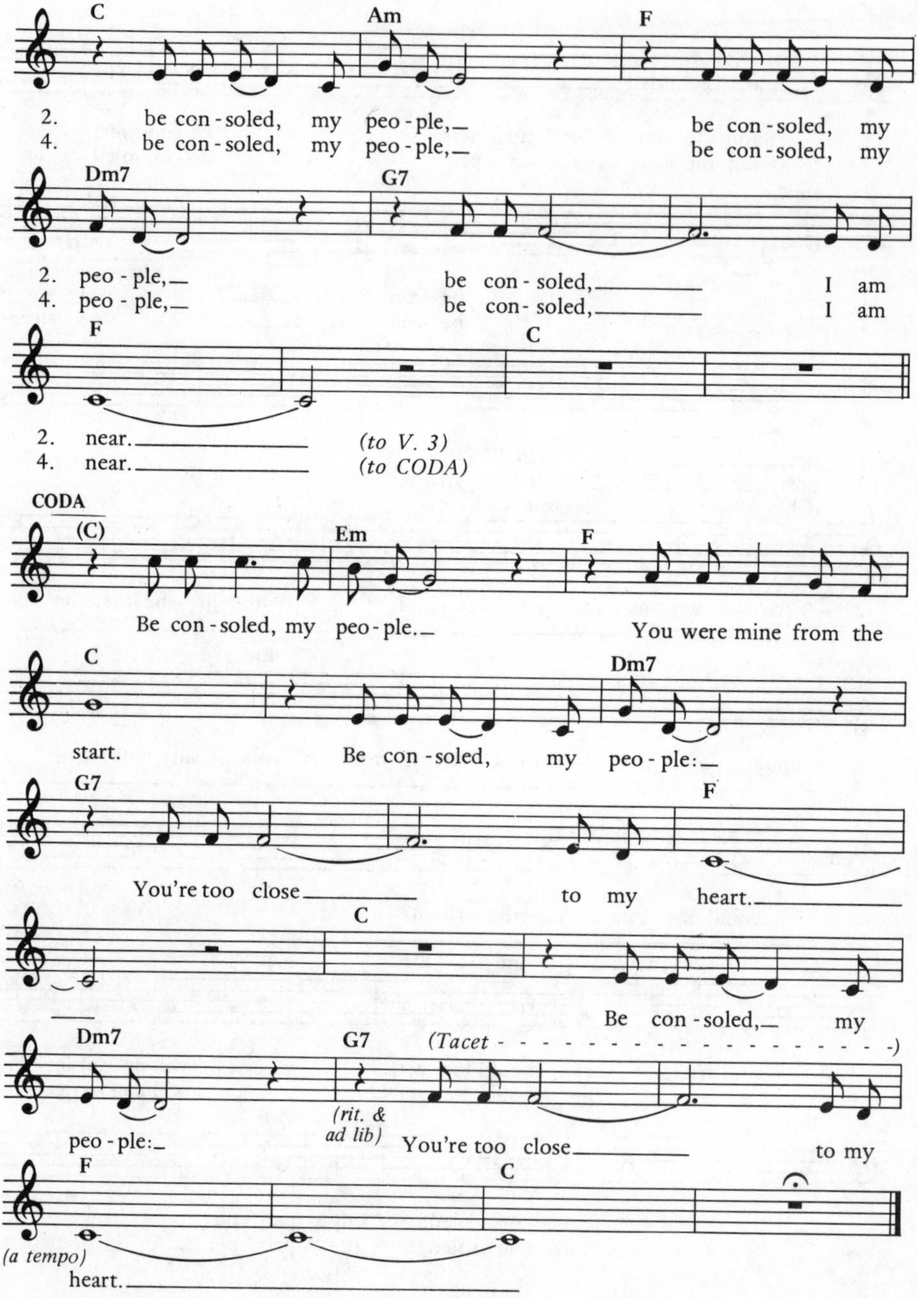

2. be con - soled, my peo - ple, — be con - soled, my
4. be con - soled, my peo - ple, — be con - soled, my

2. peo - ple, — be con - soled, _____ I am
4. peo - ple, — be con - soled, _____ I am

2. near. _____ *(to V. 3)*
4. near. _____ *(to CODA)*

CODA

Be con - soled, my peo - ple. — You were mine from the

start. Be con - soled, my peo - ple:—

You're too close _____ to my heart. _____

Be con - soled, — my

*(rit. &
ad lib)* You're too close _____ to my

peo - ple:—

(a tempo)
heart. _____

The Higher You Climb

55

Barbara Neighbors

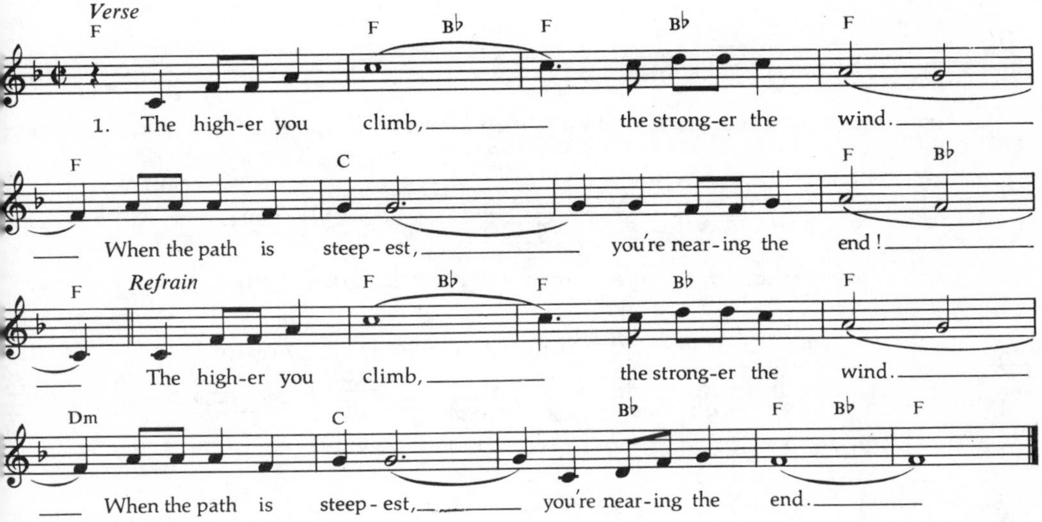

Verse

1. The high-er you climb,_____ the strong-er the wind._____
_____ When the path is steep-est,_____ you're near-ing the end!_____

Refrain

The high-er you climb,_____ the strong-er the wind._____
_____ When the path is steep-est,_____ you're near-ing the end._____

-2. Thank God for rough spots as we unfold,
For out of fire comes purest gold!

3. It's in the dark and fearsome night
The caterpillar first dreams of flight!

4. The cocoon bursts and up in the sky
There's one more worm who's learned to fly!

5. So trust in God! You cannot fall,
For all is God, and God is all!

©Copyright, 1975 by Abingdon Press. From *Singin' a Song of Joy* by Robbie Stumman and Barbara Neighbors. Used by permission.

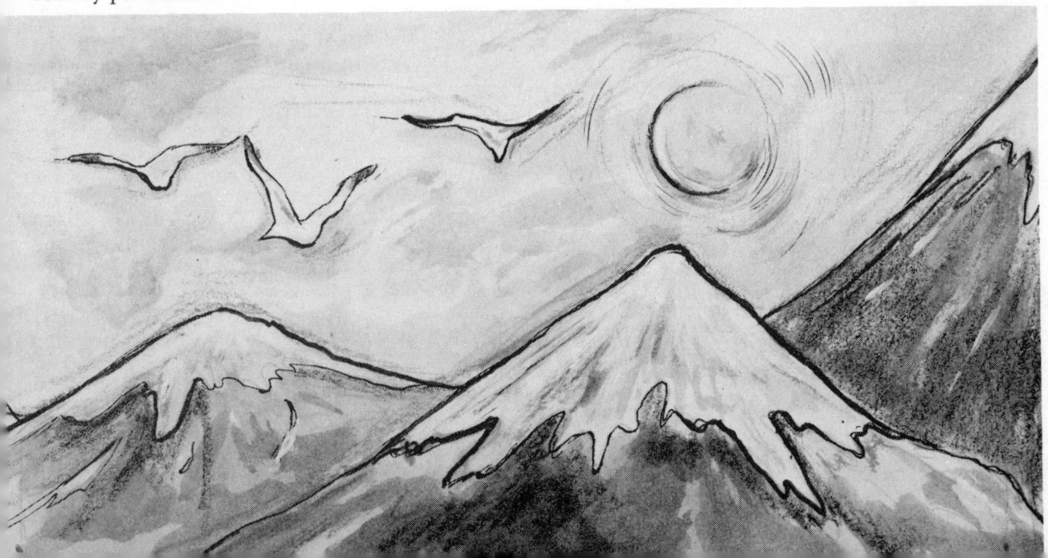

Joy Shall Come

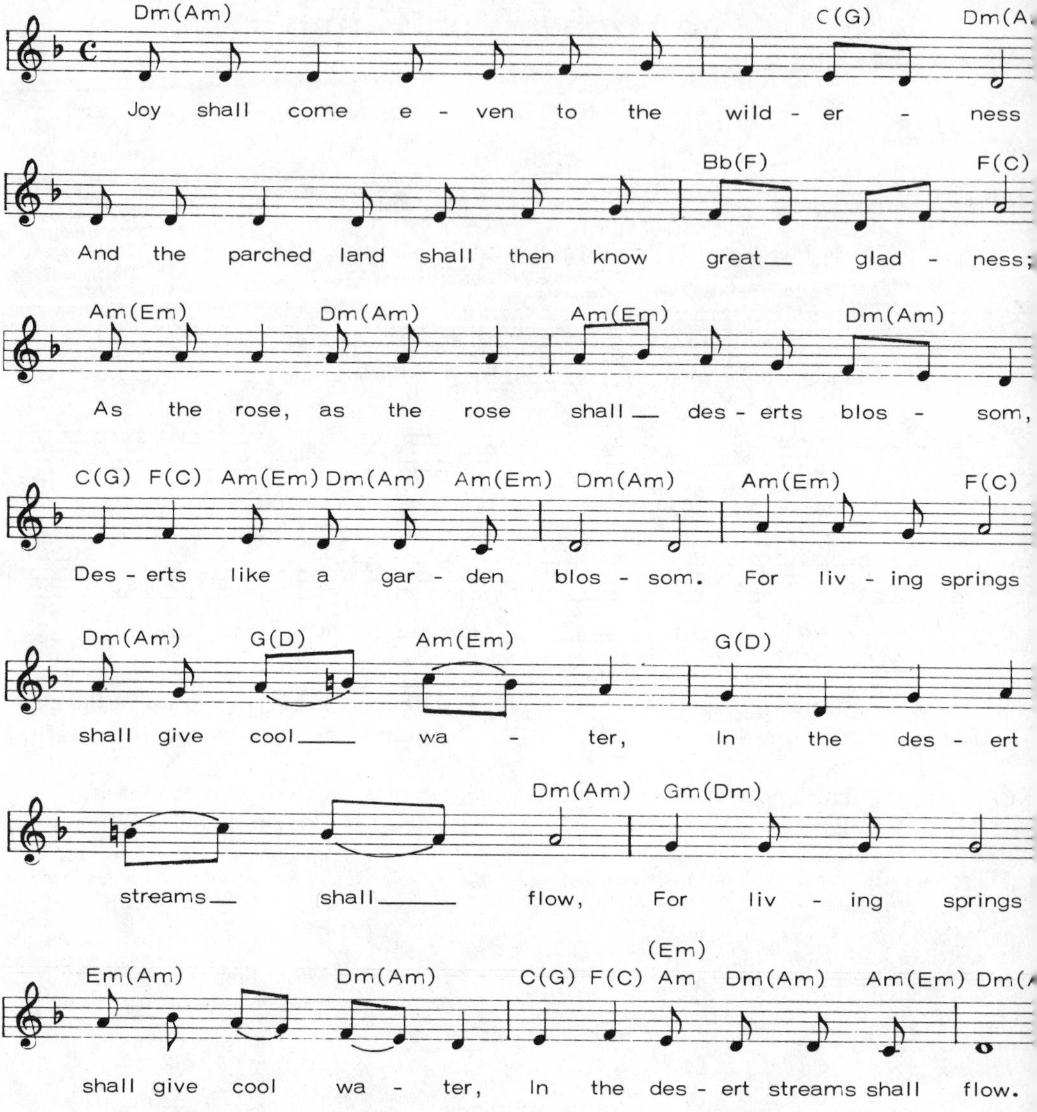

HEBREW MELO[

Joy shall come e - ven to the wild - er - ness

And the parched land shall then know great___ glad - ness;

As the rose, as the rose shall___ des - erts blos - som,

Des - erts like a gar - den blos - som. For liv - ing springs

shall give cool___ wa - ter, In the des - ert

streams___ shall___ flow, For liv - ing springs

shall give cool wa - ter, In the des - ert streams shall flow.

in thy presence there is fulness of joy and pleasure forever

psalm 16

AFFIRMATION

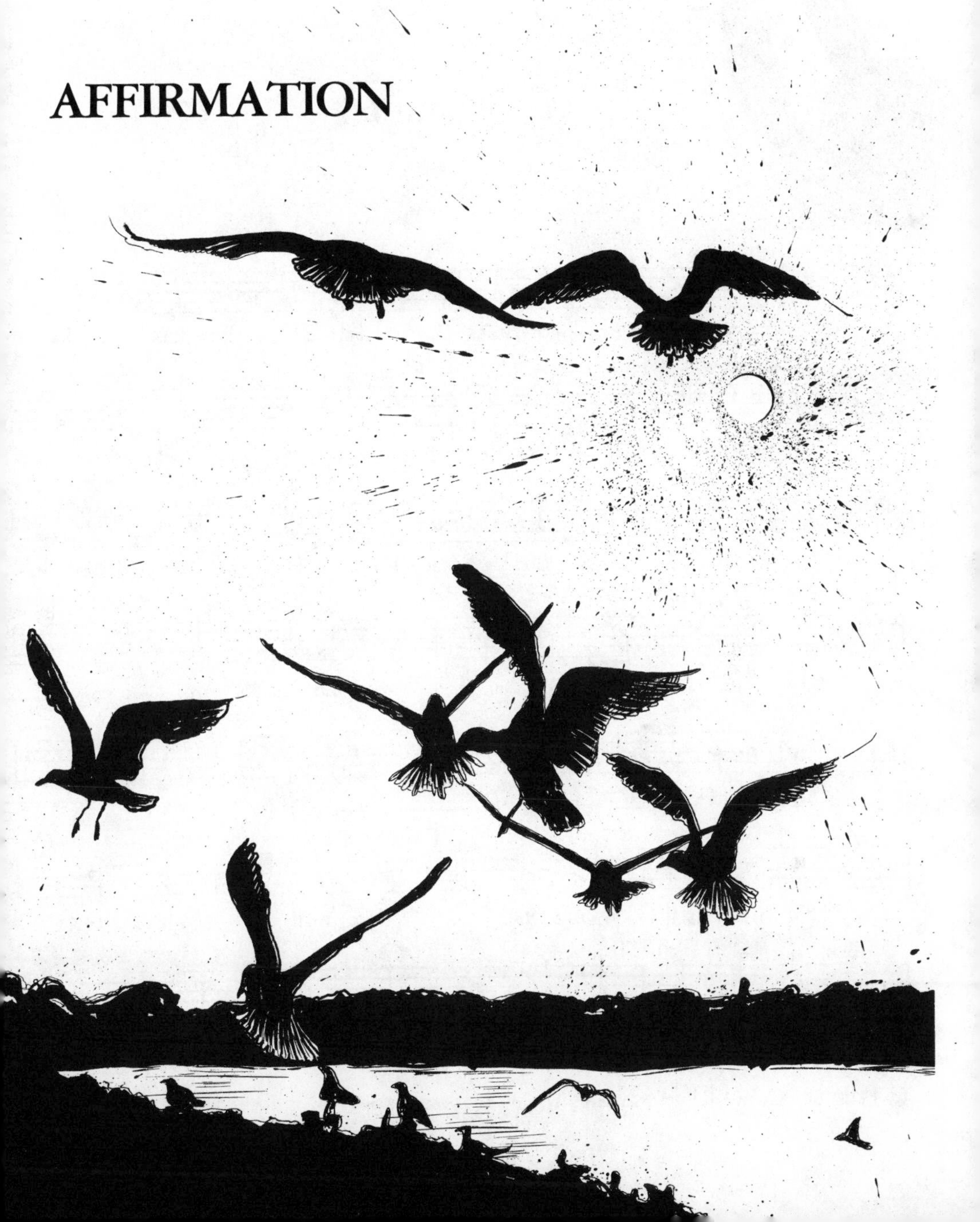

58

YOU HAVE TOUCHED ME--
I HAVE GROWN

Psalm 63

Your lov-ing-kind-ness is bet-ter than life, ___ Your lov-ing-kind-ness is bet-ter than life. My lips shall praise you thus will I bless You, Your lov-ing-kind-ness is bet-ter than life. I will lift my ___ hands up ___ in Your name ___ I will lift my ___ hands up ___ in ___ Your name. My lips shall praise You, thus will I bless You, Your lov-ing-kind-ness is bet-ter than life!

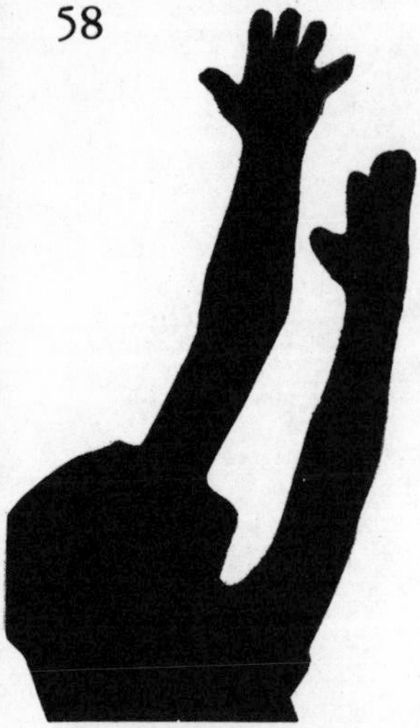

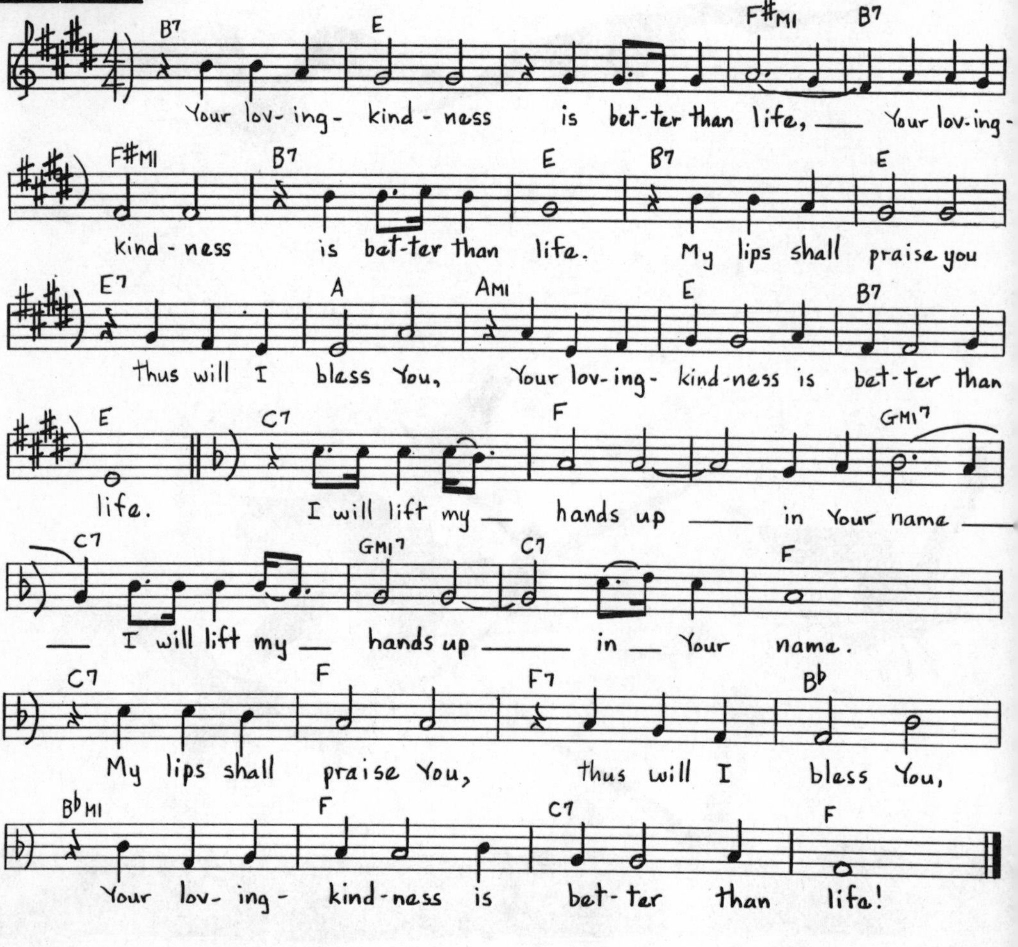

Matthew 11:28-30

Music by MARION WARRINGTON

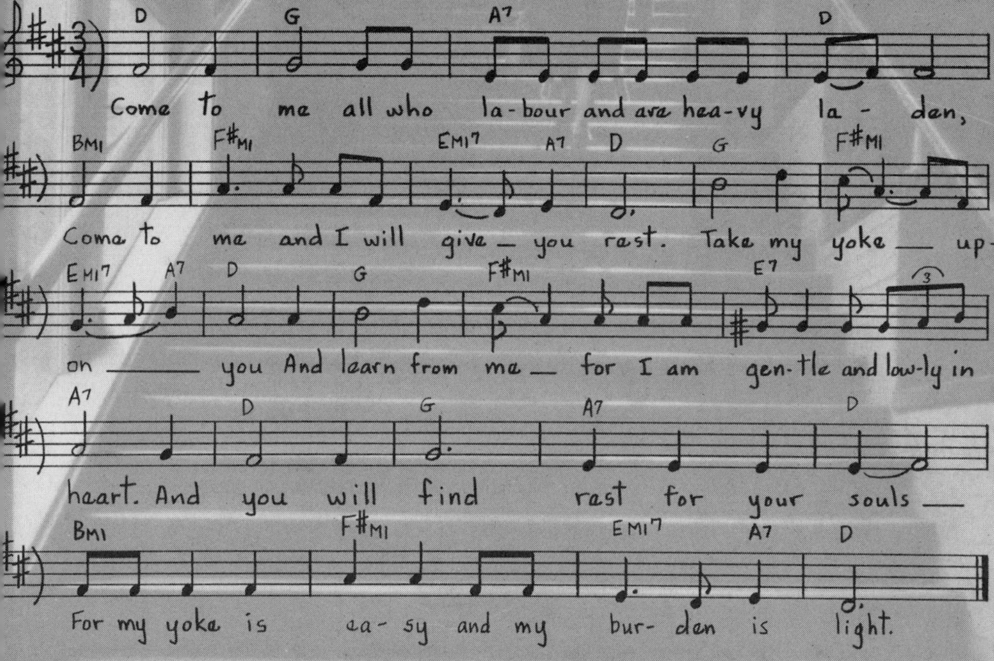

Come to me all who la-bour and are hea-vy la - den, Come to me and I will give — you rest. Take my yoke __ up-on __ you And learn from me __ for I am gen-tle and low-ly in heart. And you will find rest for your souls __ For my yoke is ea-sy and my bur-den is light.

...and I will give you rest.

I Will Not Forget You

Based on Isaiah 49:15

Carey Landry

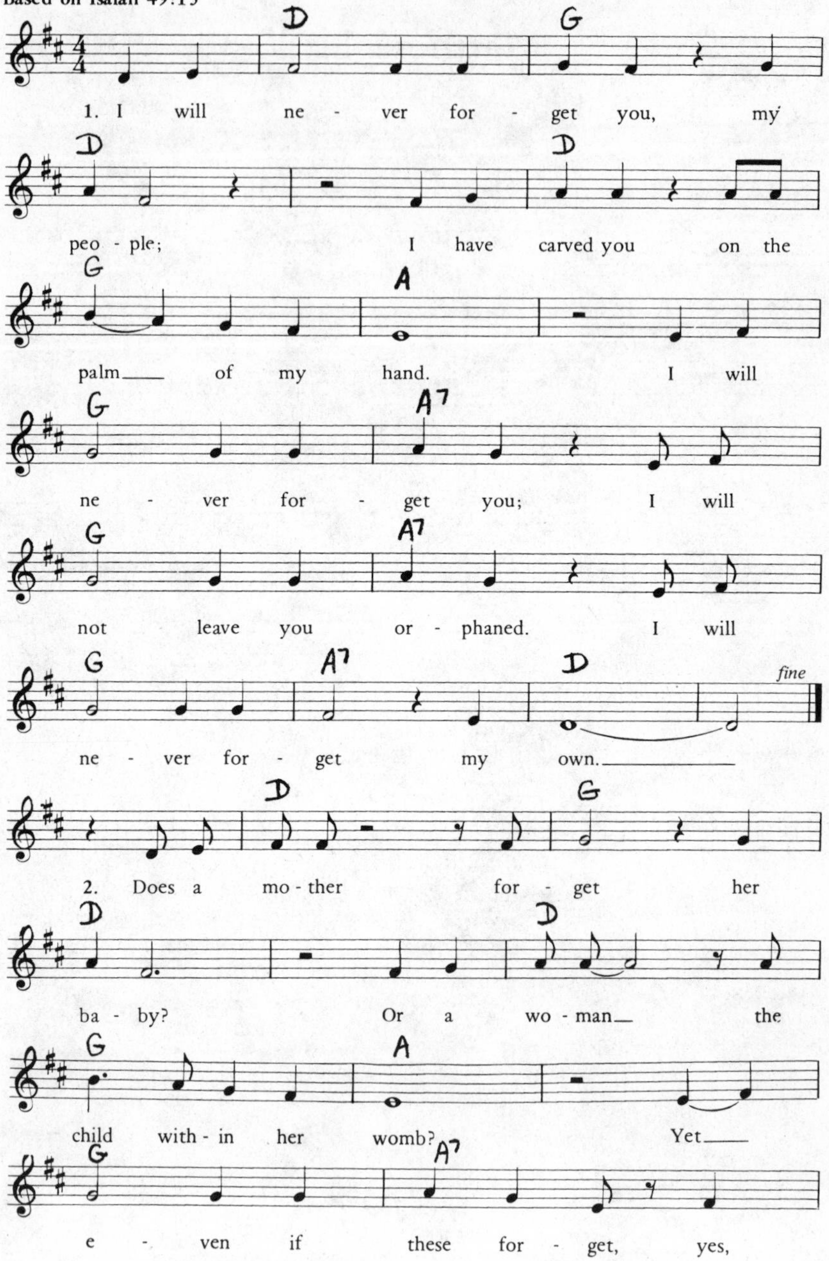

1. I will ne-ver for-get you, my peo-ple; I have carved you on the palm___ of my hand. I will ne-ver for-get you; I will not leave you or-phaned. I will ne-ver for-get my own.___

2. Does a mo-ther for-get her ba-by? Or a wo-man___ the child with-in her womb? Yet___ e-ven if these for-get, yes,

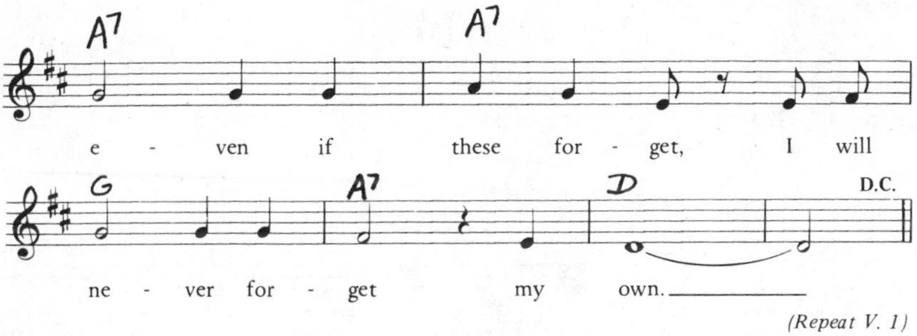

e - ven if these for - get, I will

ne - ver for - get my own._____

(Repeat V. 1)

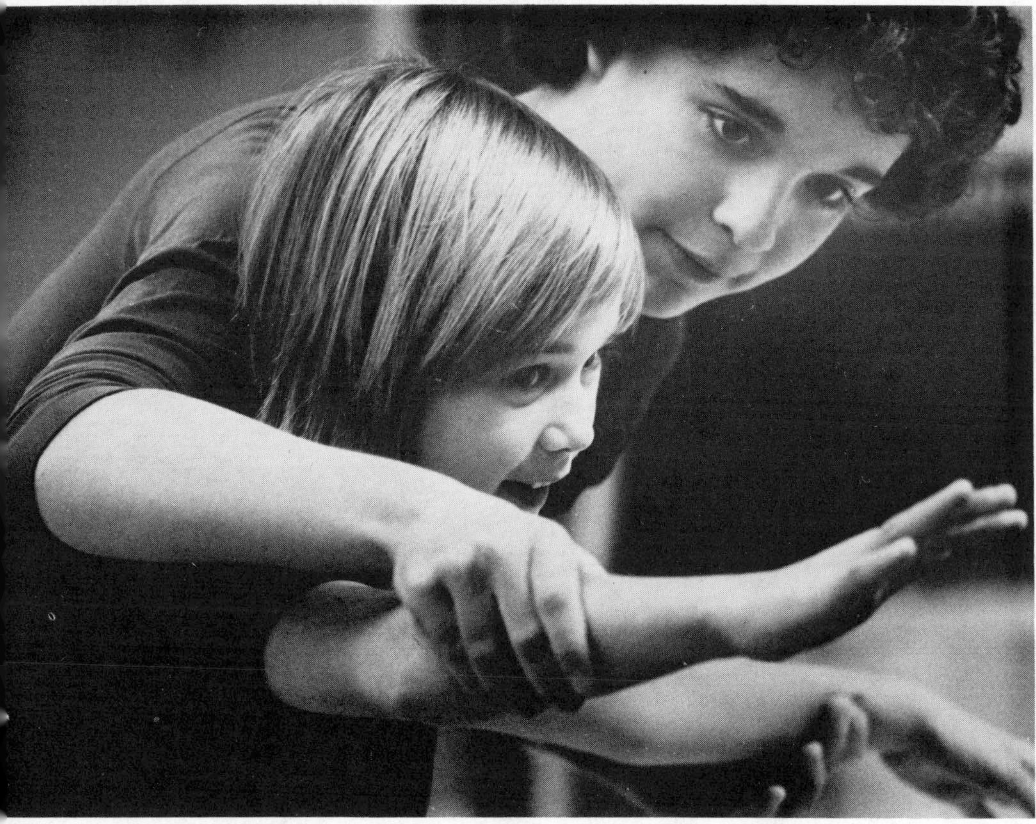

The Daily Pantagraph

'I Have Carved You on the Palm of my Hand'

Parables

From Luke 15:4-24
Capo 1 (EMI)

Judith May Newton

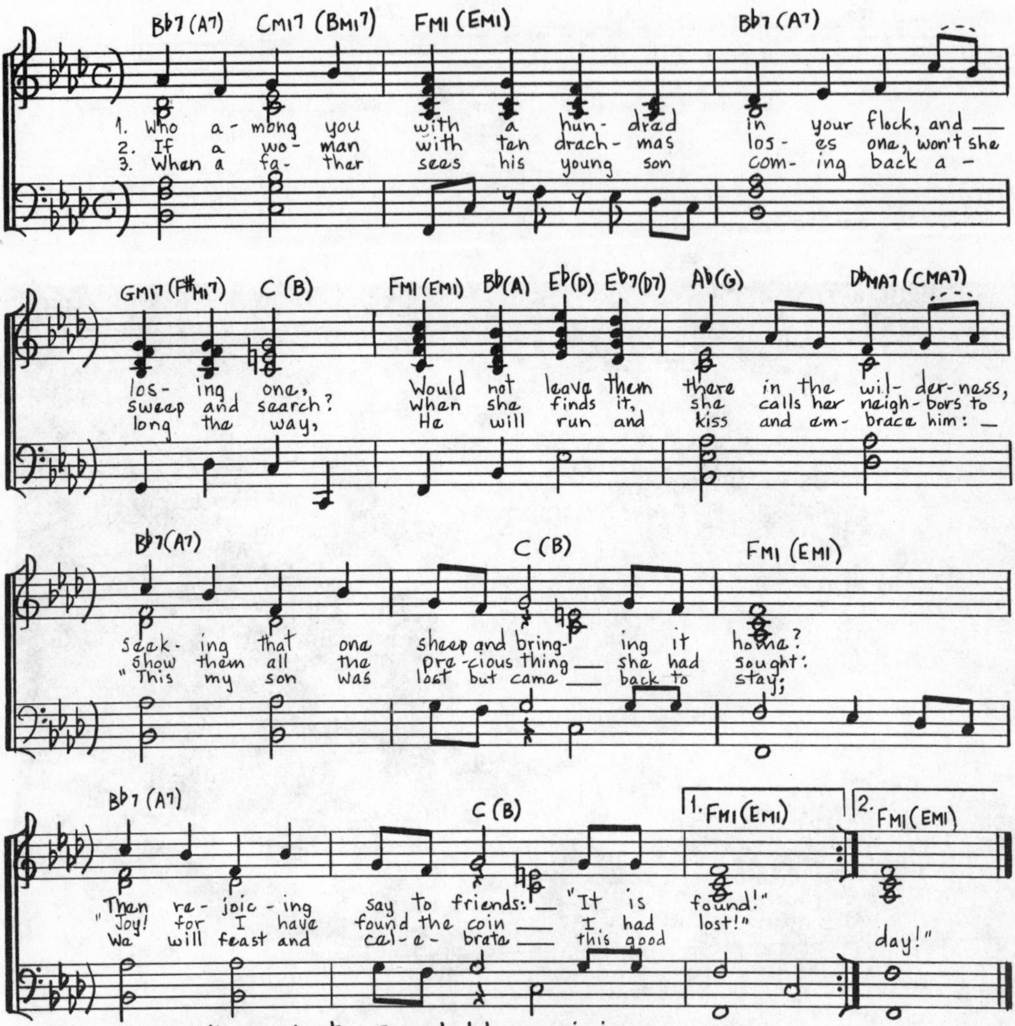

1. Who a-mong you with a hun-dred in your flock, and __
2. If a wo-man with ten drach-mas los-es one, won't she
3. When a fa-ther sees his young son com-ing back a-

los-ing one, Would not leave them there in the wil-der-ness,
sweep and search? When she finds it, she calls her neigh-bors to
long the way, He will run and kiss and em-brace him: __

seek-ing that one sheep and bring-ing it home?
"Show them all the pre-cious thing __ she had sought?
"This my son was lost but came __ back to stay;

Then re-joic-ing say to friends: __ "It is found!"
"Joy! for I have found the coin __ I had lost!"
We will feast and cel-e-brate __ this good day!"

© 1976 by Judith May Newton. Reprinted by permission.

PRAYER OF CONFESSION

We wake up and find ourselves lost from you, O God. Sometimes
like a lost sheep, through ignorance; sometimes like a lost coin,
through carelessness; sometimes like a lost child, through willful
disobedience. We make no excuses, O God; we only appeal to your
mercy. Find us, O God; bring us home again. Amen.
(by Harvey Estes. Used by permission.)

Let the Little Children Come

Words and Music by DORIS J. ELLZEY

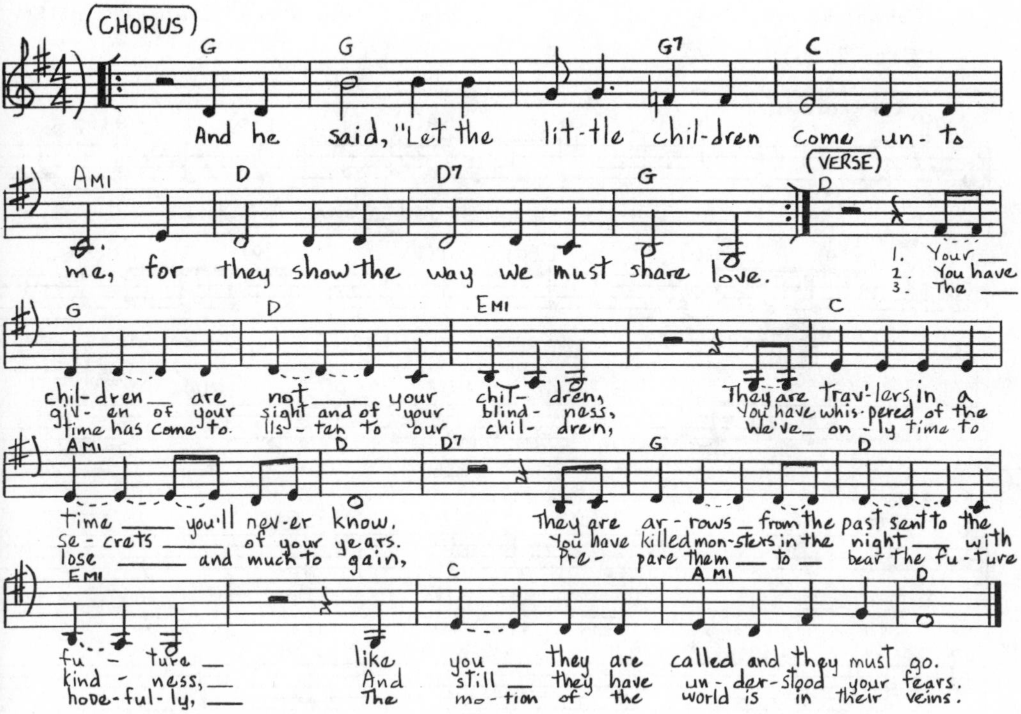

(CHORUS)
And he said, "Let the lit-tle chil-dren come un-to me, for they show the way we must share love.

(VERSE)
1. Your chil-dren__ are not__ your chil-dren, They are trav-'lers in a time __ you'll nev-er know. They are ar-rows __ from the past sent to the fu-ture __ like you __ they are called and they must go.

2. You have giv-en of your sight and of your blind-ness, You have whis-pered of the se-crets __ of your years. You have killed mon-sters in the night __ with kind-ness,__ And still __ they have un-der-stood your fears.

3. The time has come to lis-ten to our chil-dren; We've __ on-ly time to lose __ and much to gain, Pre-pare them __ to __ bear the fu-ture hope-ful-ly, __ The mo-tion of the world is in their veins.

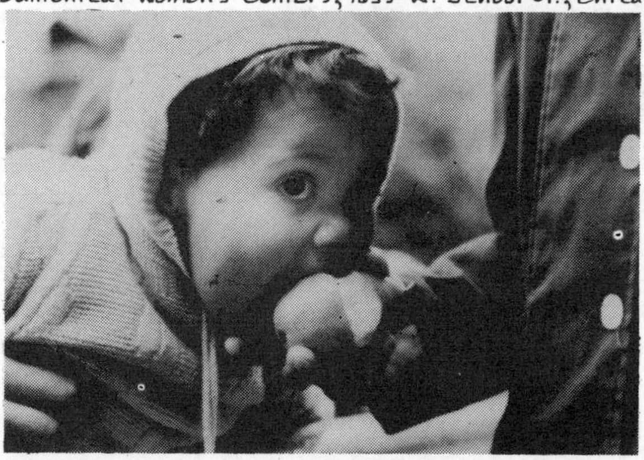

Cheryl Munn

Lose your life to find it

Bound But Free!

Romans 6

Words and Music by ART ALLEN

Capo 2 (D)

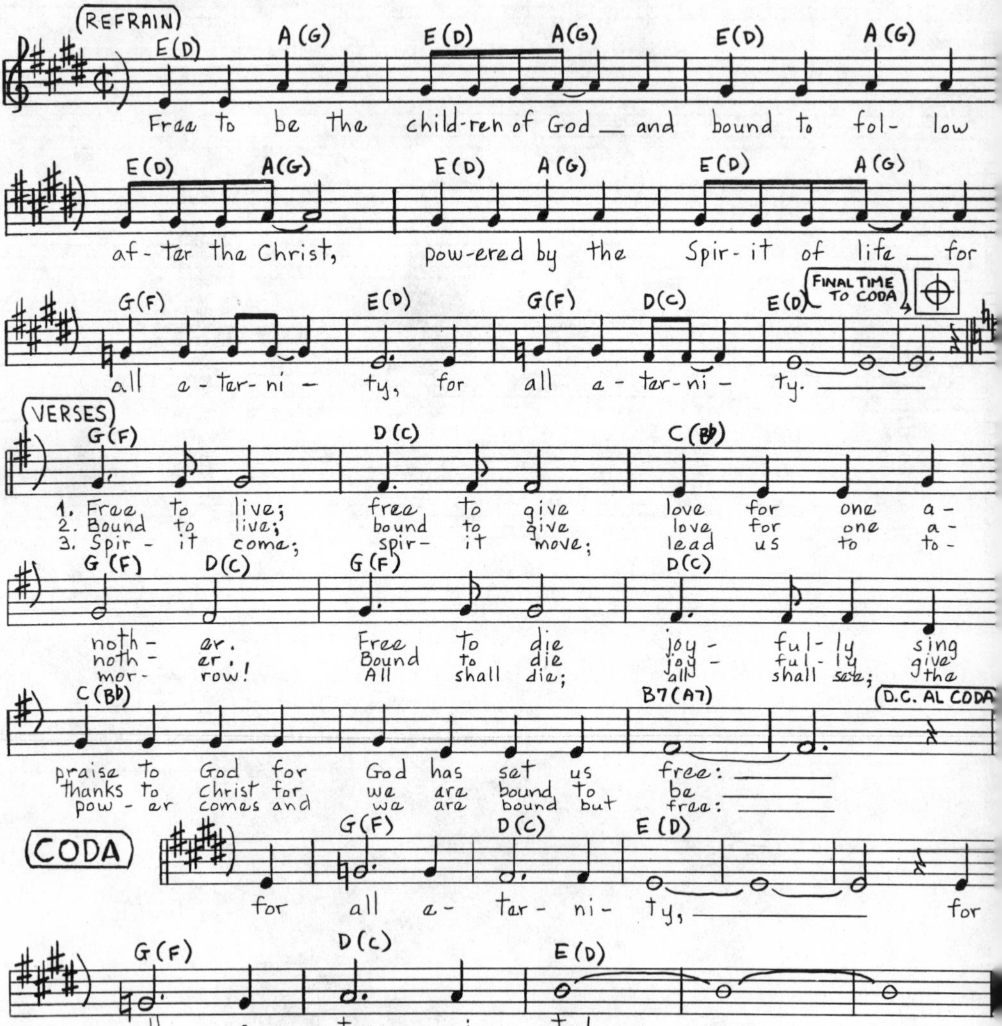

(REFRAIN)

Free to be the child-ren of God — and bound to fol-low af-ter the Christ, pow-ered by the Spir-it of life — for all a-ter-ni-ty, for all a-ter-ni-ty. —

VERSES

1. Free to live; free to give love for one a-noth-er. Free to die joy-ful-ly sing praise to God for God has set us free: —
2. Bound to live; bound to give love for one a-noth-er! Bound to die joy-ful-ly give thanks to Christ for we are bound to be: —
3. Spir-it come; spir-it move; lead us to to-mor-row! All shall die; all shall see; the pow-er comes and we are bound but free: —

CODA

for all a-ter-ni-ty, — for all a-ter-ni-ty! —

65

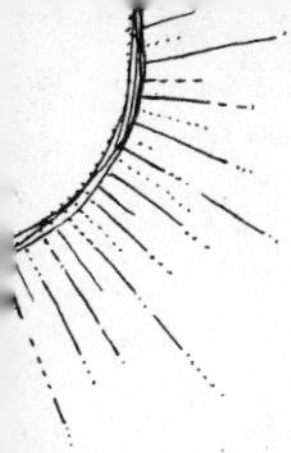

Discovery

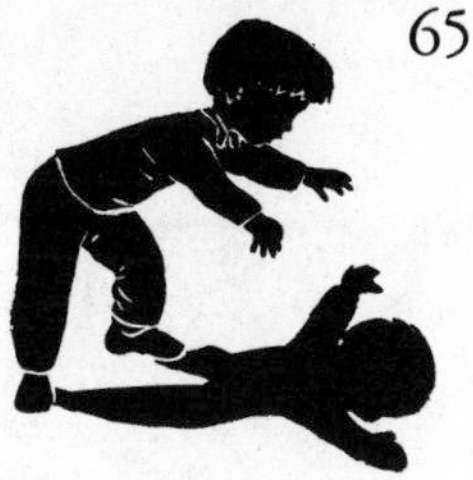

Capo 5, Play in C

Words and Music by JUDITH MAY NEWTON

Dis - cov - er - y, Dis - cov - er - y, ____ A pil - grim - age

in - to light, ____ A pil - grim - age with the light ____
1. of the Beth - le - hem
2. of the morn - ing that
3. of the ev - 'ry - day

star a - bove; ____ Star of Love ____ will lead us to
cast out fear; ____ Draw - ing near; ____ we see that no
gift of grace; ____ Ev - 'ry place ____ we'll find Christ in

Jor - dan's Dove, ____ And spir - it that pur - i - fies ____ and
one is here; ____ The tomb's just a place of rest, ____ for
ev - 'ry face; ____ As we seek the star of Love; ____ we're

o - pens our eyes ____ to God. ____
Je - sus was ____ set free. ____
on _ the move ____ to - day. ____

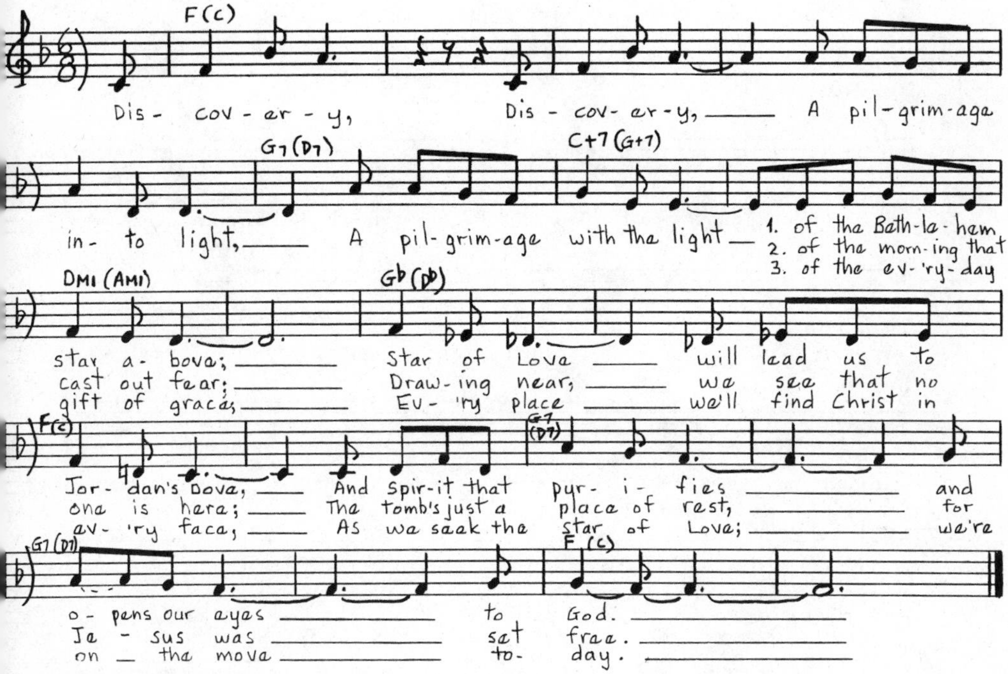

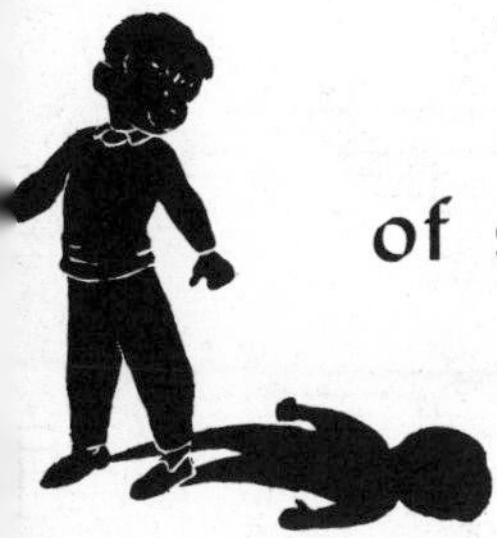

Vision is the art
of seeing things invisible

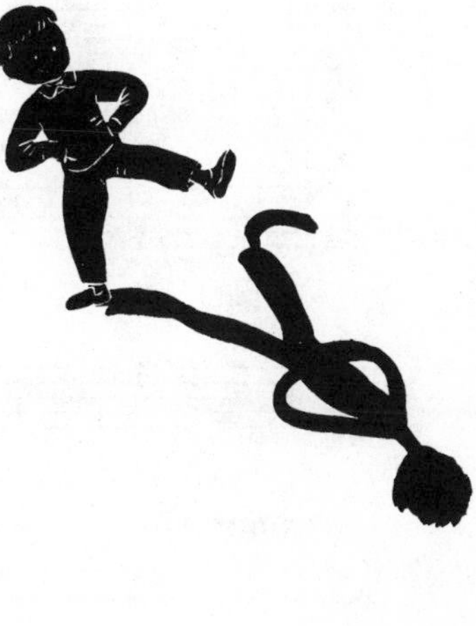

A Gentle Love Song

Joe Wise

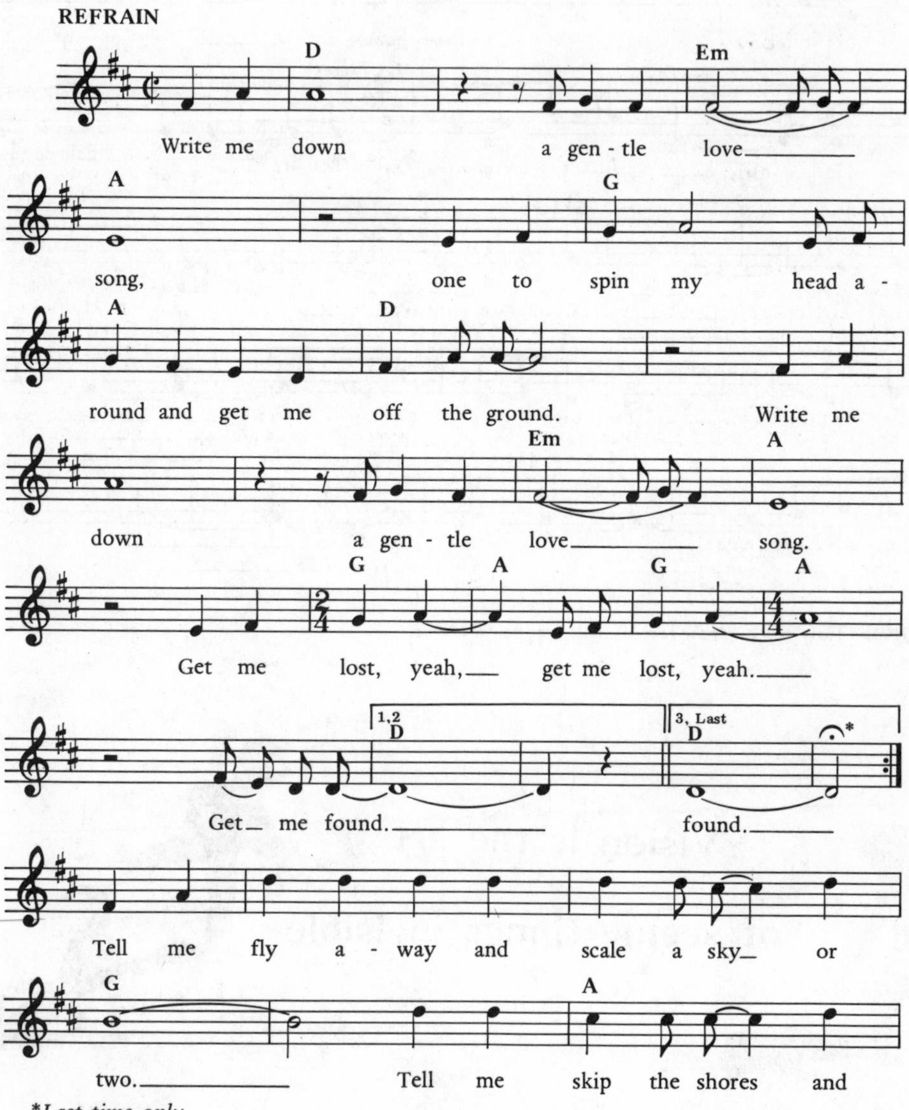

*Last time only

A GENTLE LOVE SONG, cont. (2)

D

taste the o - pen sea. Give me half a start_ and

Em A

I'll be gone_ 'til morn - in'.

G A G A

Look for sun - rise,___ catch the star - flies.___

D G

Watch for me. I'll bring it back,

A D G

I'll bring it back, bring it back, my friend, and

A D G

give it all_ to you.___ I'll bring it back,

A D G

I'll bring it back, bring it back, my friend, and

A D

give it all___ to you.

VERSE

(Tacet - - - - - - - -) Em A

1. I saw a wound - ed fawn run snow blind, lost and
2. I saw a clown with - out his grease - paint cry - in'

D Bm

1. crazed out in a for - est,___ seen a
2. soft - ly on a sub - way,___ seen a

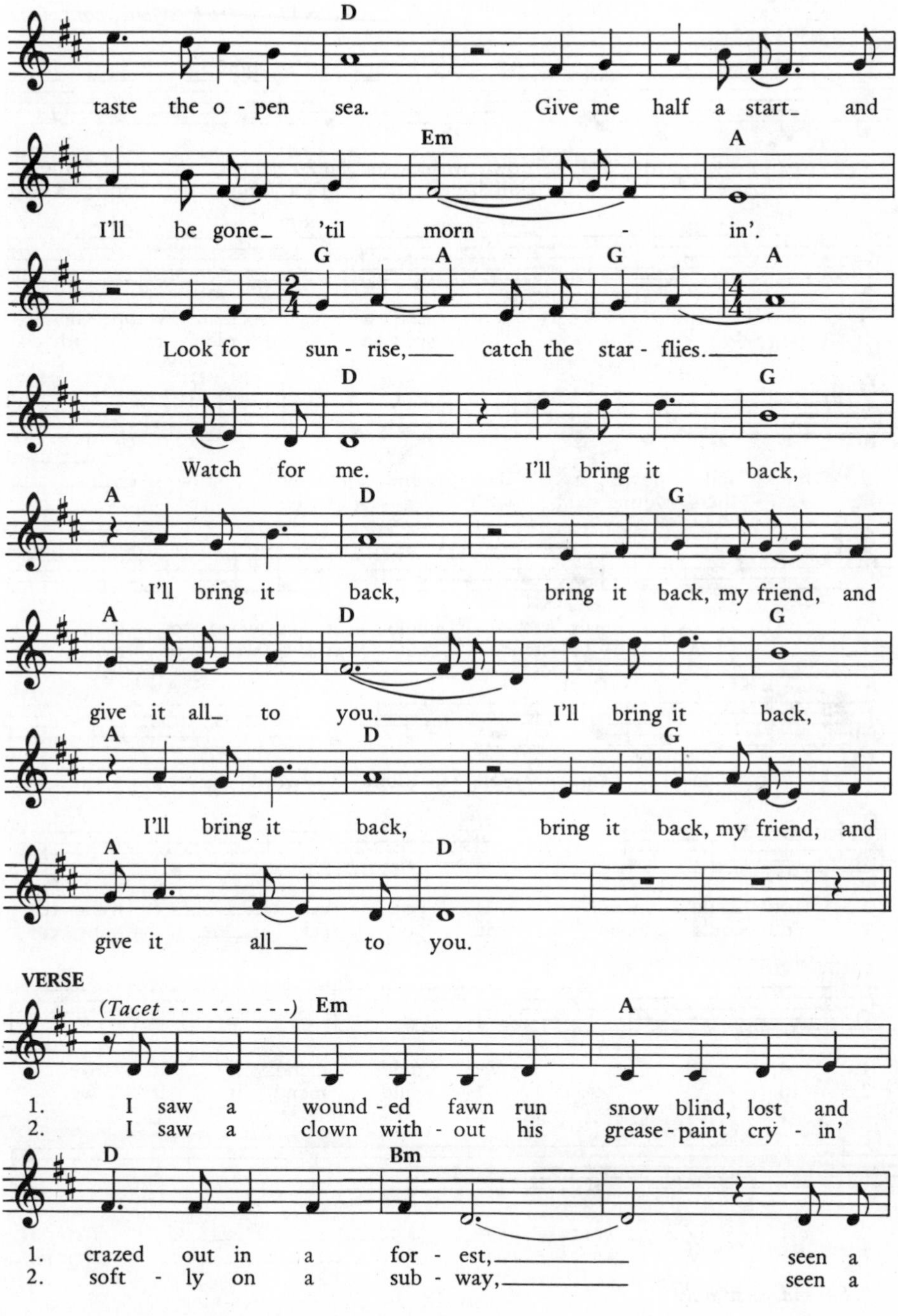

68

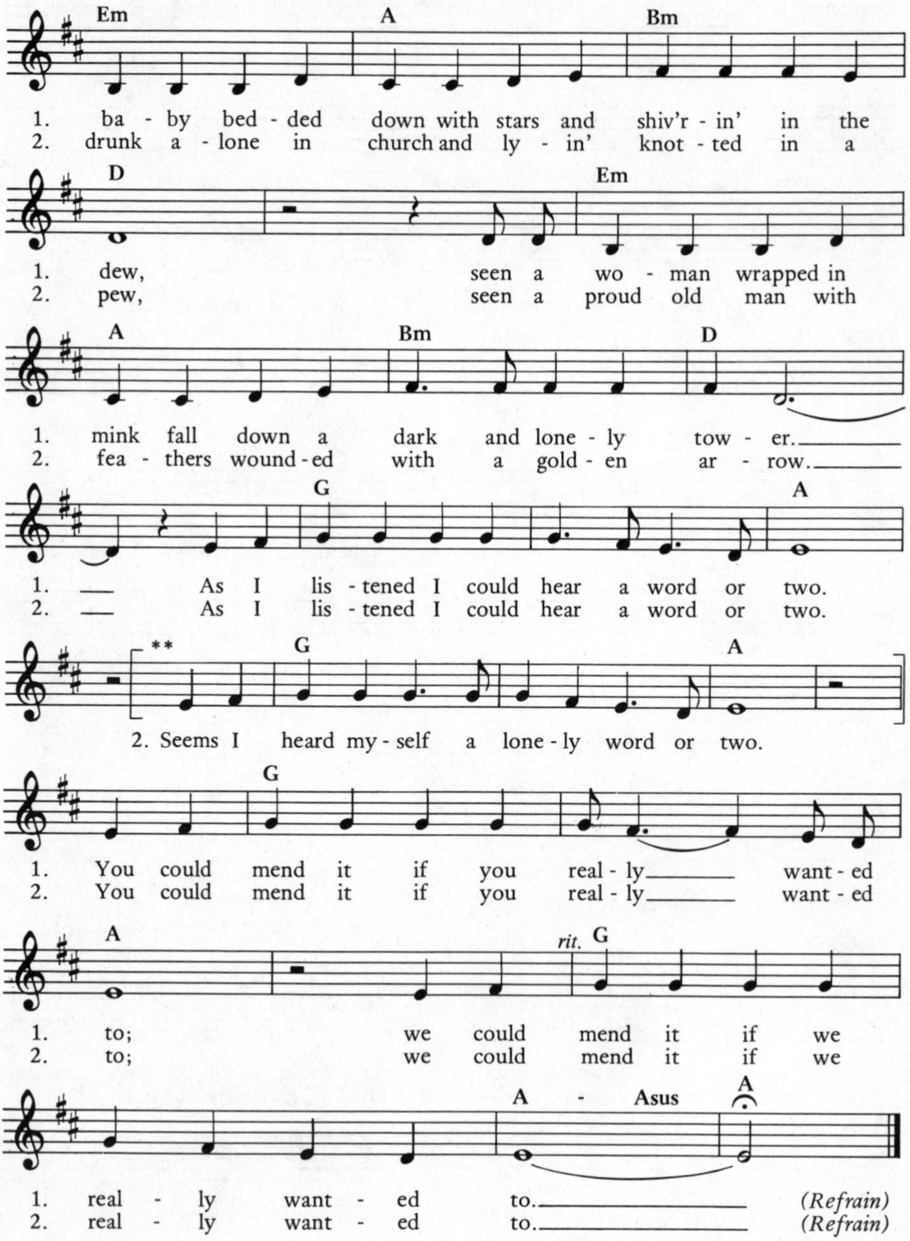

1. ba - by bed - ded down with stars and shiv'r - in' in the
2. drunk a - lone in church and ly - in' knot - ted in a

1. dew, seen a wo - man wrapped in
2. pew, seen a proud old man with

1. mink fall down a dark and lone - ly tow - er.____
2. fea - thers wound - ed with a gold - en ar - row.____

1. ____ As I lis - tened I could hear a word or two.
2. ____ As I lis - tened I could hear a word or two.

2. Seems I heard my - self a lone - ly word or two.

1. You could mend it if you real - ly_____ want - ed
2. You could mend it if you real - ly_____ want - ed

1. to; we could mend it if we
2. to; we could mend it if we

1. real - ly want - ed to._____ (Refrain)
2. real - ly want - ed to._____ (Refrain)

**Second verse only

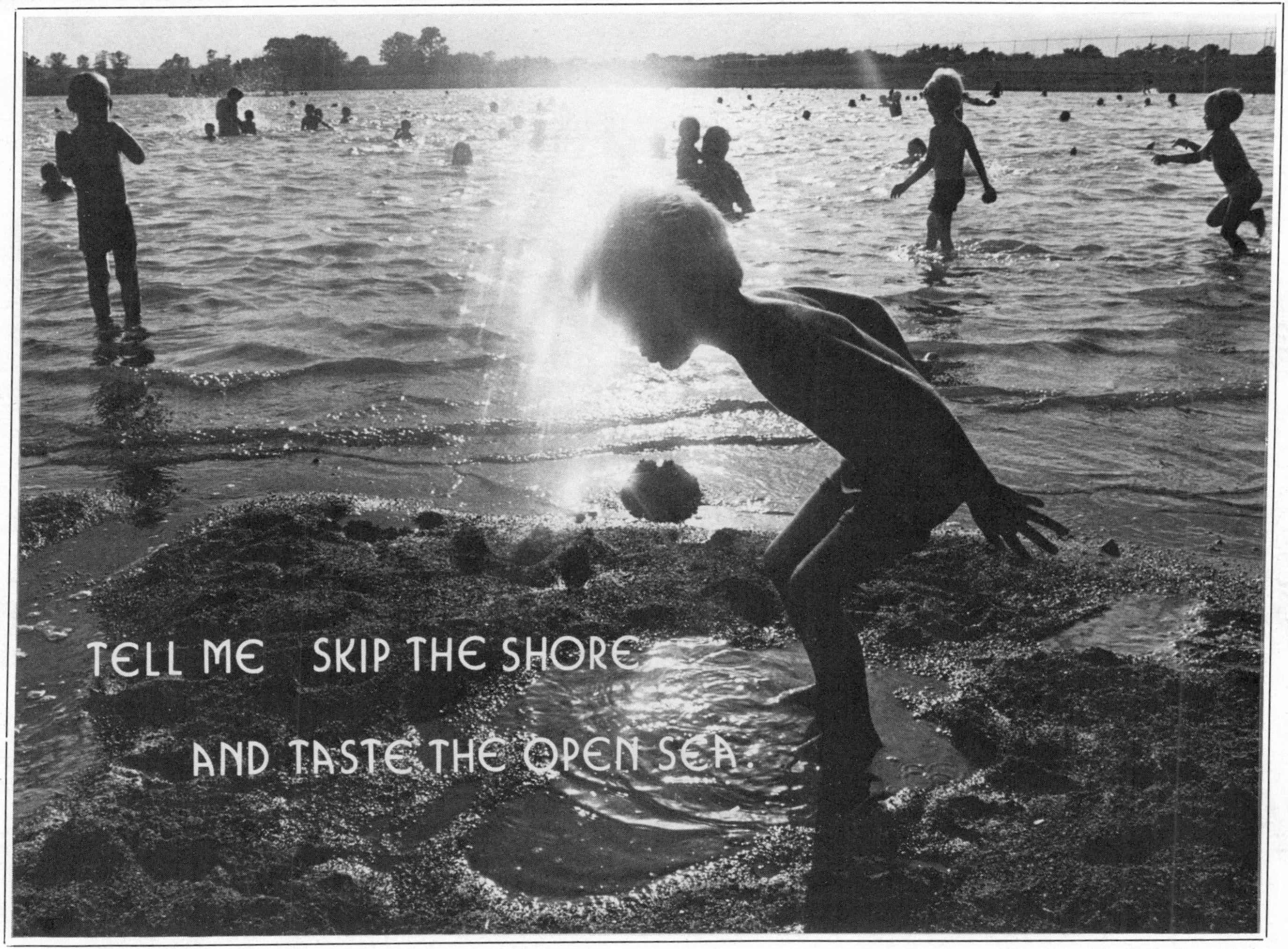

TELL ME SKIP THE SHORE AND TASTE THE OPEN SEA.

The Daily Pantagraph

Blessed Are Those

Joe Wise

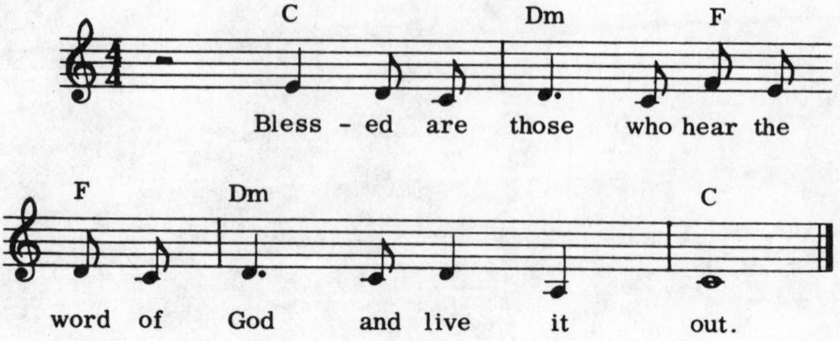

Bless - ed are those who hear the

word of God and live it out.

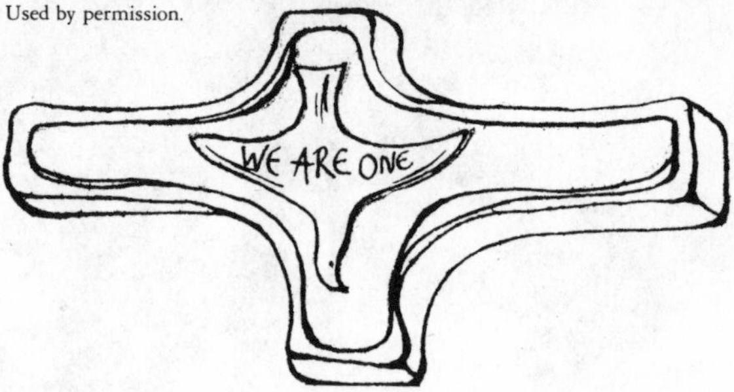

Jesus

Jamaican Melody

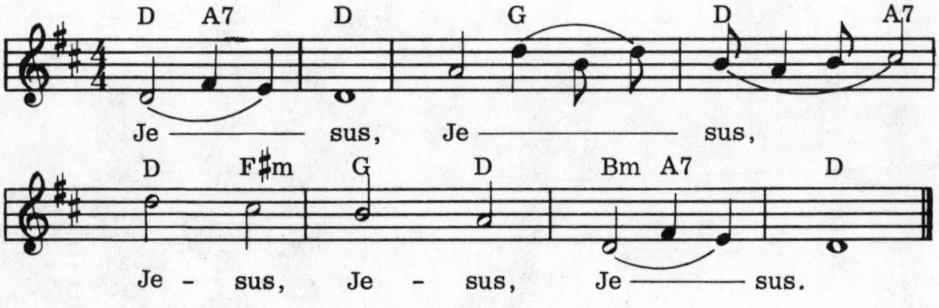

Je —— sus, Je —— sus,

Je - sus, Je - sus, Je —— sus.

2. He died; He died;
He died; He died;
He died.

3. He rose again;
He rose again;
He rose, He rose;
He rose again.

4. He lives in me;
He lives in me;
He lives, He lives;
He lives in me.

5. He's coming soon;
He's coming soon;
He's coming soon;
He's coming soon.

Simple Gifts

Shaker Hymn

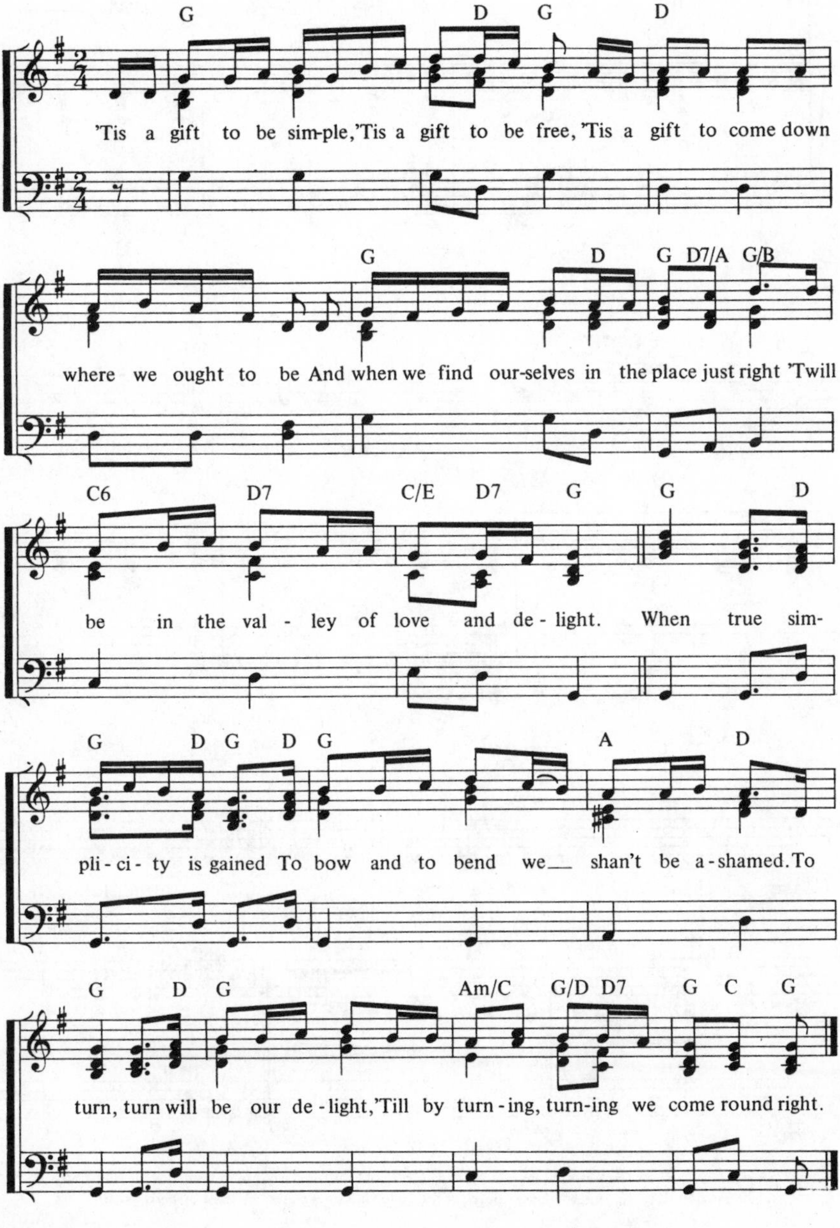

Faith Is Such a Simple Thing

Words and Music by
AL CARMINES

Faith is such a sim-ple thing, It can't talk, but

on - ly sing, It can't rea - son, but can dance.

Take a chance, take a chance. Life is full of

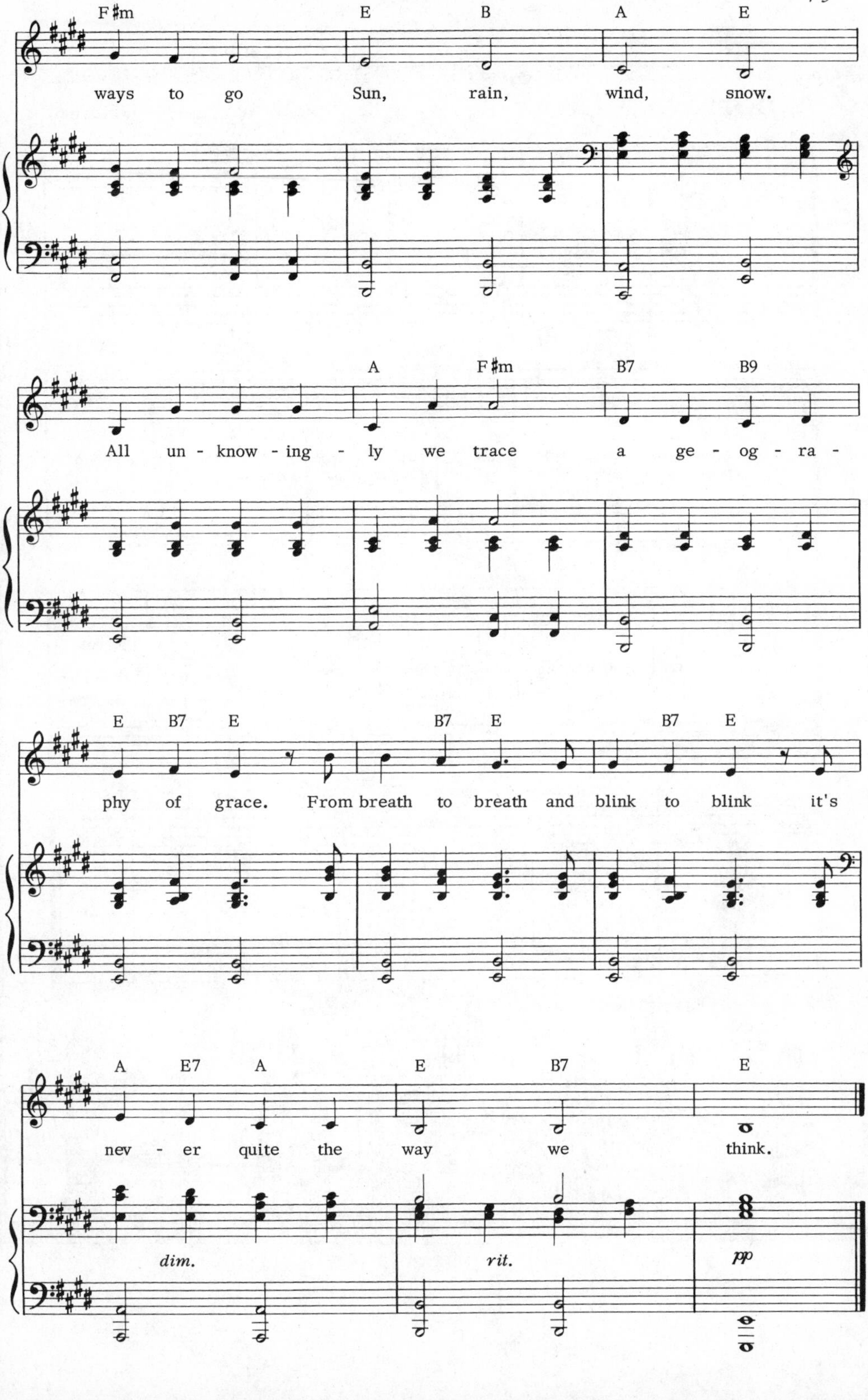
F♯m E B A E
ways to go Sun, rain, wind, snow.
A F♯m B7 B9
All un - know - ing - ly we trace a ge - og - ra -
E B7 E B7 E B7 E
phy of grace. From breath to breath and blink to blink it's
A E7 A E B7 E
nev - er quite the way we think.
dim.
rit.
pp

A Borrowed Cross

Judith May Newton

1. A bor-rowed room to come to life in, A bor--rowed cross to die on; A gift that some---one else has brought, A way that some---one else has taught; A bor---rowed tomb to lie in.

2. Re- ceiv----ing bless-ing at the Jor---dan, Be- com---ing God's own sign then; Re- ceiv----ing God's own plan with grace and act----ing for the hu------man race, Our Christ chose life by dy - - - - - - ing.

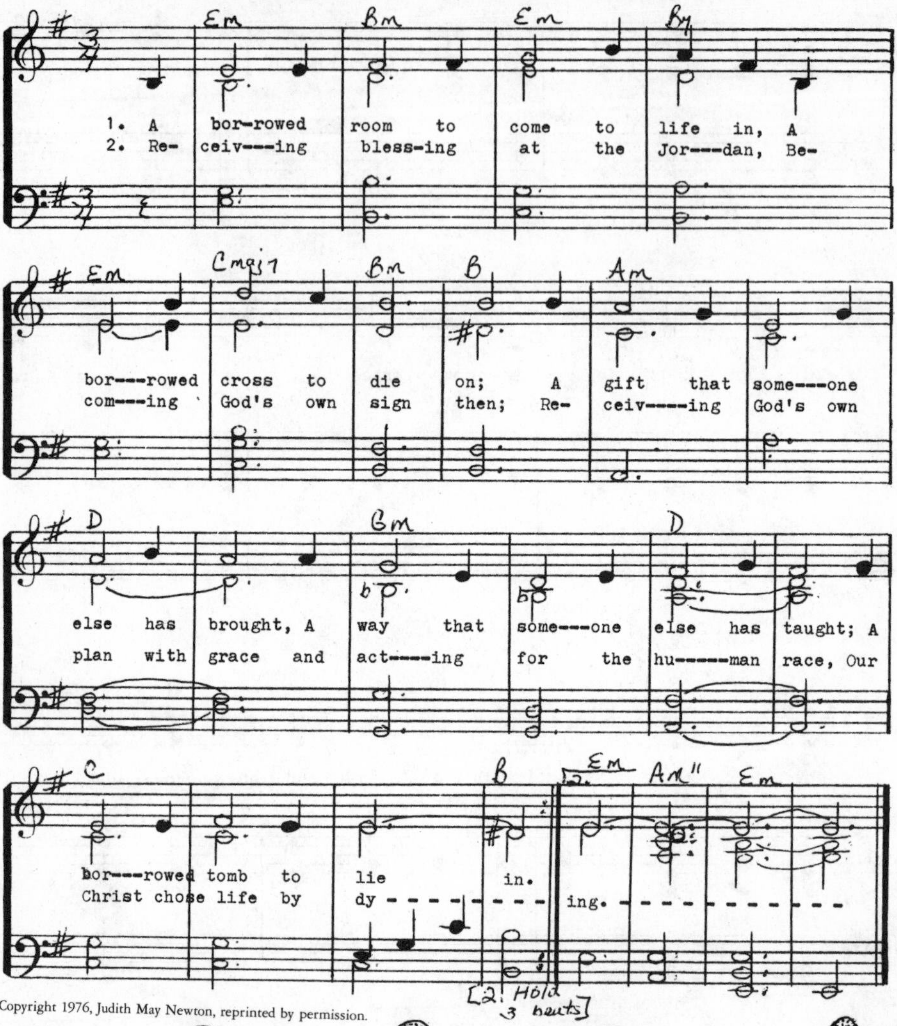

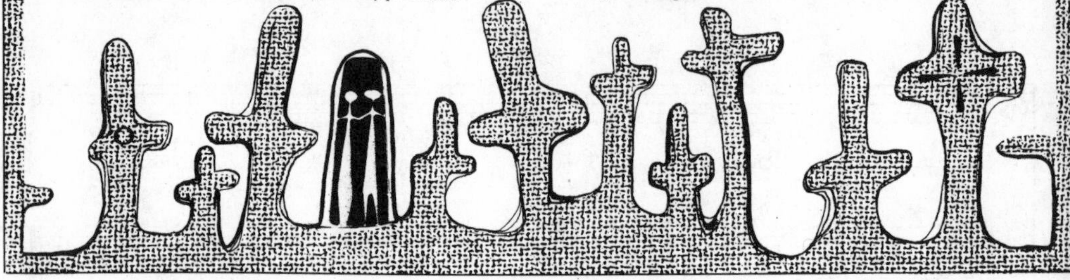

Peace Time

Words and Music
by REV. CAREY LANDRY

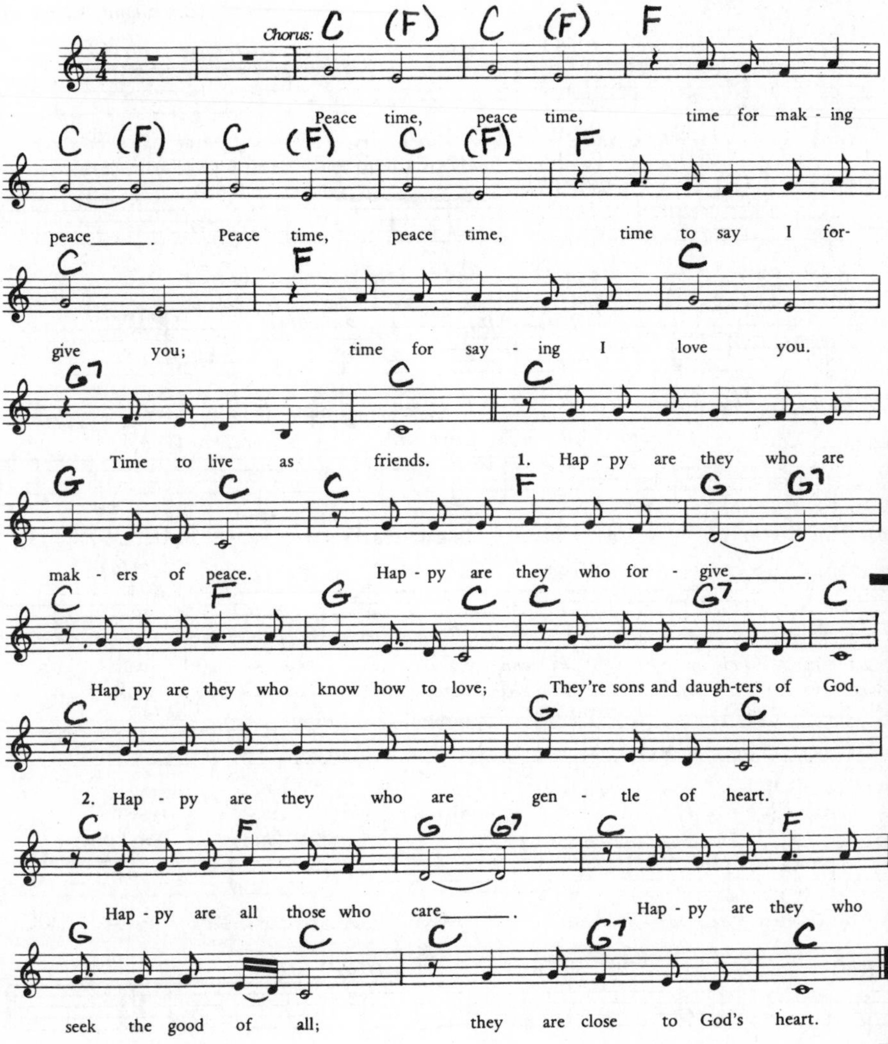

Peace time, peace time, time for mak - ing peace___. Peace time, peace time, time to say I for-give you; time for say - ing I love you. Time to live as friends.

1. Hap - py are they who are mak - ers of peace. Hap - py are they who for - give___. Hap-py are they who know how to love; They're sons and daugh-ters of God.

2. Hap - py are they who are gen - tle of heart. Hap - py are all those who care___. Hap - py are they who seek the good of all; they are close to God's heart.

the peacemakers

Blessed are

Who Knows the Face of God?

76

Tom Neufer Emswiler

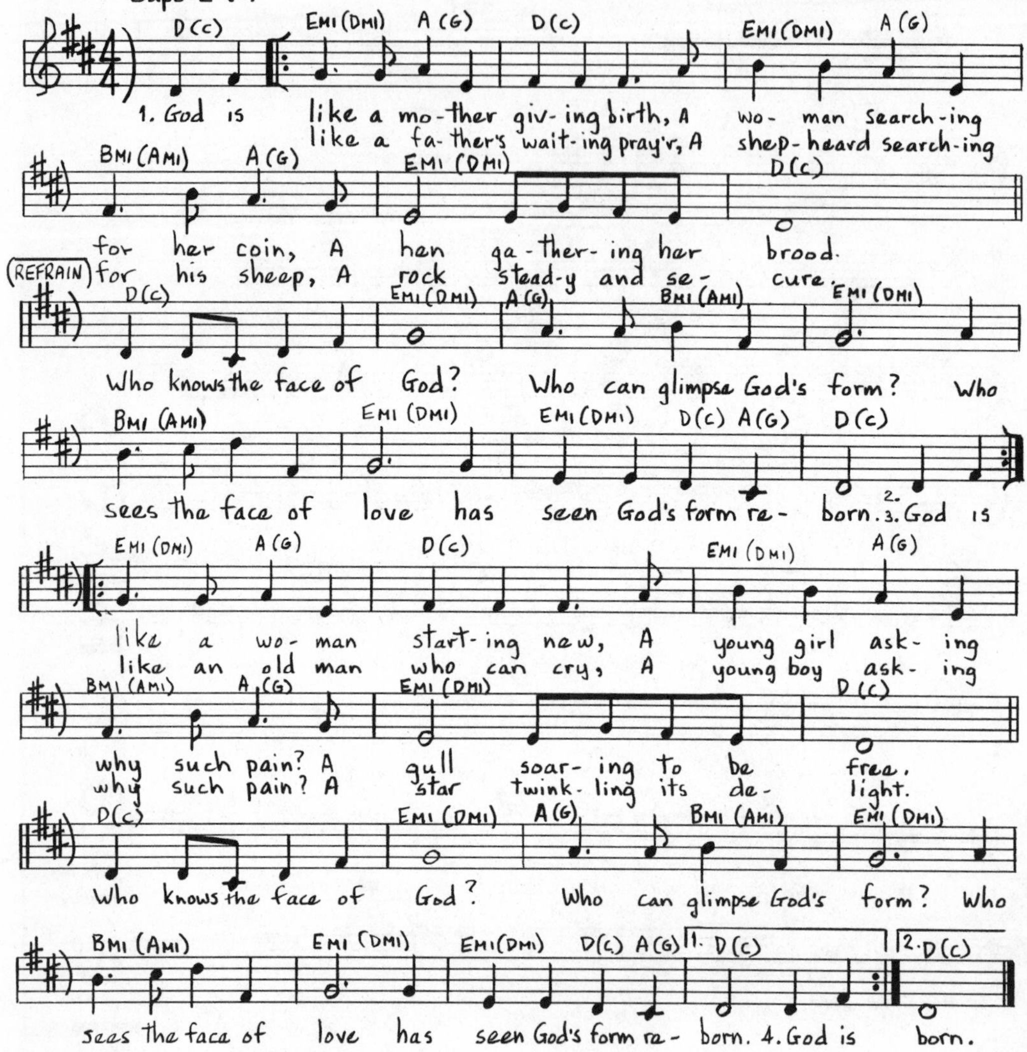

Is your God too small?

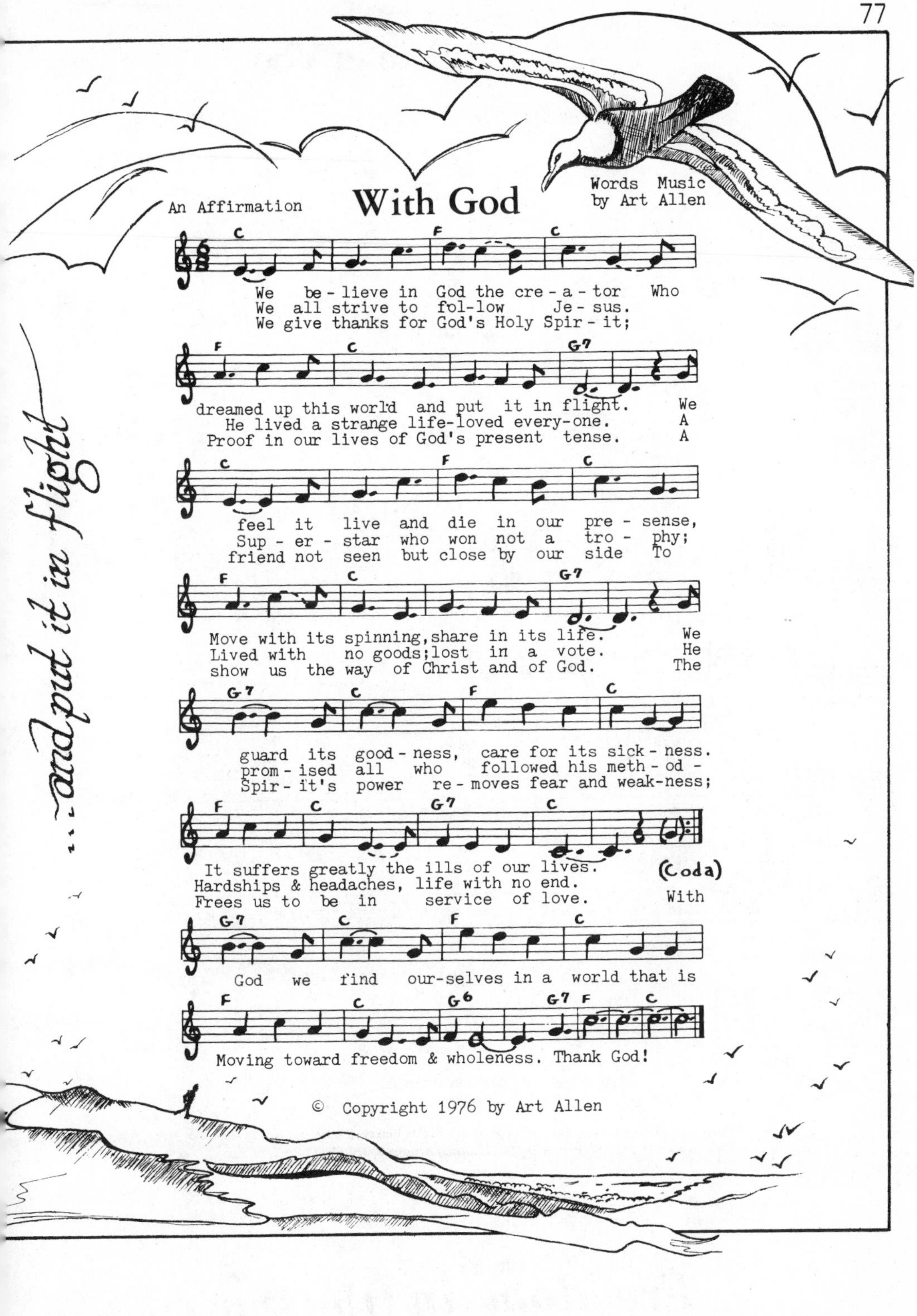

An Affirmation

With God

Words Music
by Art Allen

We be-lieve in God the cre-a-tor Who
We all strive to fol-low Je-sus.
We give thanks for God's Holy Spir-it;

dreamed up this world and put it in flight. We
He lived a strange life-loved every-one. A
Proof in our lives of God's present tense. A

feel it live and die in our pre-sense,
Sup-er-star who won not a tro-phy;
friend not seen but close by our side To

Move with its spinning, share in its life. We
Lived with no goods; lost in a vote. He
show us the way of Christ and of God. The

guard its good-ness, care for its sick-ness.
prom-ised all who followed his meth-od-
Spir-it's power re-moves fear and weak-ness;

It suffers greatly the ills of our lives. (Coda)
Hardships & headaches, life with no end.
Frees us to be in service of love. With

God we find our-selves in a world that is

Moving toward freedom & wholeness. Thank God!

... and put it in flight

I Believe in You

Joe Wise

(ASCAP)

Capo 2, play G

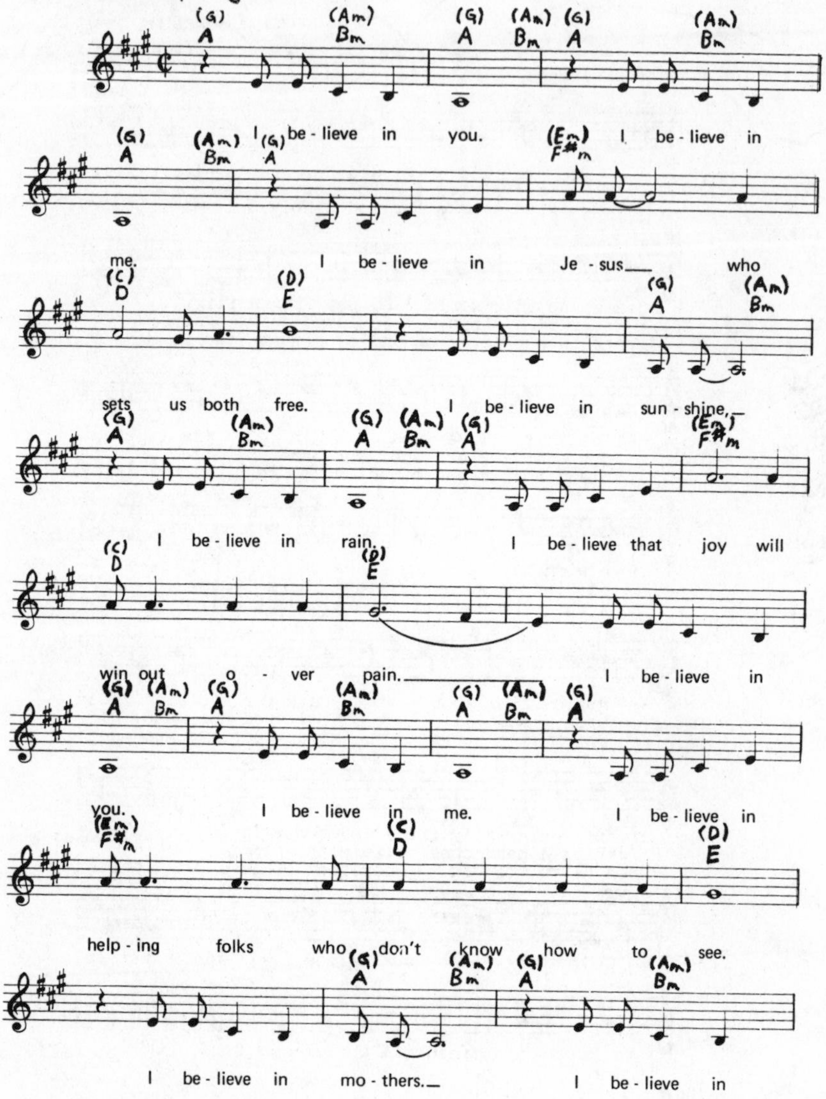

Freedom in the Spirit

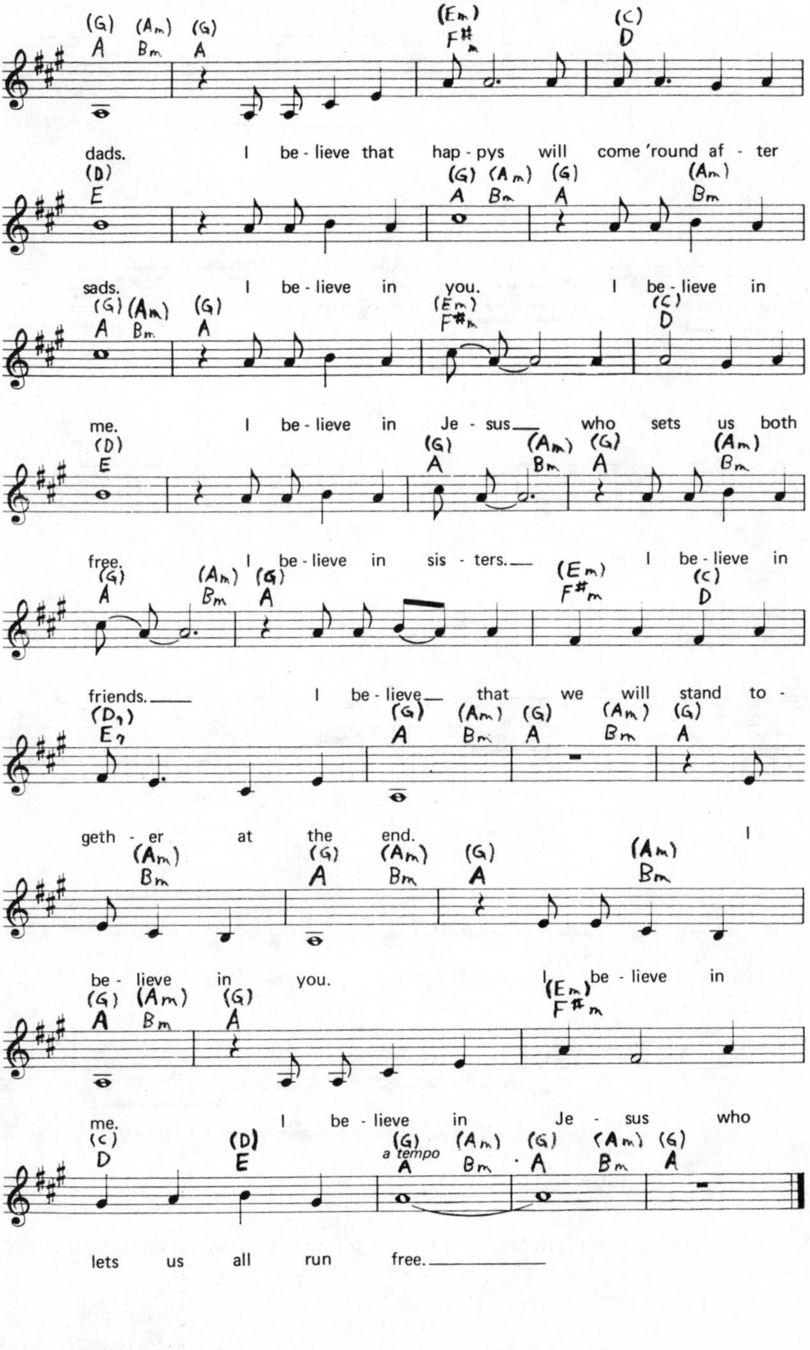

dads.   I be-lieve that hap-pys will come 'round af-ter

sads.   I be-lieve in you.   I be-lieve in

me.   I be-lieve in Je-sus___ who sets us both

free.   I be-lieve in sis-ters.___   I be-lieve in

friends.___   I be-lieve___ that we will stand to-

geth-er at the end.   I

be-lieve in you.   I be-lieve in

me.   I be-lieve in Je-sus who

lets us all run free.___

My Name

Barbara Neighbors

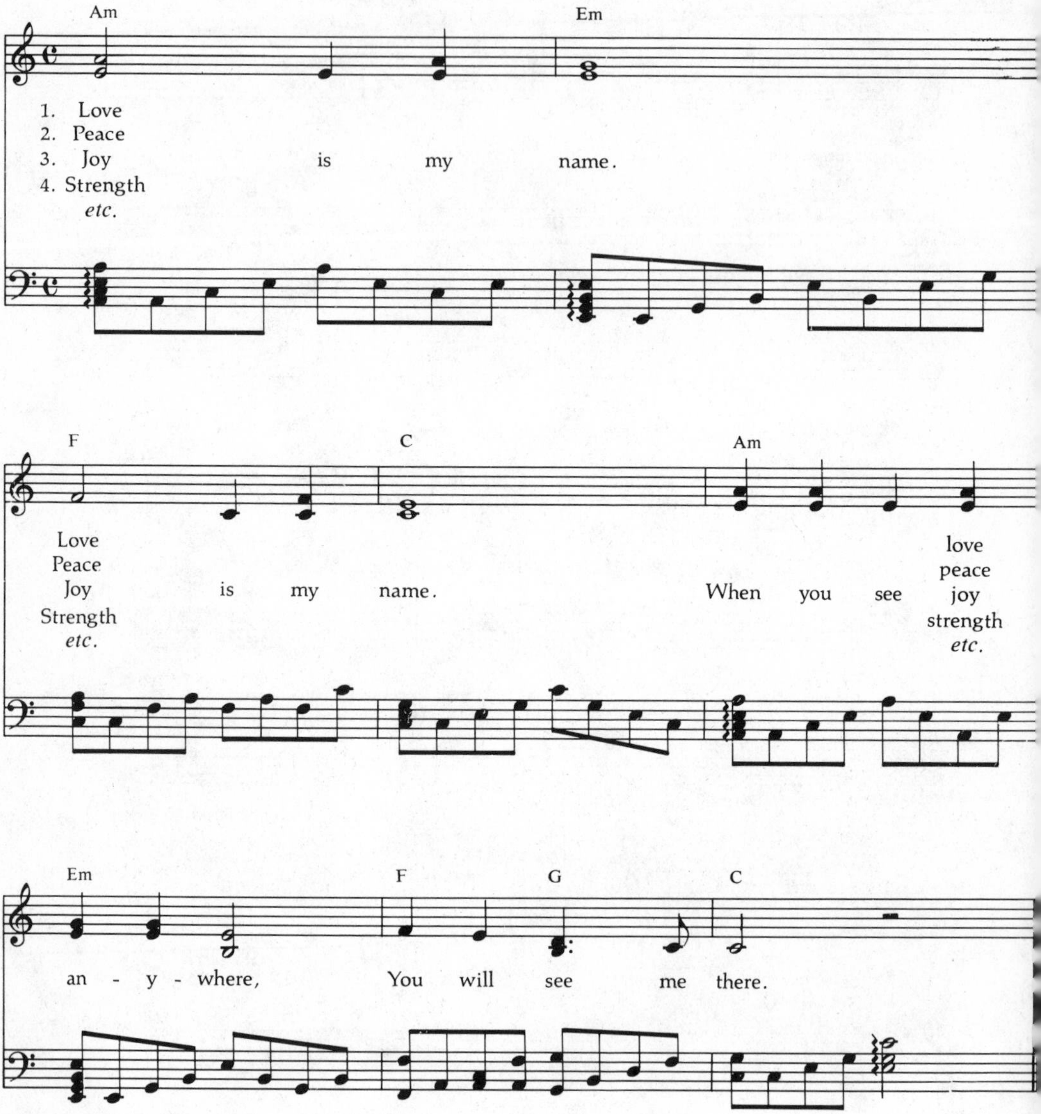

1. Love
2. Peace
3. Joy   is   my   name.
4. Strength
   etc.

Love   love
Peace   peace
Joy   is   my   name.   When you see joy
Strength   strength
etc.   *etc.*

an - y - where,   You will see   me there.

COMMUNION

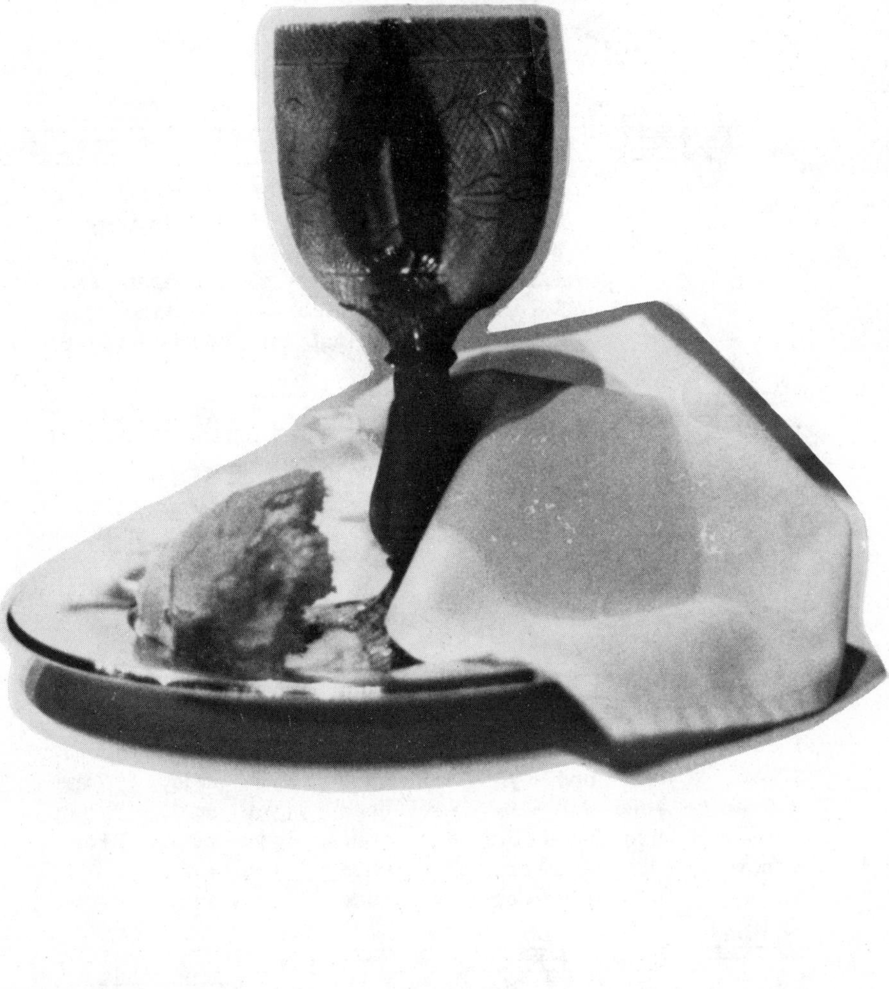

Cheryl Munn

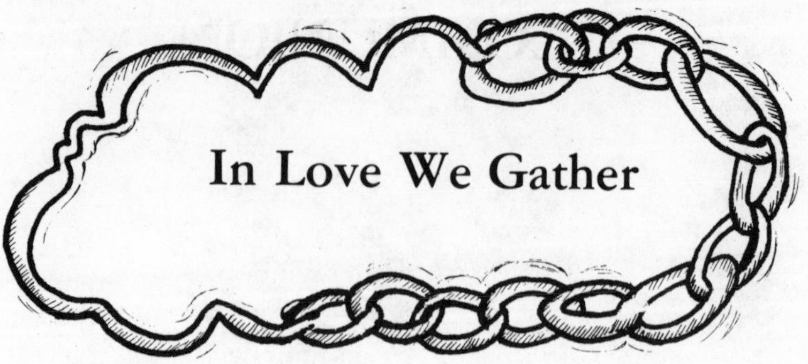

In Love We Gather

Robert J. Schaffer

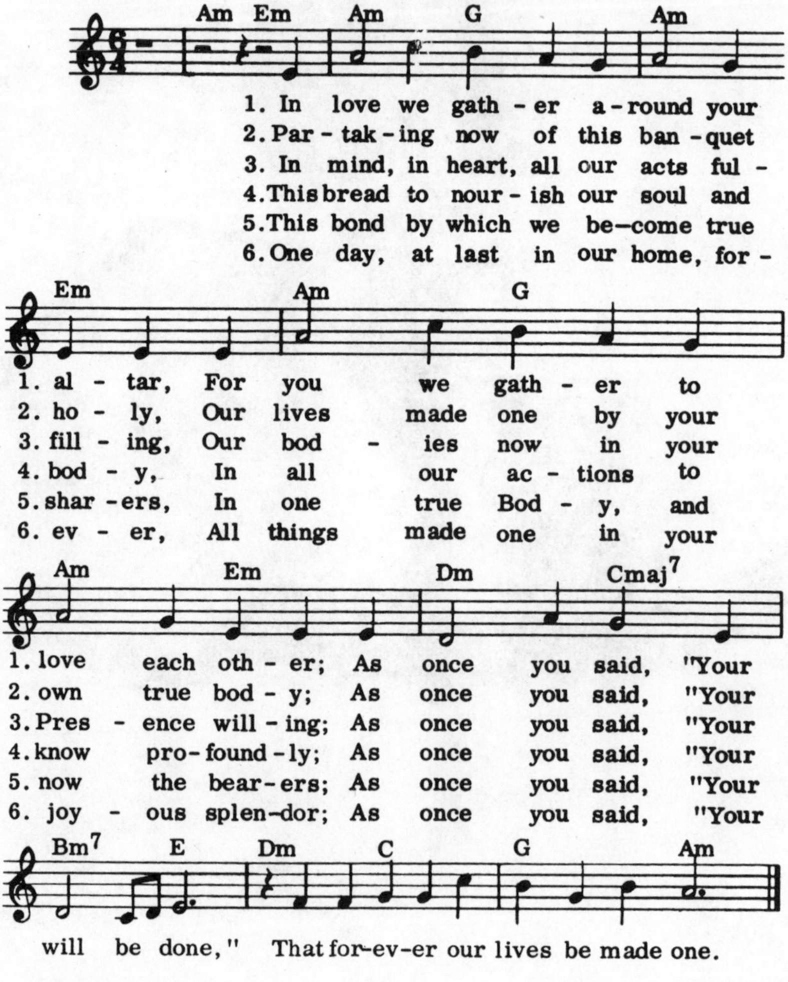

1. In love we gath - er a - round your
2. Par - tak - ing now of this ban - quet
3. In mind, in heart, all our acts ful -
4. This bread to nour - ish our soul and
5. This bond by which we be—come true
6. One day, at last in our home, for -

1. al - tar, For you we gath - er to
2. ho - ly, Our lives made one by your
3. fill - ing, Our bod - ies now in your
4. bod - y, In all our ac - tions to
5. shar - ers, In one true Bod - y, and
6. ev - er, All things made one in your

1. love each oth - er; As once you said, "Your
2. own true bod - y; As once you said, "Your
3. Pres - ence will - ing; As once you said, "Your
4. know pro - found - ly; As once you said, "Your
5. now the bear - ers; As once you said, "Your
6. joy - ous splen-dor; As once you said, "Your

will be done," That for-ev-er our lives be made one.

I Am Meat and I Am Drink

JOHN KILLINGER   VANDERBILT   ANNE KILLINGER

1. Are you hun-gry, are you tired? Do you feel that you're a-lone? If you
2. Eat for health and eat for wealth, Eat your way to joy di-vine. Let your
3. Take my food in-to your heart, Feel the spir-it, feel the power. Let it
4. Spread the word that food is here, Call the peo-ple far and near; Let them
5. We will show the world our love, We will pass the food a-round. We will
6. When this age has passed a-way, All its glo-ry in de-cay, We will

1. do, then come with me and Find a strength be-yond your own, I am
2. life de-pend on me — On this bread and on this wine,
3. hap-pen to you now — Come a-live this ve-ry hour.
4. ga-ther at the ta-ble; Shout it out and let them hear.
5. praise the name of Christ — Till all earth has heard the sound!
6. still be go-ing strong — On the food we share to-day.

meat and I am drink, I am bread and I am wine. Taste and see how good I am When your life is joined to mine.

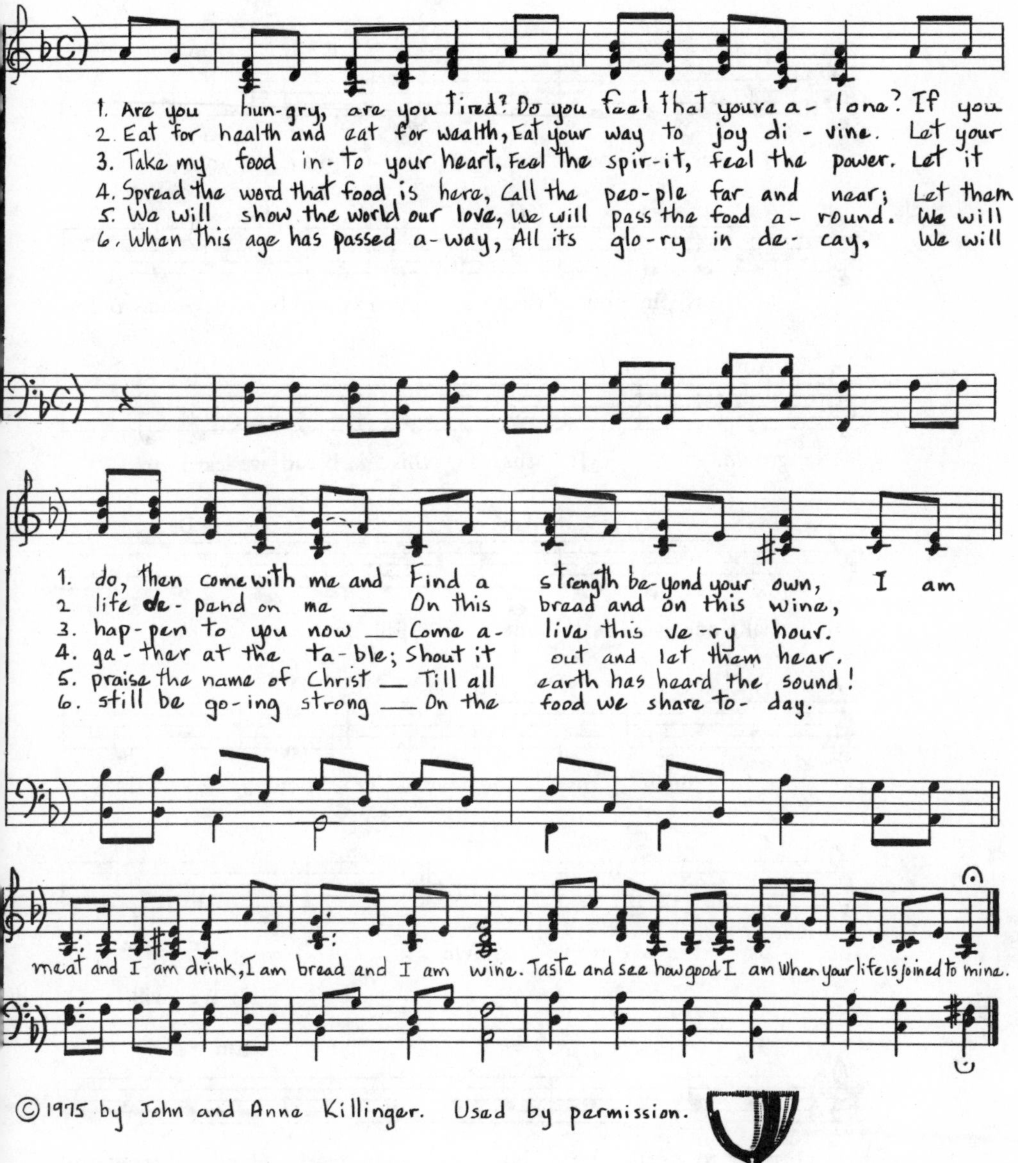

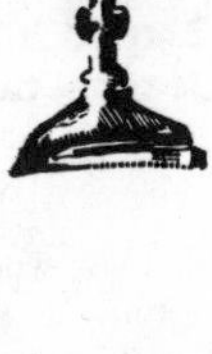

Jesus In Our Hands

Joe Wise
(ASCAP)

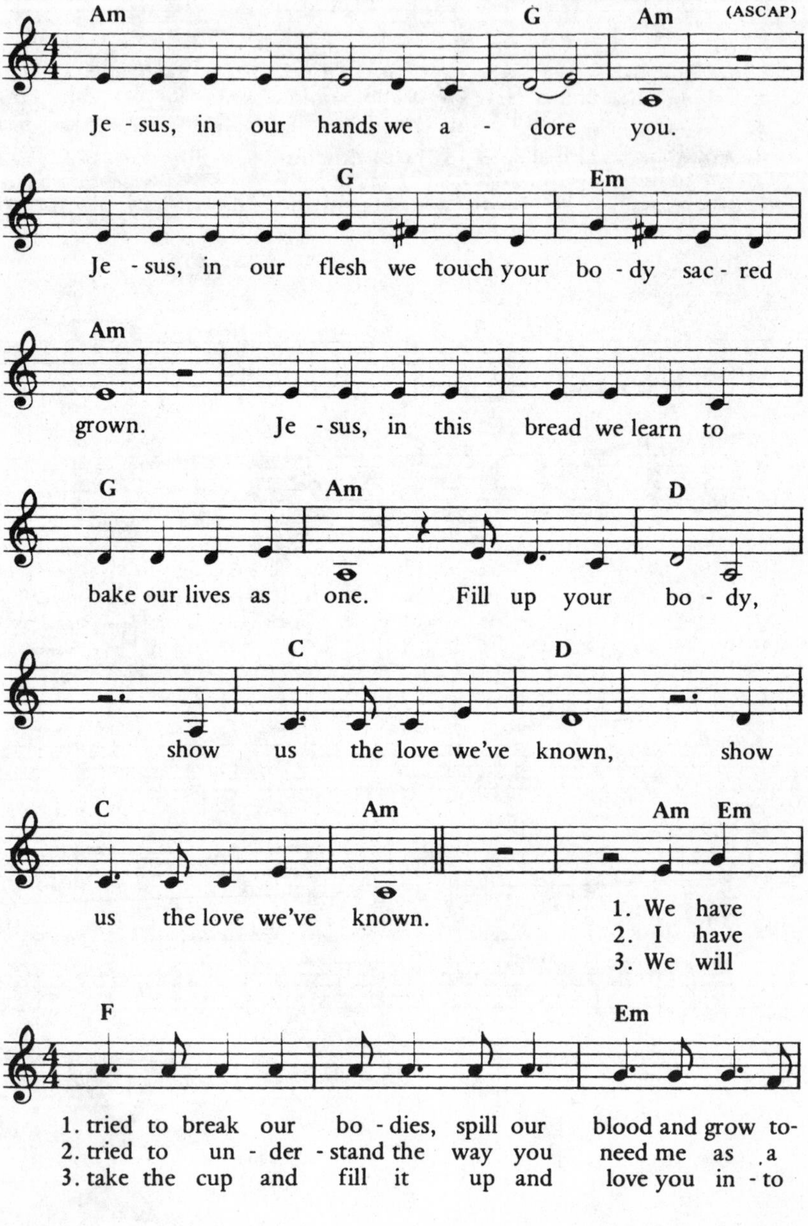

Je - sus, in our hands we a - dore you.

Je - sus, in our flesh we touch your bo - dy sac - red

grown. Je - sus, in this bread we learn to

bake our lives as one. Fill up your bo - dy,

show us the love we've known, show

us the love we've known.

1. We have
2. I have
3. We will

1. tried to break our bo - dies, spill our blood and grow to-
2. tried to un - der - stand the way you need me as a
3. take the cup and fill it up and love you in - to

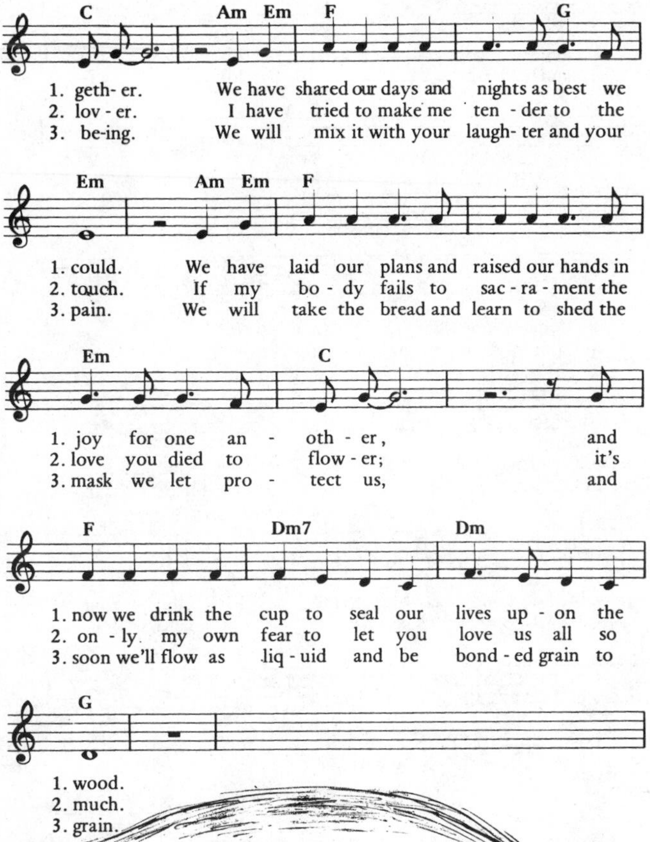

1. geth- er.   We have shared our days and   nights as best we
2. lov - er.   I have   tried to make me   ten - der to   the
3. be-ing.   We will   mix it with your   laugh- ter and your

1. could.   We have   laid our plans and   raised our hands in
2. touch.   If my   bo - dy fails to   sac - ra - ment the
3. pain.   We will   take the bread and   learn to shed the

1. joy   for one   an -   oth - er,   and
2. love   you died   to   flow - er;   it's
3. mask   we let   pro -   tect us,   and

1. now we   drink the   cup to   seal our   lives up - on   the
2. on - ly   my own   fear to   let you   love us all   so
3. soon we'll   flow as   liq - uid   and be   bond - ed grain   to

1. wood.
2. much.
3. grain.

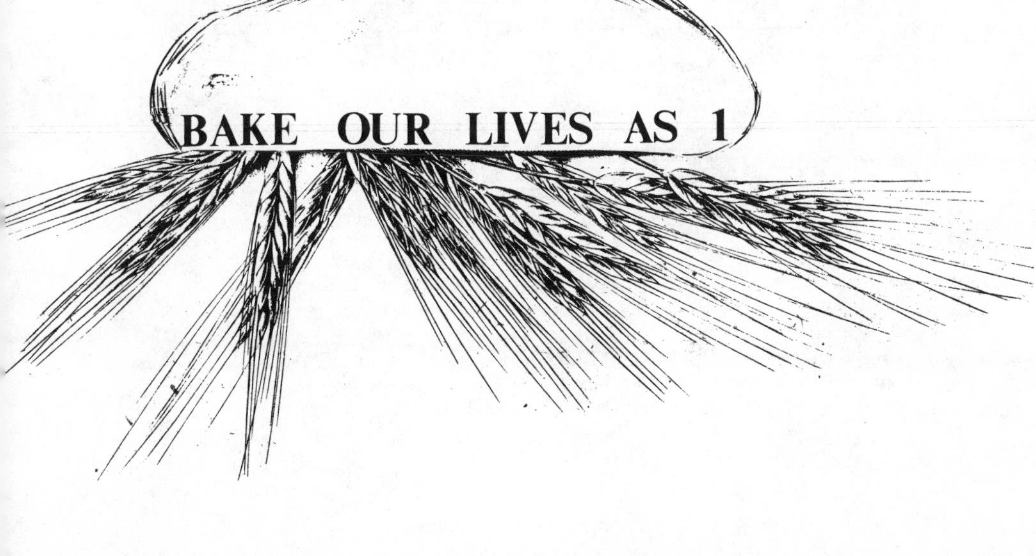

BAKE OUR LIVES AS 1

Re-Member Me

Joe Wise

Take and eat; ————— this is my
Take and eat; ————— this is my

Bo - dy, (—————) bro - ken on
(—————) gift, my - self giv - en in

cross-es too lone - ly to men - tion. ————
love in the face of re - jec - tion. ————

Take and drink; this is my Blood, ————
Take and drink; this is my Life. ————

spilled on your al - leys and lost in your
Know it's my pledge now to be with you

hall - ways. ———— Re - mem - ber me,
al - ways. ———— Re - mem - ber me,

1st ending   2nd ending

Re - mem-ber me.
Re - mem-ber   me.

1. I could - n't be here, ————
2. I ride on your bus, ————
3. I count on your love, ————
4. I live in your house, ————

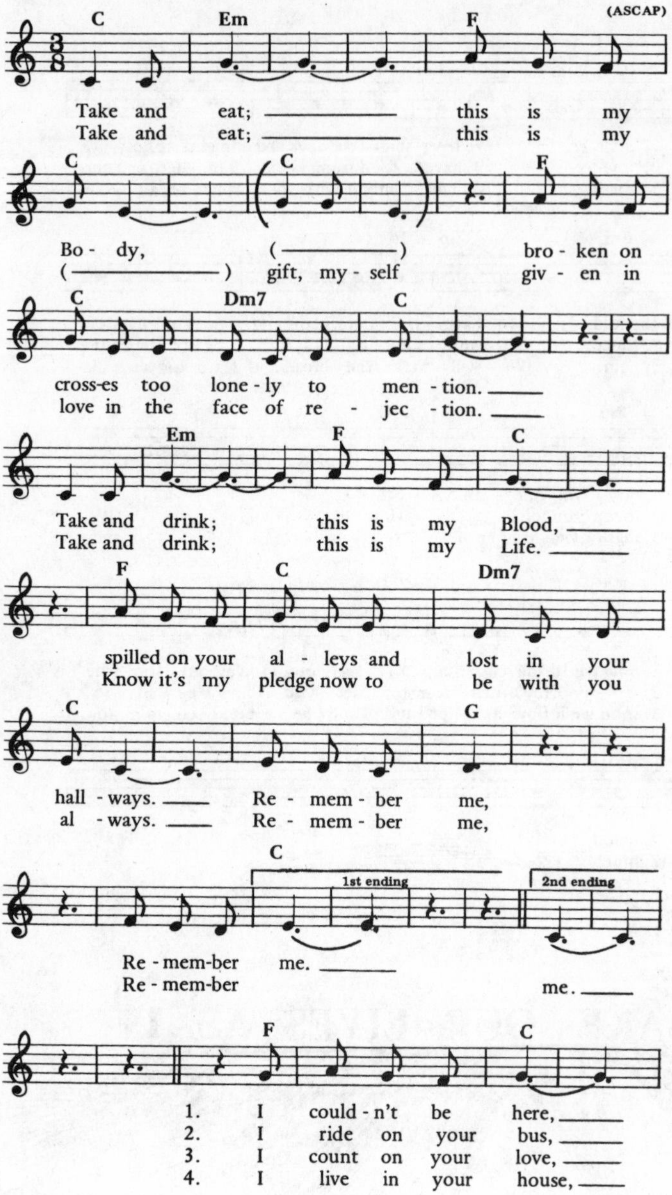

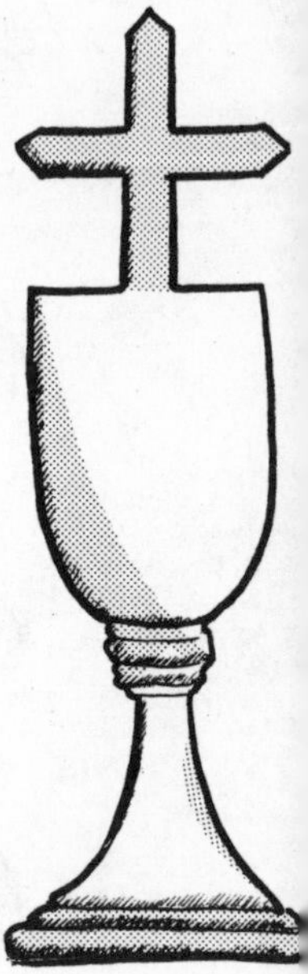

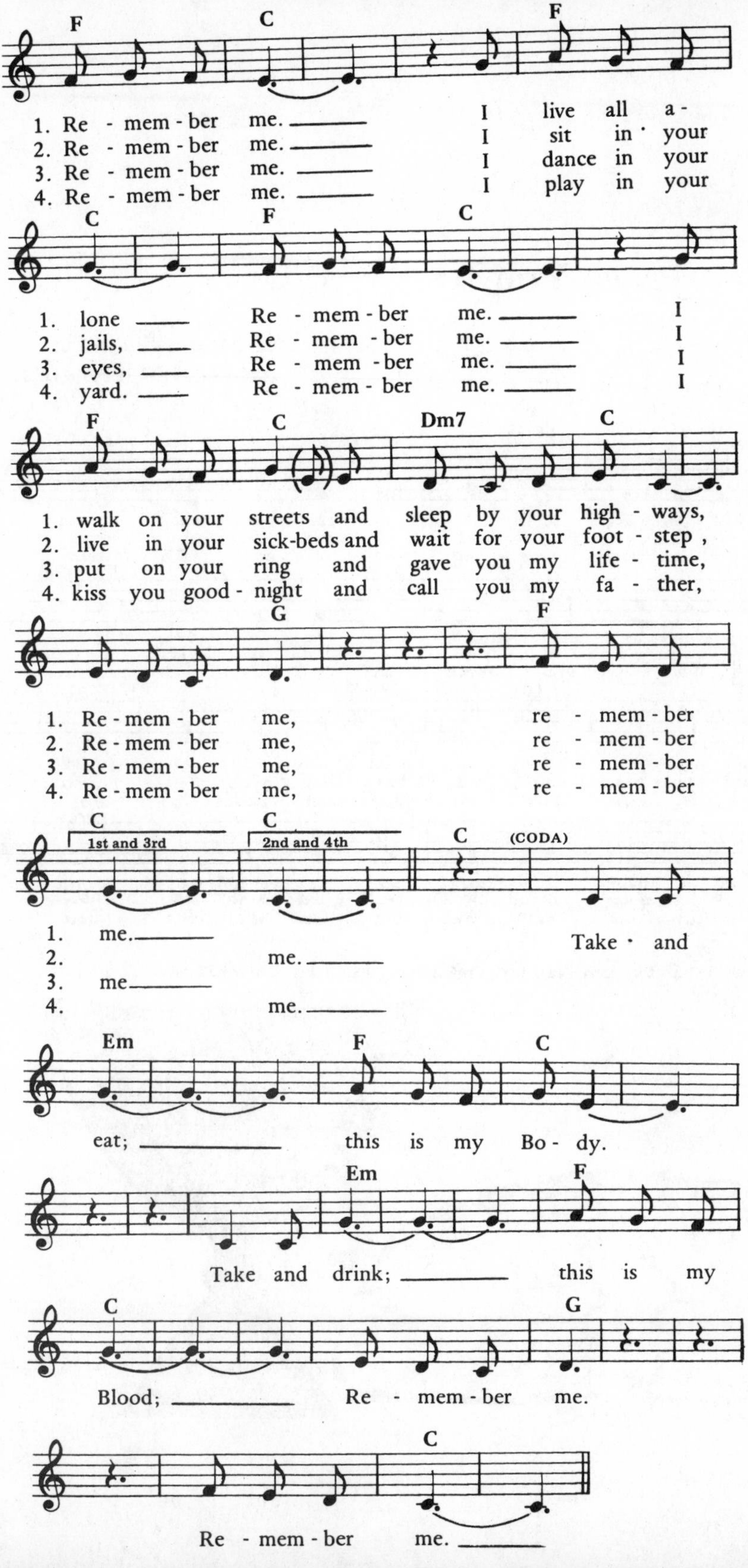

1. Re - mem - ber me. _____ I live all a -
2. Re - mem - ber me. _____ I sit in your
3. Re - mem - ber me. _____ I dance in your
4. Re - mem - ber me. _____ I play in your

1. lone _____ Re - mem - ber me. _____ I
2. jails, _____ Re - mem - ber me. _____ I
3. eyes, _____ Re - mem - ber me. _____ I
4. yard. _____ Re - mem - ber me. _____ I

1. walk on your streets and sleep by your high - ways,
2. live in your sick-beds and wait for your foot - step,
3. put on your ring and gave you my life - time,
4. kiss you good - night and call you my fa - ther,

1. Re - mem - ber me, re - mem - ber
2. Re - mem - ber me, re - mem - ber
3. Re - mem - ber me, re - mem - ber
4. Re - mem - ber me, re - mem - ber

1st and 3rd   2nd and 4th   (CODA)

1. me. _____
2. me. _____
3. me. _____
4. me. _____ Take and

eat; _____ this is my Bo - dy.

Take and drink; _____ this is my

Blood; _____ Re - mem - ber me.

Re - mem - ber me. _____

Jesus, You Are With Us

Words and Music by
Tom Neufer Emswiler

Capo 1 (D)

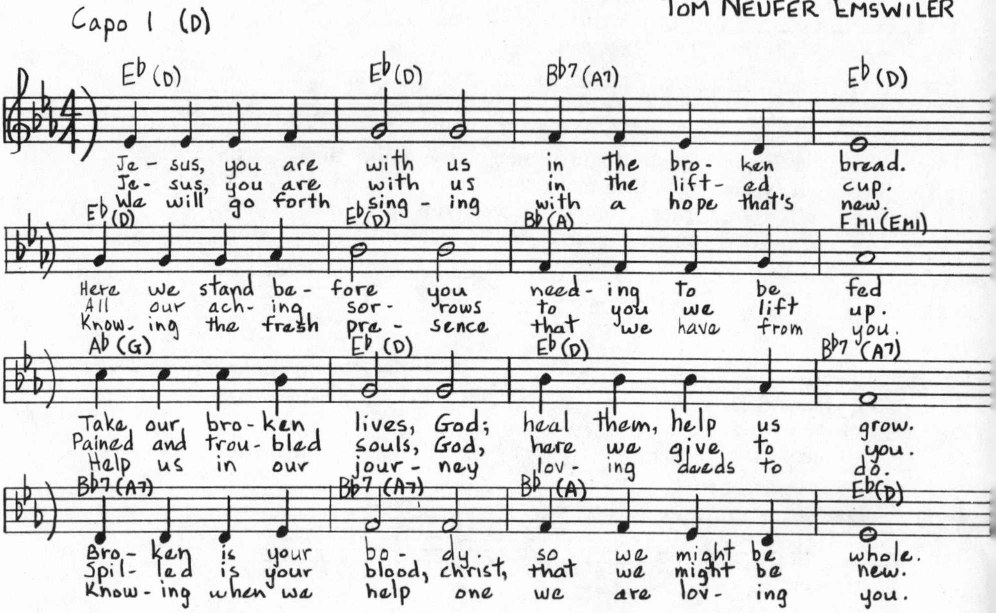

Je-sus, you are with us in the bro-ken bread.
Je-sus, you are with us in the lift-ed cup.
We will go forth sing-ing with a hope that's new.

Here we stand be-fore you need-ing to be fed
All our ach-ing sor-rows to you we lift up.
Know-ing the fresh pre-sence that we have from you.

Take our bro-ken lives, God; heal them, help us grow.
Pained and trou-bled souls, God; here we give to you.
Help us in our jour-ney lov-ing deeds to do.

Bro-ken is your bo-dy. so we might be whole.
Spil-led is your blood, Christ, that we might be new.
Know-ing when we help one we are lov-ing you.

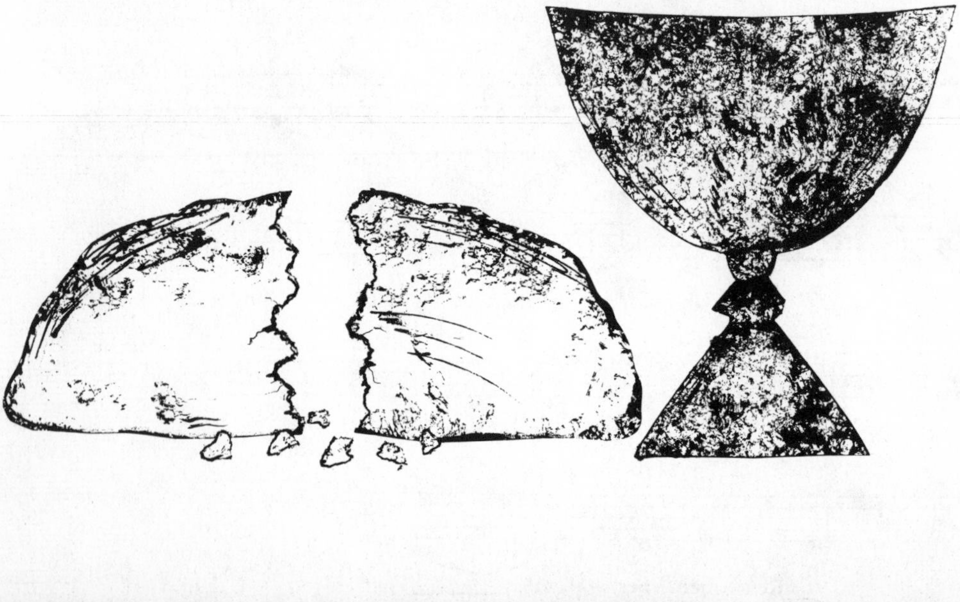

DEDICATION

And

BENEDICTION

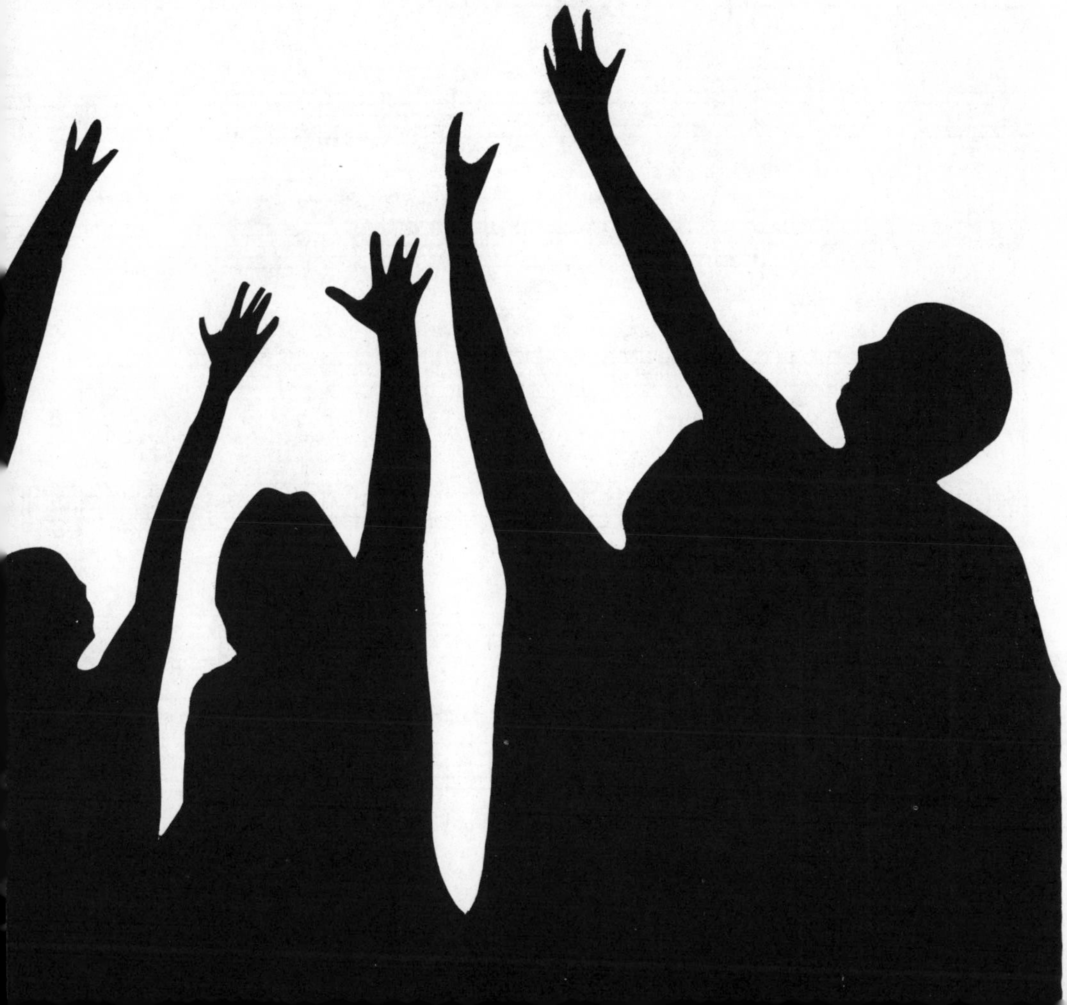

90

Live Into Hope

From Luke 4:18-19
Jane Parker Huber, 1976

Truro : L.M.
T. Williams' <u>Psalmodia Evangelica</u>, 1789

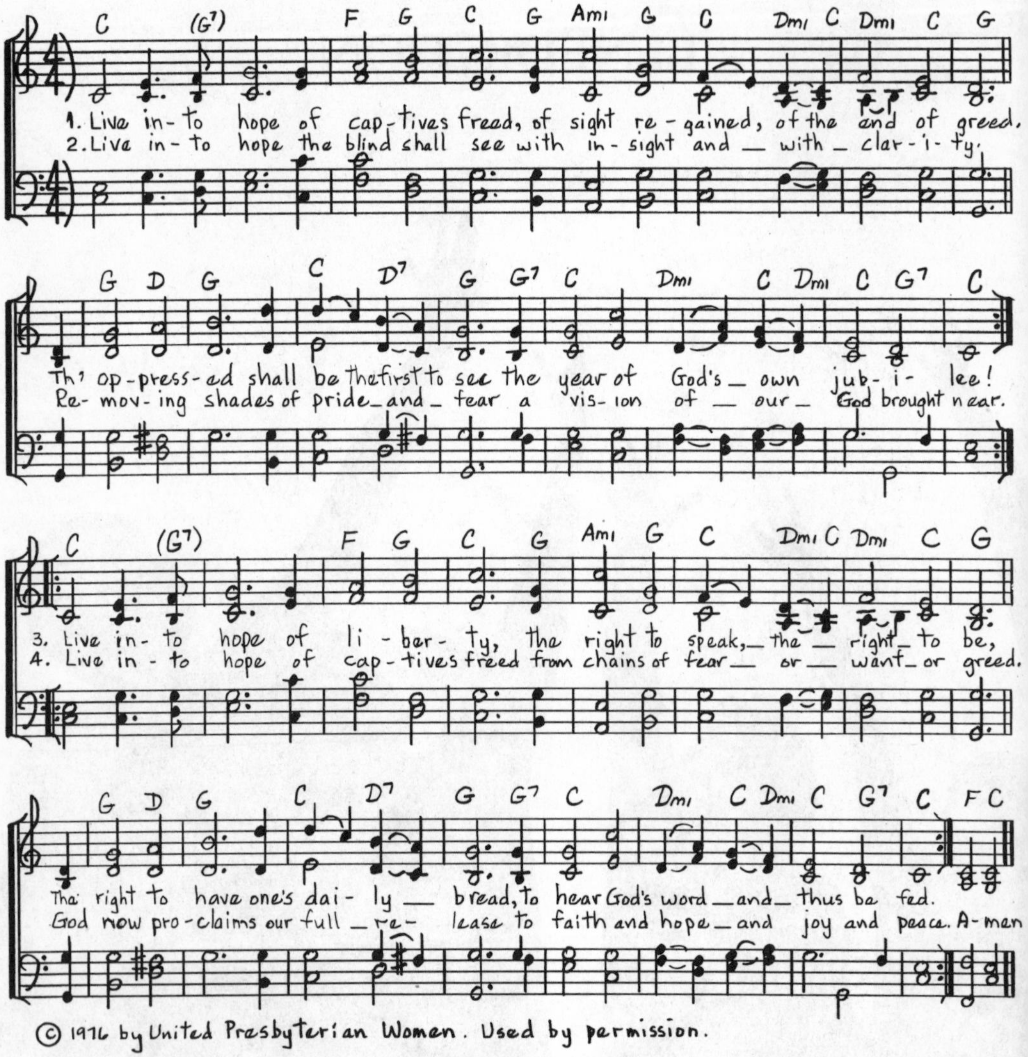

1. Live in-to hope of cap-tives freed, of sight re-gained, of the end of greed.
2. Live in-to hope the blind shall see with in-sight and _ with _ clar-i-ty.

Th' op-press-ed shall be the first to see the year of God's own jub-i-lee!
Re-mov-ing shades of pride _ and _ fear a vis-ion of _ our _ God brought near.

3. Live in-to hope of li-ber-ty, the right to speak, _ the _ right _ to be,
4. Live in-to hope of cap-tives freed from chains of fear _ or _ want _ or greed.

The right to have one's dai-ly _ bread, to hear God's word _ and _ thus be fed.
God now pro-claims our full _ re-lease to faith and hope _ and joy and peace. A-men

Mine Are the Hungry

Kenneth I. Morse

Wilbur E. Brumbaugh

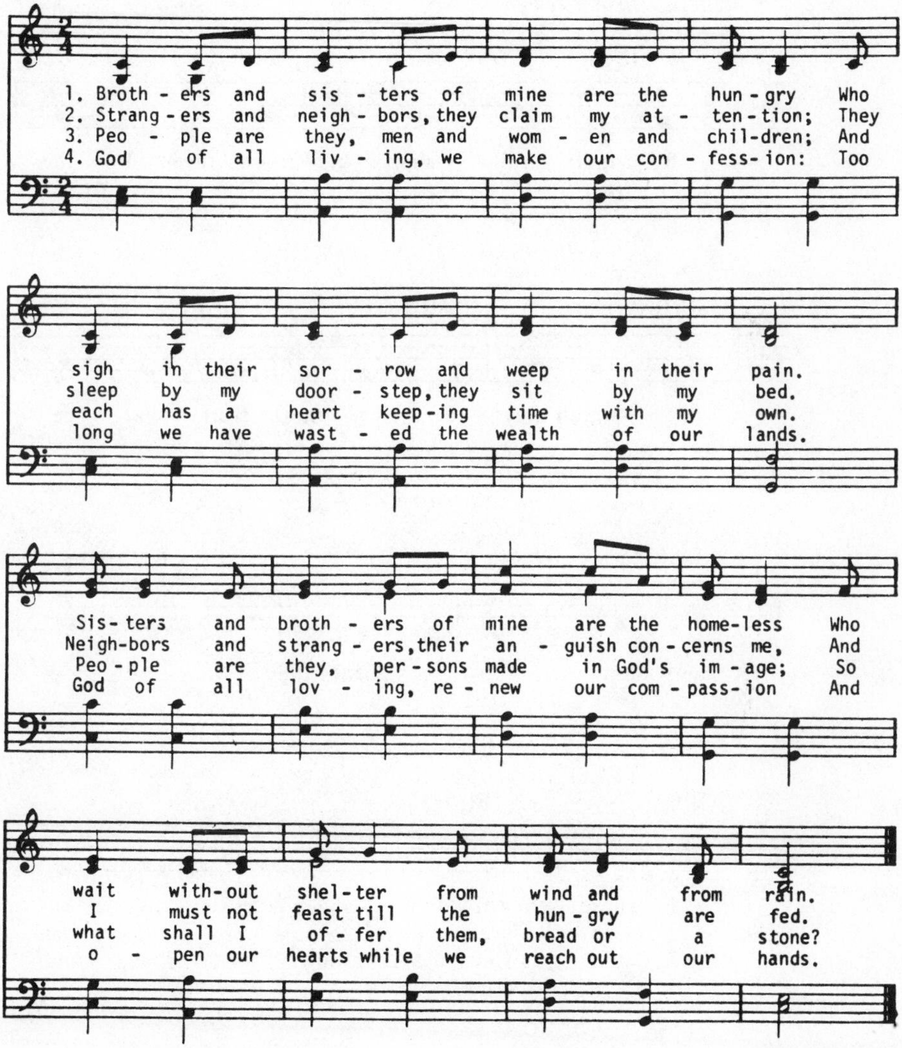

1. Broth-ers and sis-ters of mine are the hun-gry Who
2. Strang-ers and neigh-bors, they claim my at-ten-tion; They
3. Peo-ple are they, men and wom-en and chil-dren; And
4. God of all liv-ing, we make our con-fess-ion: Too

sigh in their sor-row and weep in their pain.
sleep by my door-step, they sit by my bed.
each has a heart keep-ing time with my own.
long we have wast-ed the wealth of our lands.

Sis-ters and broth-ers of mine are the home-less Who
Neigh-bors and strang-ers, their an-guish con-cerns me, And
Peo-ple are they, per-sons made in God's im-age; So
God of all lov-ing, re-new our com-pass-ion And

wait with-out shel-ter from wind and from rain.
I must not feast till the hun-gry are fed.
what shall I of-fer them, bread or a stone?
o-pen our hearts while we reach out our hands.

'I Was Hungry and . . .'

By Their Fruit

Capo 1 play ( )

Moderate bright tempo
CHORUS

Sebastian Temple

By their fruit shall ye know them, by the

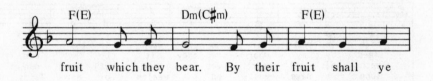

fruit which they bear. By their fruit shall ye

Fine

know, not by the gar - ments they wear. _____

VERSES

1. There are wolves in sheep's cloth - ing that
2. Date ___ trees bear no ol - ives and
3. My ___ fruits are long suf - f'ring and

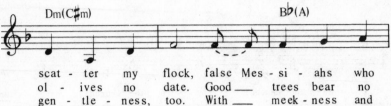

scat - ter my flock, false Mes - si - ahs who
ol - ives no date. Good __ trees bear no
gen - tle - ness, too. With __ meek - ness and

claim __ that they're Christ the Rock. But it's
bad fruit as love bears no hate. You can
faith - ful - ness, joy that is true. Love __

eas - y to see, that these pro - phets aren't
tell by the fruit just how an - y tree
and self - con - trol with __ good - ness and

real - ly of me. ____
us - es its root. ____
peace for your soul. ____

We Are the Church

Richard Avery
Donald Marsh

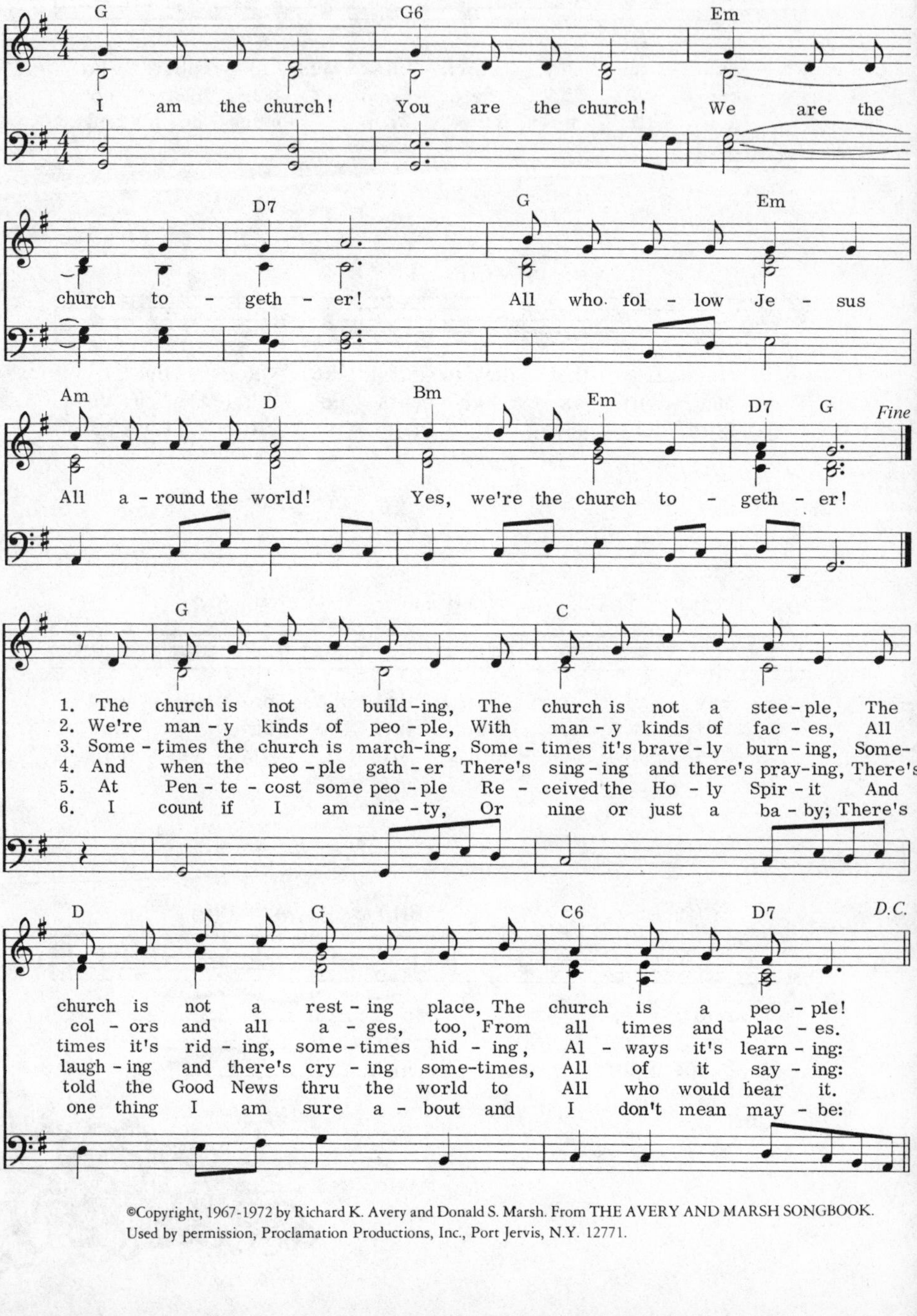

I am the church! You are the church! We are the church to - geth - er! All who fol - low Je - sus All a - round the world! Yes, we're the church to - geth - er!

1. The church is not a build - ing, The church is not a stee - ple, The church is not a rest - ing place, The church is a peo - ple!
2. We're man - y kinds of peo - ple, With man - y kinds of fac - es, All col - ors and all a - ges, too, From all times and plac - es.
3. Some - times the church is march - ing, Some - times it's brave - ly burn - ing, Some - times it's rid - ing, some - times hid - ing, Al - ways it's learn - ing:
4. And when the peo - ple gath - er There's sing - ing and there's pray - ing, There's laugh - ing and there's cry - ing some - times, All of it say - ing:
5. At Pen - te - cost some peo - ple Re - ceived the Ho - ly Spir - it And told the Good News thru the world to All who would hear it.
6. I count if I am nine - ty, Or nine or just a ba - by; There's one thing I am sure a - bout and I don't mean may - be:

Awaken Us, God

(Note: Repeat refrain after each verse)

Words and Music by TOM NEUFER EMSWILER

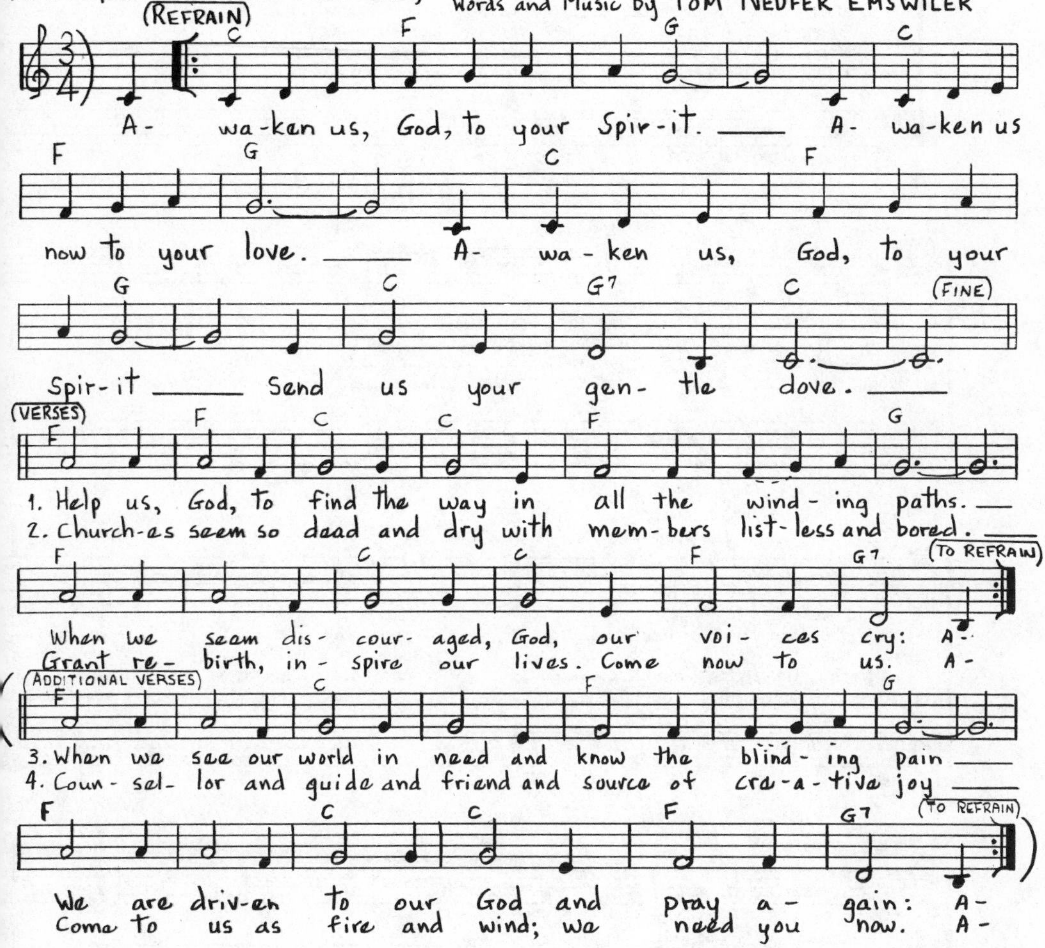

(REFRAIN)

A- wa-ken us, God, to your Spir-it. ___ A- wa-ken us now to your love. ___ A- wa-ken us, God, to your Spir-it ___ Send us your gen-tle dove. ___

(VERSES)

1. Help us, God, to find the way in all the wind-ing paths. ___
2. Church-es seem so dead and dry with mem-bers list-less and bored. ___

(TO REFRAIN)

When we seem dis-cour-aged, God, our voi-ces cry: A-
Grant re- birth, in- spire our lives. Come now to us. A-

(ADDITIONAL VERSES)

3. When we see our world in need and know the blind-ing pain ___
4. Coun-sel- lor and guide and friend and source of cre-a-tive joy ___

(TO REFRAIN)

We are driv-en to our God and pray a- gain: A-
Come to us as fire and wind; we need you now. A-

COME TO US AS FIRE AND WIND

Sing Love Songs

Richard Ave
Donald Mars

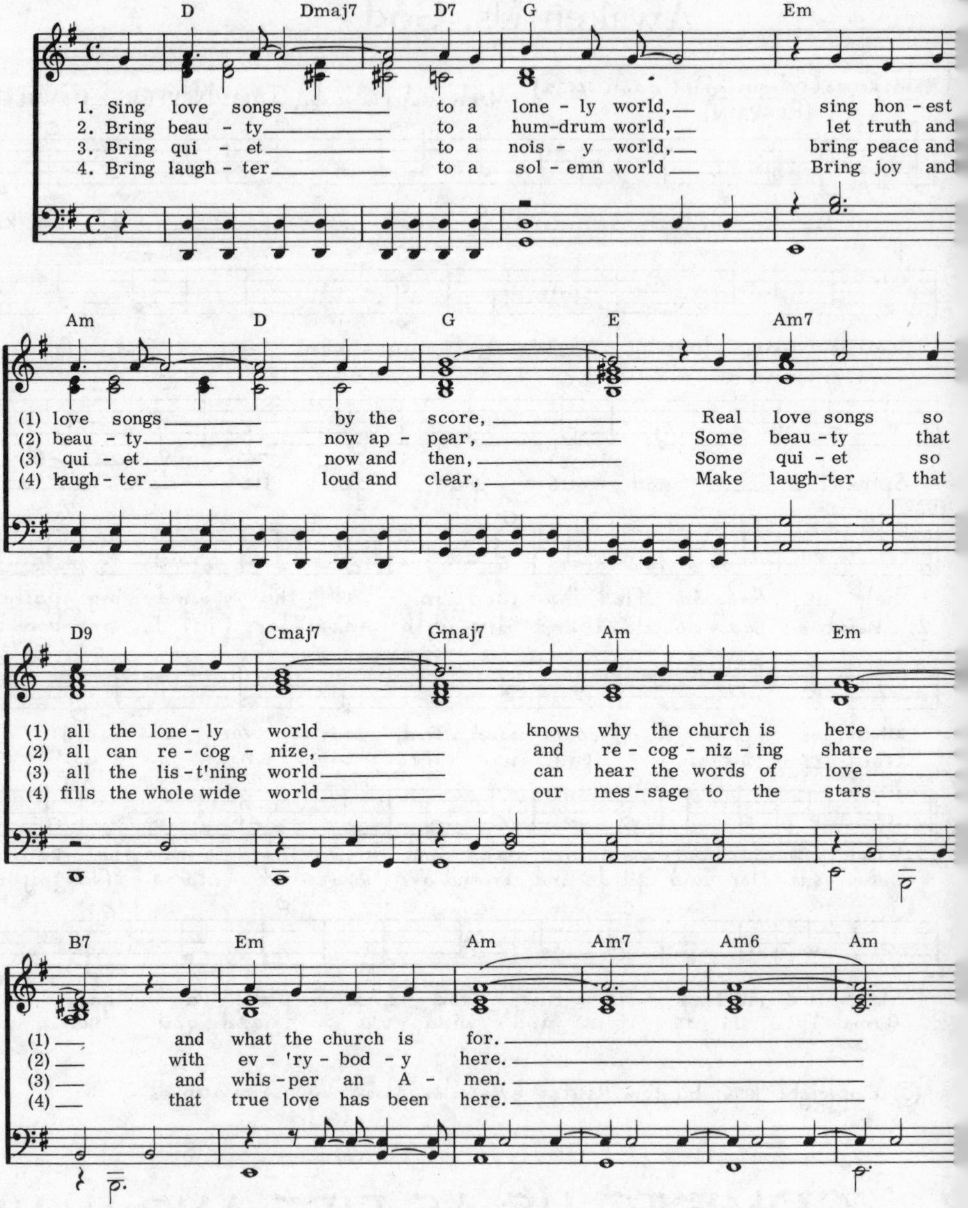

You Are the Salt of the Earth

Richard Avery
Donald Marsh

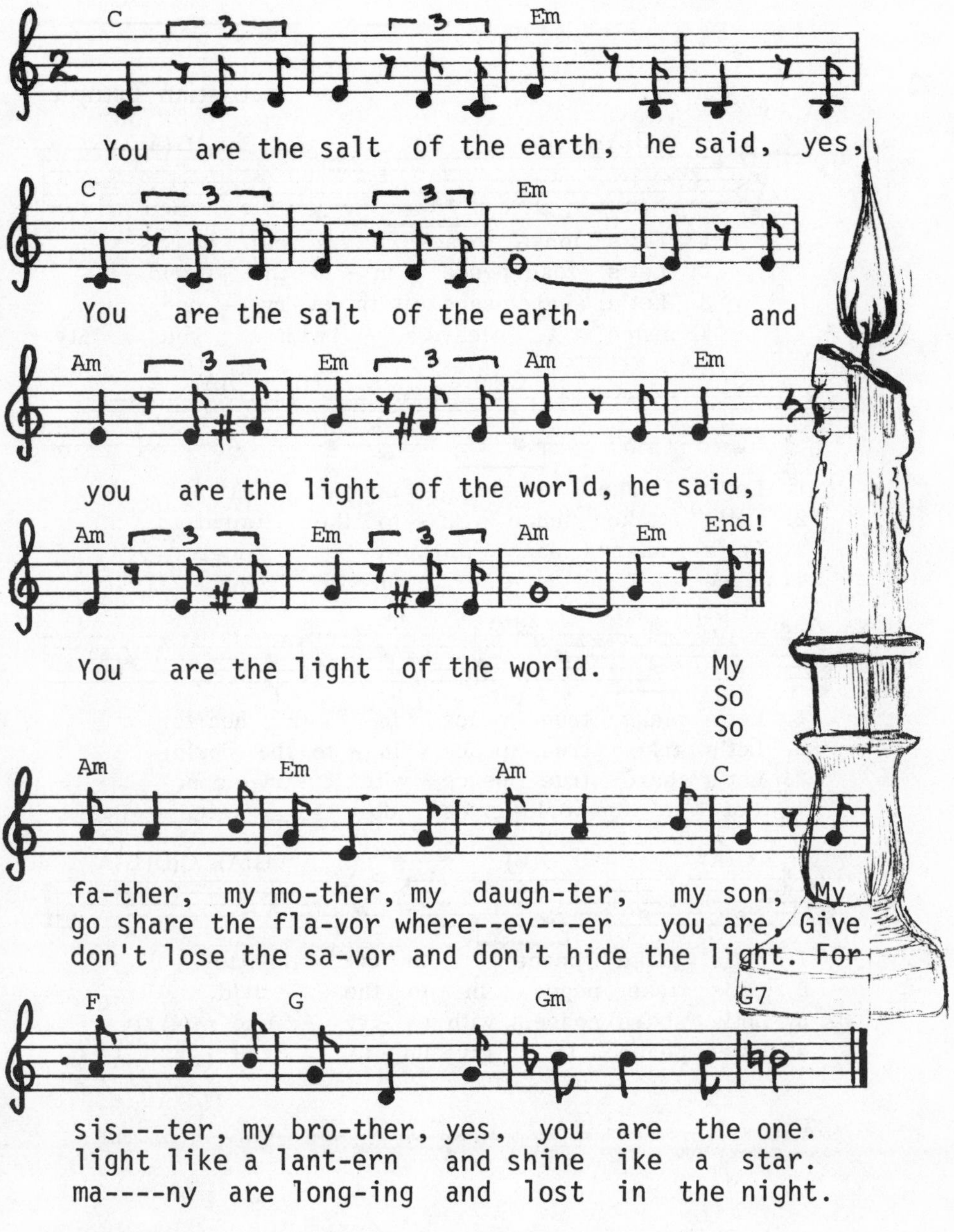

You are the salt of the earth, he said, yes,

You are the salt of the earth. and

you are the light of the world, he said,

You are the light of the world. My
So
So

fa-ther, my mo-ther, my daugh-ter, my son, My
go share the fla-vor where--ev---er you are, Give
don't lose the sa-vor and don't hide the light. For

sis---ter, my bro-ther, yes, you are the one.
light like a lant-ern and shine ike a star.
ma----ny are long-ing and lost in the night.

Let's Make Peace

Sebastian Temple

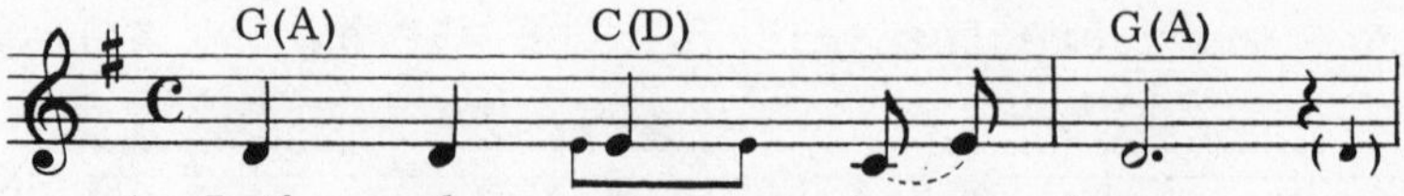

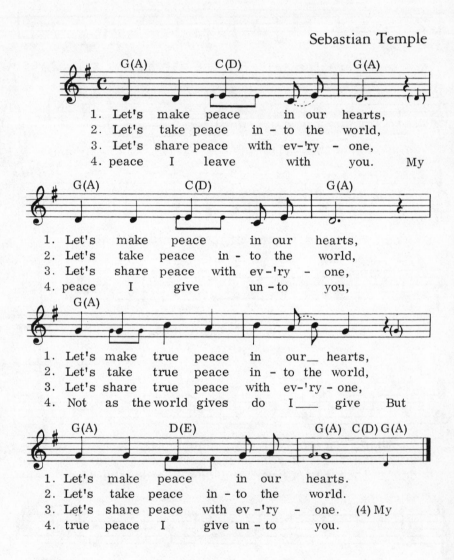

1. Let's make peace in our hearts,
2. Let's take peace in - to the world,
3. Let's share peace with ev-'ry - one,
4. peace I leave with you. My

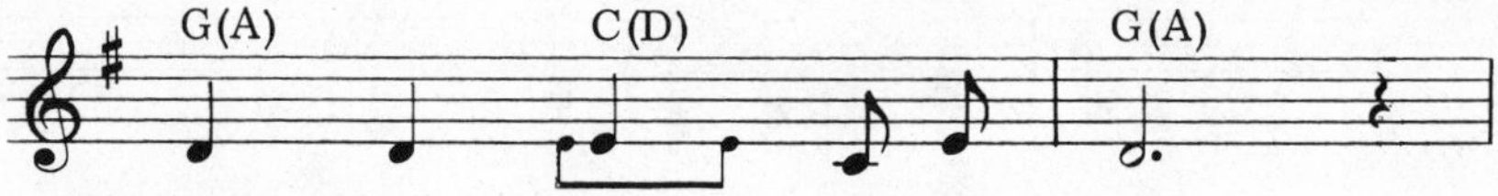

1. Let's make peace in our hearts,
2. Let's take peace in - to the world,
3. Let's share peace with ev-'ry - one,
4. peace I give un - to you,

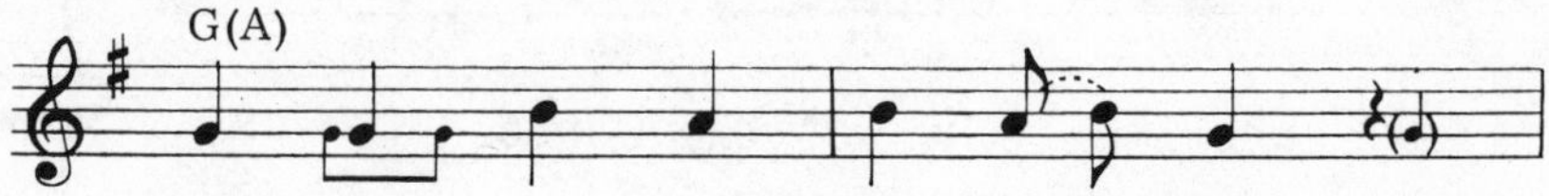

1. Let's make true peace in our＿ hearts,
2. Let's take true peace in - to the world,
3. Let's share true peace with ev-'ry - one,
4. Not as the world gives do I＿ give But

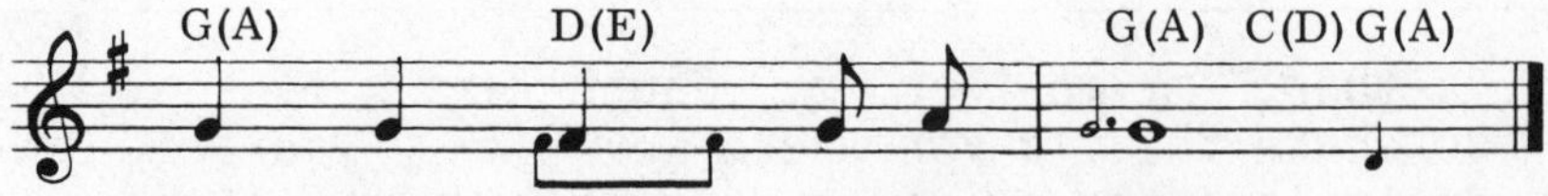

1. Let's make peace in our hearts.
2. Let's take peace in - to the world.
3. Let's share peace with ev -'ry - one. (4) My
4. true peace I give un - to you.

This Is My Gift

Joe Wise

1-3. This is my gift. This is my song. This is my
5. This is my gift. This is my song. This is my

1-3. claim on to-mor__ row_____. My dare to be wrong
5. claim on to-mor__ row_____. My dare to be wrong

1-3. from all my yes-ter-days_; with all my hopes in times to
5. this is my song, my life___, how-e-ver long, how-e-ver

1-3. come. This is my gift, my God. This is my song.
5. lost. This is my gift, my God. This is my song.

2. You wrote the words in flesh_____ so long a-go;
4. It is your gift, my God_____, and now it's mine.

2. I write the tune in mine_____. So far to
4. It is my gift, my God_____, and now it's

2. go_____. It is the wed-ding now of God and
4. yours_____. It is the wed-ding now of God and

2. flesh; you say, I take you now, and I say, yes. This is my
4. flesh; you say, I take you now, and I say, yes. This is my

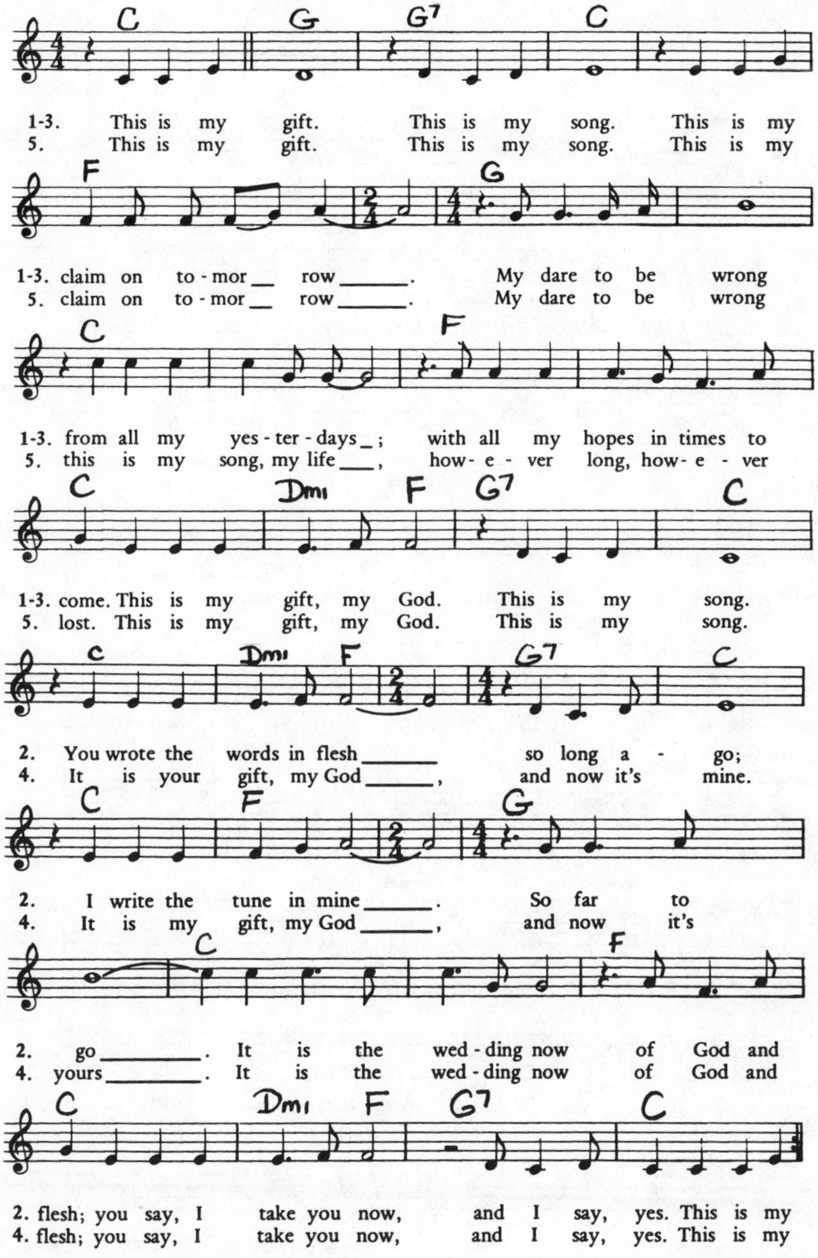

100

Song of Thanksgiving

Words and Music by DARRYL DUCOTE

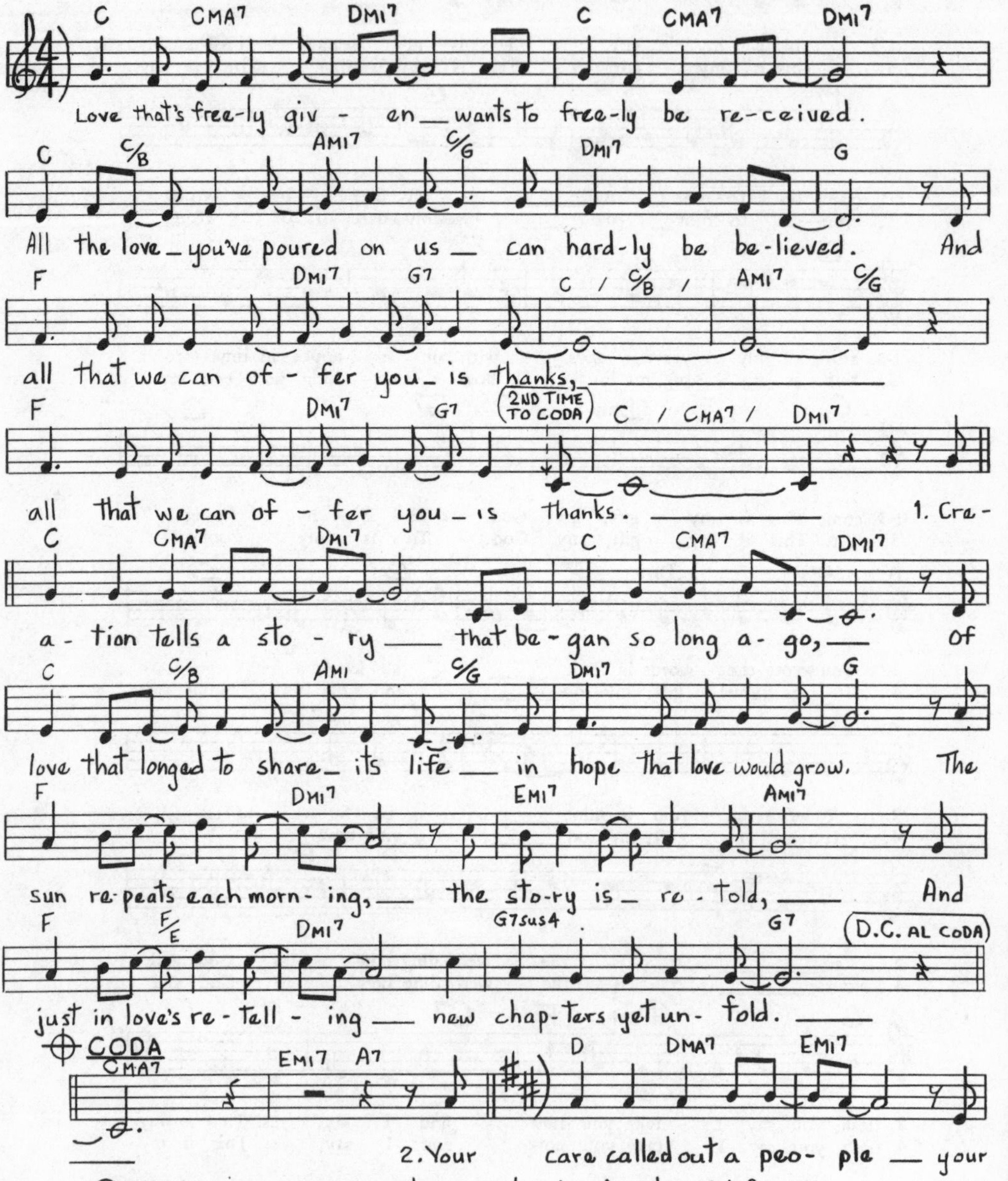

Song of Thanksgiving

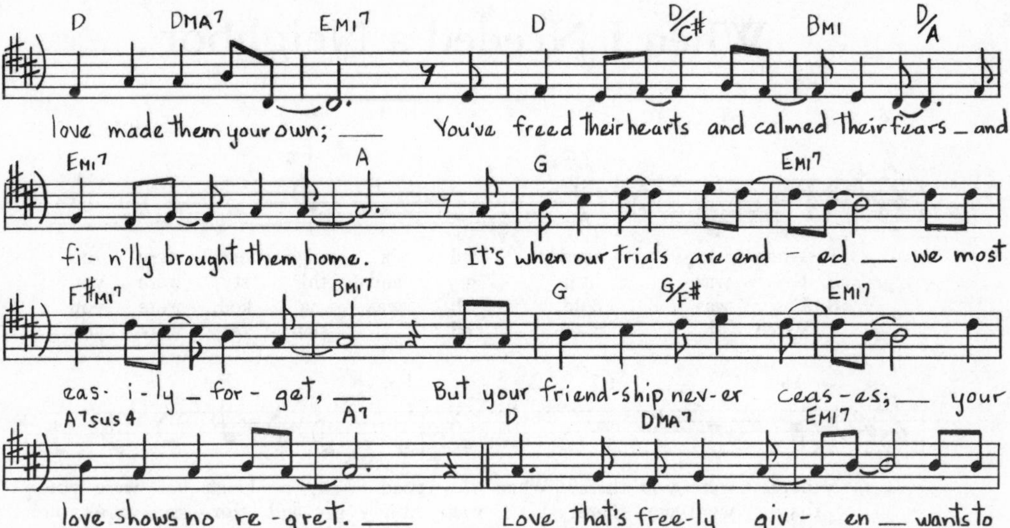

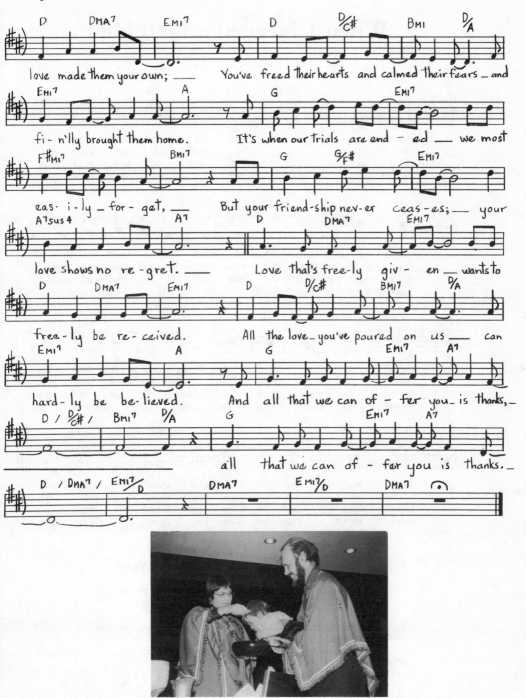

love made them your own; ___ You've freed their hearts and calmed their fears _ and
fi - n'lly brought them home. It's when our trials are end - ed ___ we most
eas - i - ly _ for - get, ___ But your friend-ship nev-er ceas-es; ___ your
love shows no re-gret. ___ Love that's free-ly giv - en ___ wants to
free-ly be re - ceived. All the love _ you've poured on us ___ can
hard-ly be be-lieved. And all that we can of - fer you _ is thanks, ___
all that we can of - fer you is thanks. _

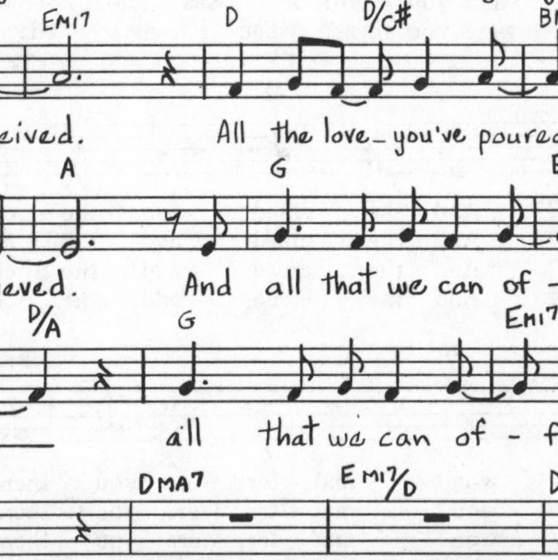

When I Needed a Neighbor

Sydney Carter

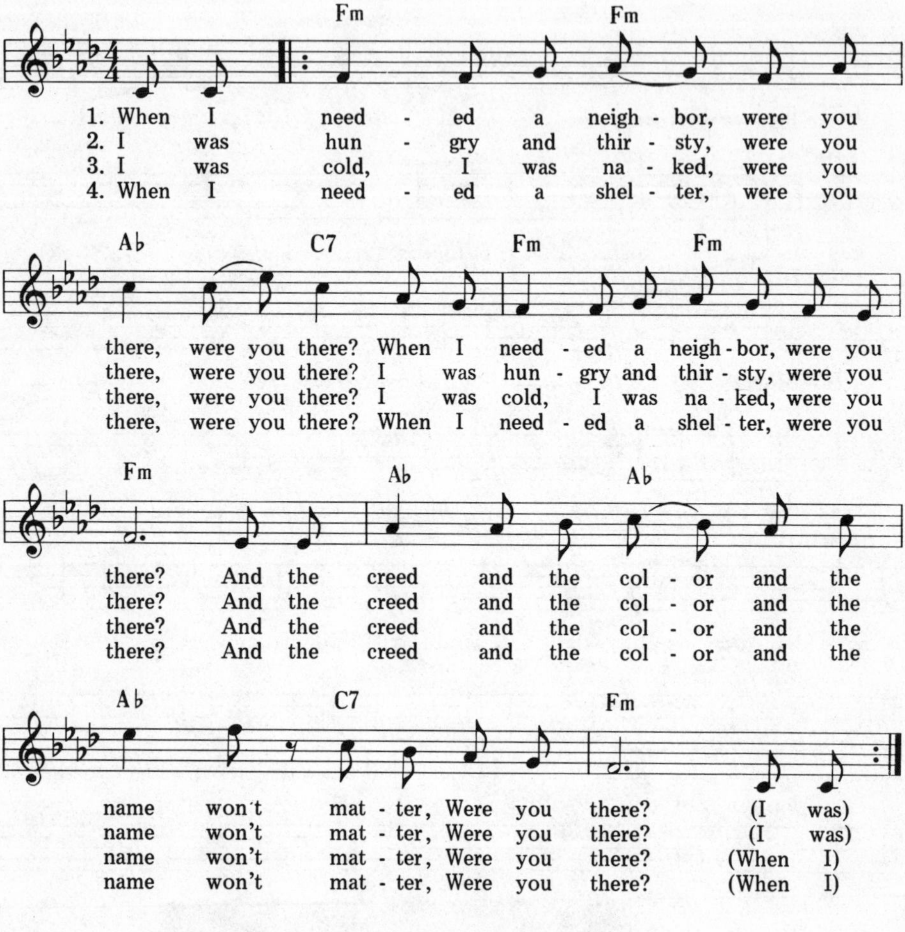

5. When I needed a healer, were you there, were you there?
   When I needed a healer, were you there?
   And the creed and the color and the name won't matter,
   Were you there? (Wherever)

6. Wherever you travel, I'll be there, I'll be there,
   Wherever you travel, I'll be there.
   And the creed and the color and the name won't matter,
   I'll be there.

Let Me Know Love

Capo 5, Play in C

Words and Music by CAROLYN McDADE

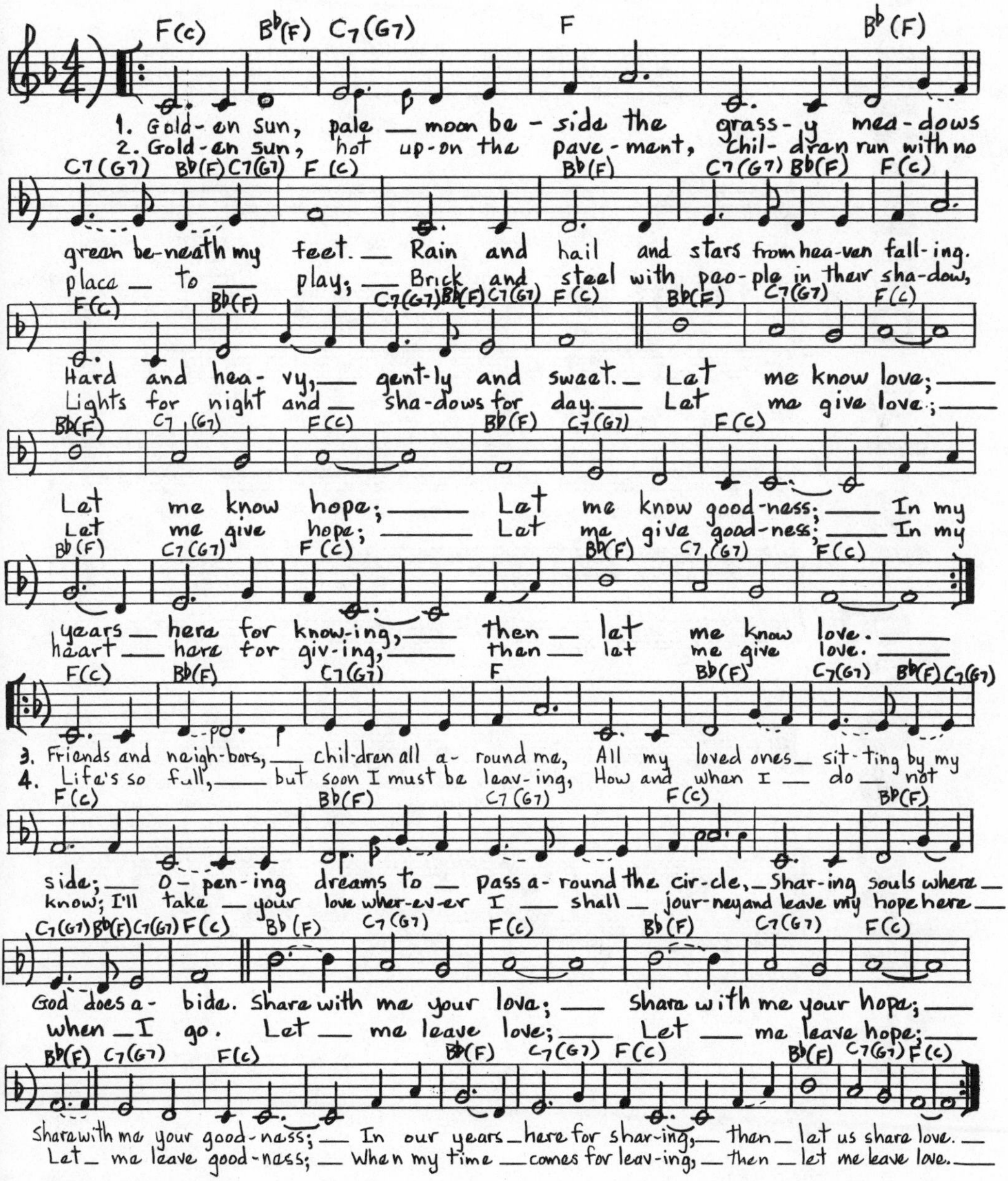

if the song is to continue

There's a Bright New World

Robbie Stumman

A joyful song that can be used anytime and anywhere, the tempo is bouncy and shouldn't be too slow. The refrain is easy to teach to a group, and the verses can be sung by soloists.

There's a bright new world shining under the sun, Where a smile and a touch of love comes from ev-'ry- one.

1. Let's sing a song for the lit-tle ones who
2. Let's dance a waltz with the but-ter-flies who
3. Let's show our-selves just what we can do with

we must do the singing !

Gifts of Love

Words and Music by ART ALLEN

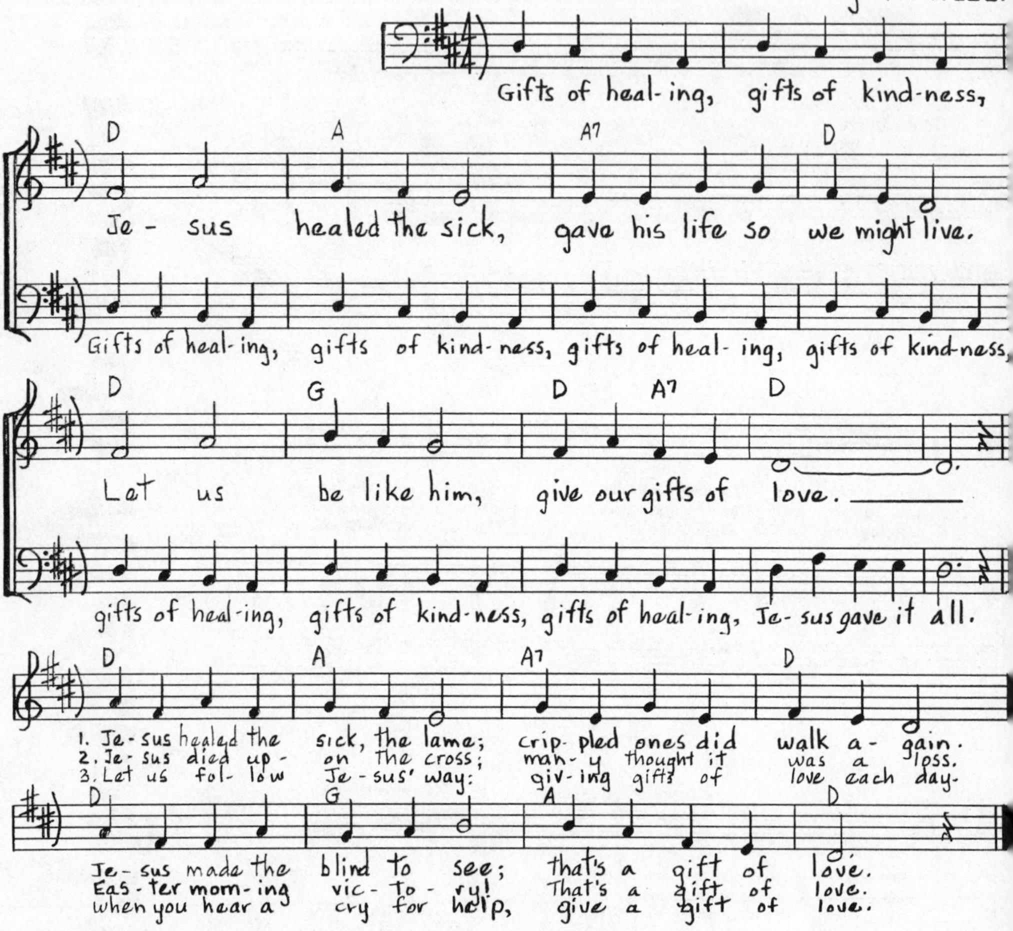

© Copyright 1974 by Art Allen. Used by permission.

Give a gift of love today!

One But Not the Same

An Offertory Round
Ephesians 4

Words & Music
by Art Allen

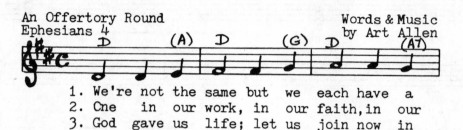

1. We're not the same but we each have a
2. One in our work, in our faith, in our
3. God gave us life; let us join now in

gift to bring; Multicolored, multilingual -
loy - al - ty; One in our hope for new
har - mo - ny. Christ set us free; let us

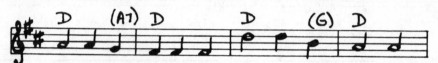

O what an of-fer-ing! Each in our own way
birth of hu-man-i-ty; One in our vi-sion,
follow the Spirit's lead. Let the whole world see

coming to celebrate God's gift of love for the
One in our will to be sharing the love God has
we're one community; One in our hope we shall

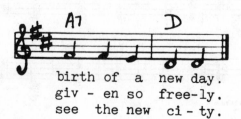

birth of a new day.
giv - en so free-ly.
see the new ci - ty.

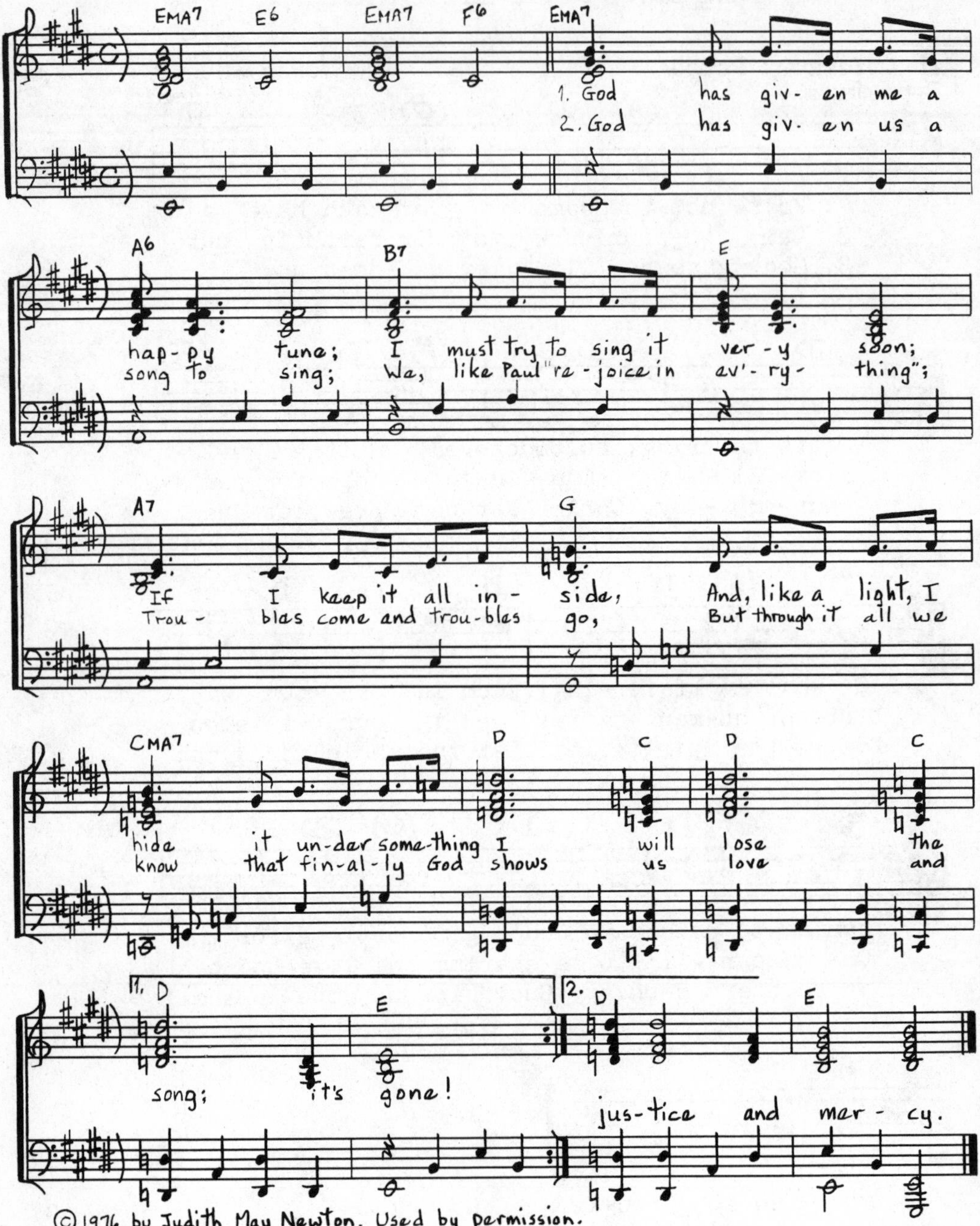

Sing It Soon

108

For friends at Baika Girls School and Baika Women's College, Osaka, Japan

Words and Music by JUDITH MAY NEWTON

1. God has giv-en me a hap-py tune; I must try to sing it ver-y soon; If I keep it all in-side, And, like a light, I hide it un-der some-thing I will lose the song; it's gone!

2. God has giv-en us a song to sing; We, like Paul "re-joice in ev'-ry-thing"; Trou-bles come and trou-bles go, But through it all we know that fin-al-ly God shows us love and jus-tice and mer-cy.

Discipleship

Words and Music by JUDITH MAY NEWTON

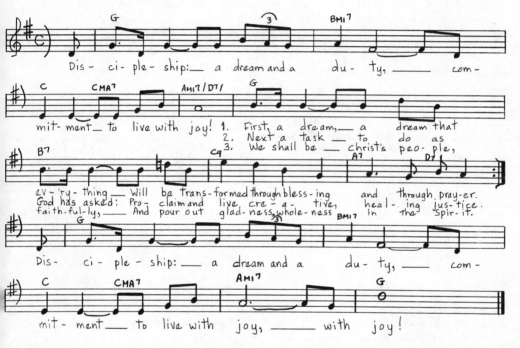

Dis- ci- ple- ship: __ a dream and a du- ty, __ com-

mit- ment __ to live with joy!
1. First a dream, __ a dream that
2. Next a task __ to do as
3. We shall be __ christ's peo- ple,

ev- 'ry- thing __ Will be Trans- formed through bless- ing and through pray- er.
God has asked: Pro- claim and live cre- a- tive, heal- ing jus- tice.
faith- ful- ly, __ And pour out glad- ness, whole- ness in the Spir- it.

Dis- ci- ple- ship: __ a dream and a du- ty, __ com-

mit- ment __ to live with joy, __ with joy!

110

A Better Country

Words and Music by Ruth Duck

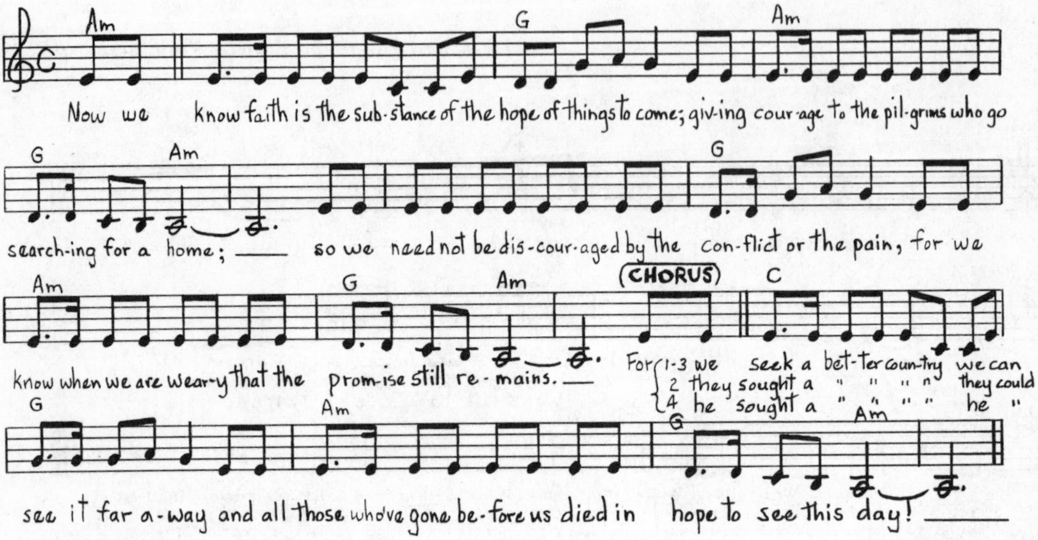

Now we know faith is the sub-stance of the hope of things to come; giv-ing cour-age to the pil-grims who go

search-ing for a home; ___ so we need not be dis-cour-aged by the con-flict or the pain, for we

know when we are wear-y that the prom-ise still re-mains. ___ For (1-3) we seek a bet-ter coun-try we can
(2) they sought a " " " " they could
(4) he sought a " Am " " he "

see it far a-way and all those who've gone be-fore us died in hope to see this day! ___

2. 'Twas by faith our sister Sarah bore a child in years of age;
'Twas by faith the Hebrew children dared escape the Pharoah's rage.
Mary and her sister Martha by their faith saw Laz'rus rise,
And faith saved an outcast woman who gave welcome to God's spies,

CHORUS

3. We are carrying a treasure in a vessel made of clay;
Though the storm winds sweep across us, we are never swept away;
Although many are against us, we are never left alone,
And our hope lives on inside us through no power of our own,

CHORUS

4. Through the witness of these faithful, then, let all despair be gone,
Like a great cloud they surround us and their spirits lead us on.
Like our pioneer and savior who did once endure the cross,
Who for joy that was before him did not fear to suffer loss,

CHORUS (repeat the last line —) And all those who've gone before us
in hope to see this day!
From Hebrews 11 + 12 and II Cor. 4

© 1976 Ruth Duck. Used by permission.

You Don't Reach Out By Pushin'

Words and Music by DORIE ELLZEY

(Repeat CHORUS after each verse)

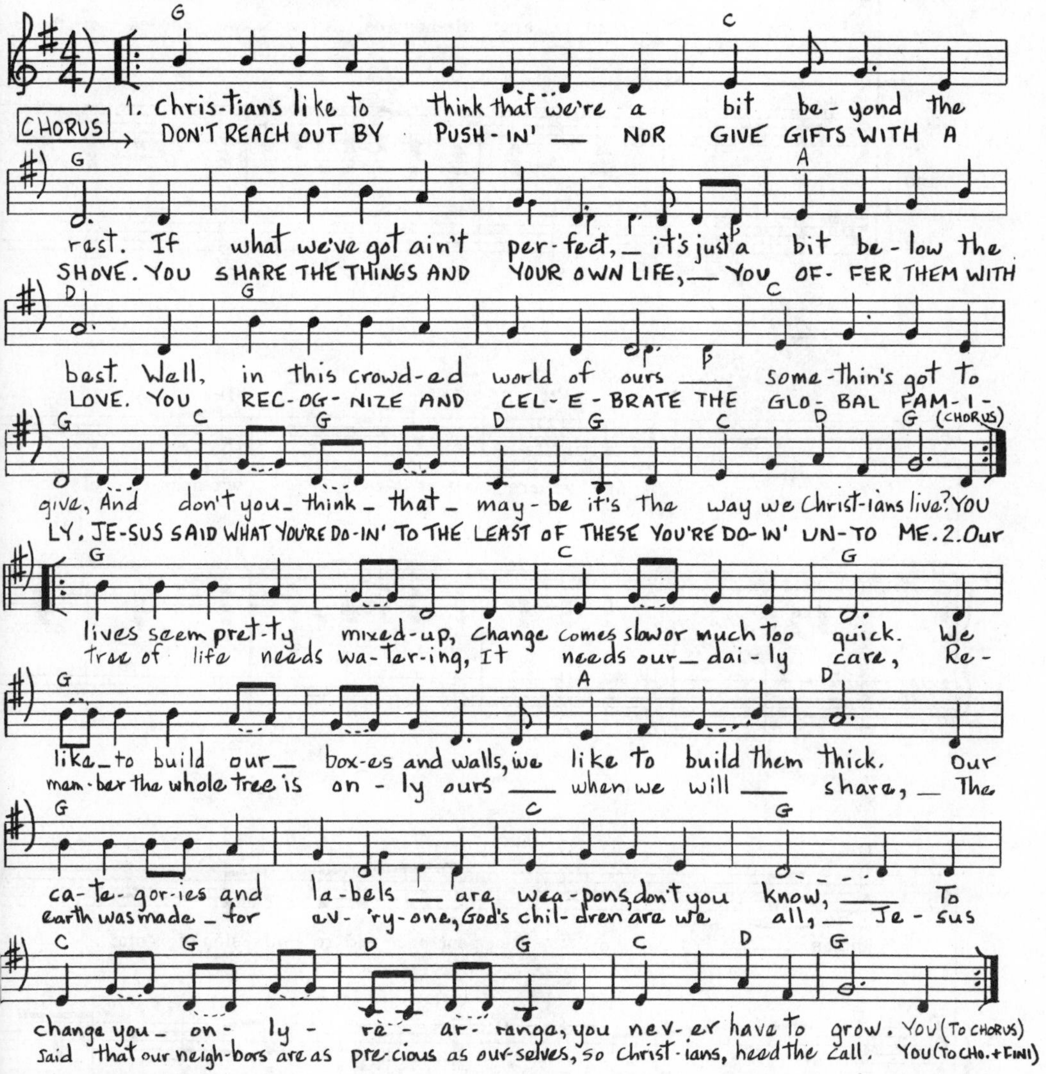

CHORUS

1. chris-tians like to think that we're a bit be-yond the rest. If what we've got ain't per-fect,— it's just a bit be-low the best. Well, in this crowd-ed world of ours __ some-thin's got to give, And don't you think that may-be it's the way we Christ-ians live? YOU

DON'T REACH OUT BY PUSH-IN' __ NOR GIVE GIFTS WITH A SHOVE. YOU SHARE THE THINGS AND YOUR OWN LIFE,— YOU OF-FER THEM WITH LOVE. YOU REC-OG-NIZE AND CEL-E-BRATE THE GLO-BAL FAM-I-LY. JE-SUS SAID WHAT YOU'RE DO-IN' TO THE LEAST OF THESE YOU'RE DO-IN' UN-TO ME. 2. Our

lives seem pret-ty mixed-up, Change comes slow or much too quick. We like to build our box-es and walls, we like to build them thick. Our ca-te-gor-ies and la-bels __ are wea-pons, don't you know, __ To change you __ on-ly re-ar-range, you nev-er have to grow. You (To CHORUS)

tree of life needs wa-ter-ing, It needs our dai-ly care, Re-mem-ber the whole tree is on-ly ours __ when we will __ share, __ The earth was made __ for ev-'ry-one, God's chil-dren are we all, __ Je-sus said that our neigh-bors are as pre-cious as our-selves, so Christ-ians, heed the call. You (To CHO. + FINE)

Ye Are Witnesses

Words and Music b
AL CARMINES

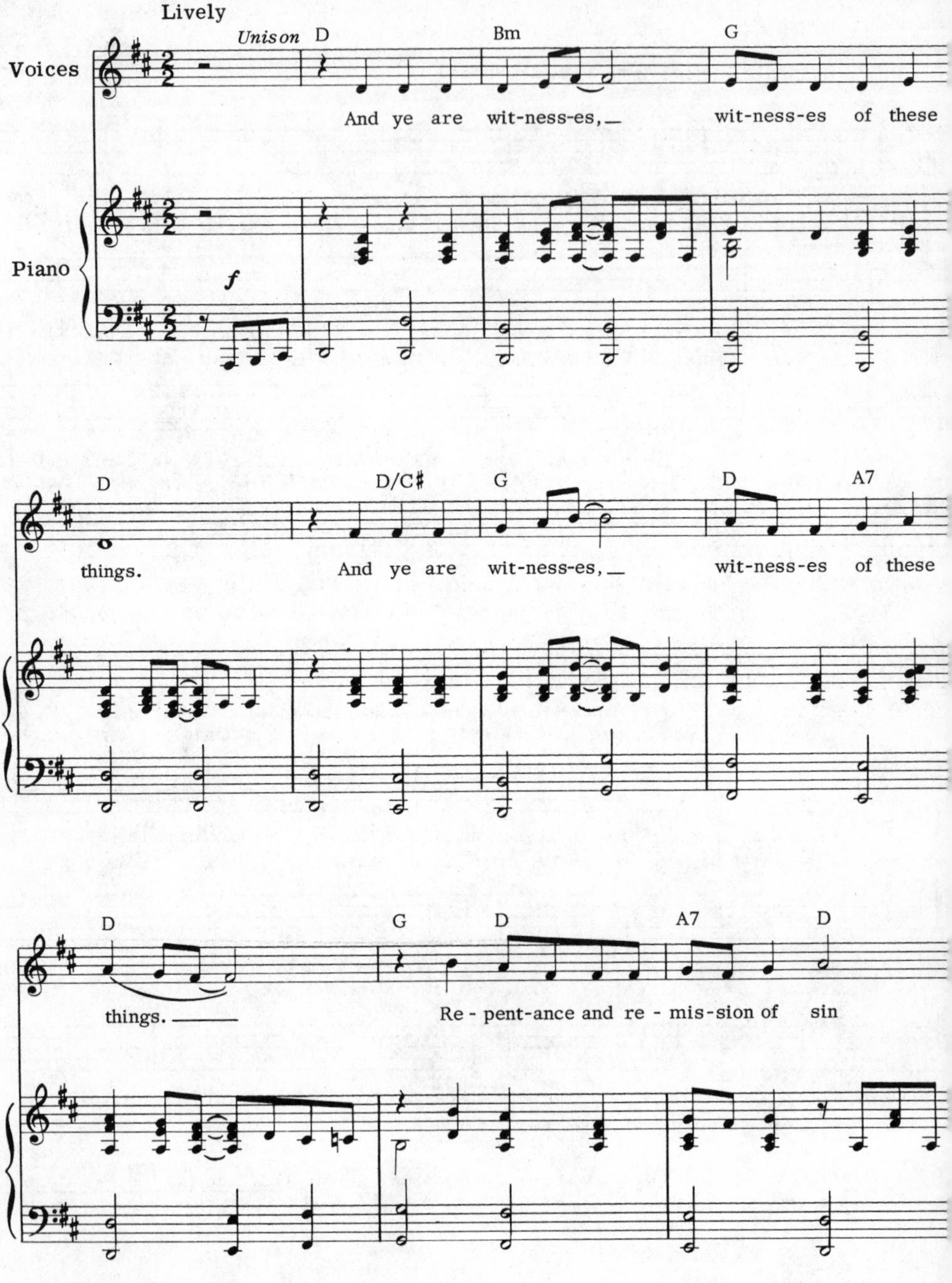

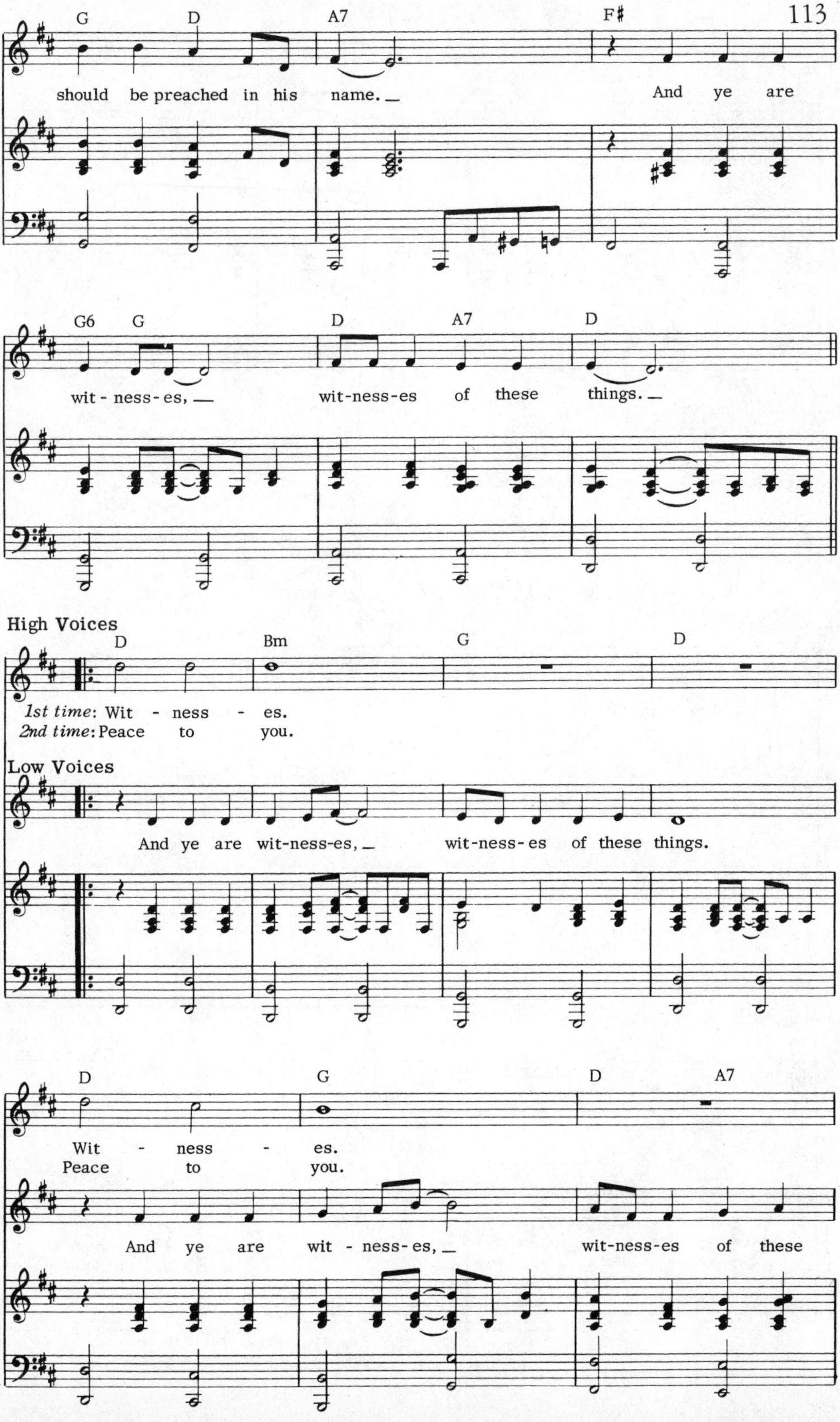
G D A7 F#
should be preached in his name.
And ye are
G6 G D A7 D
wit-ness-es,
wit-ness-es of these things.
High Voices
D Bm G D
1st time: Wit - ness - es.
2nd time: Peace to you.
Low Voices
And ye are wit-ness-es,
wit-ness-es of these things.
D G D A7
Wit - ness - es.
Peace to you.
And ye are wit - ness-es,
wit-ness-es of these

114

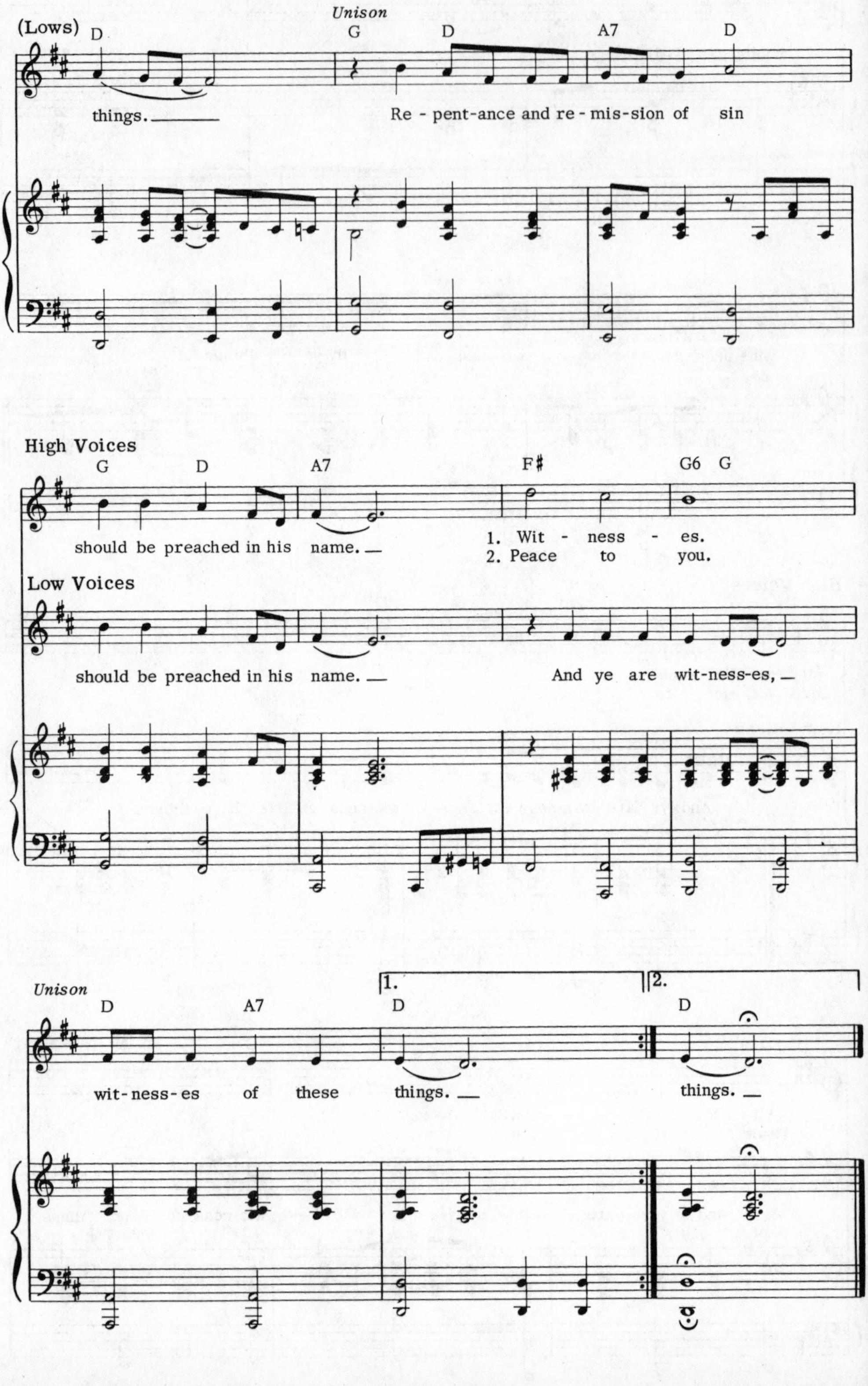

Go to Galilee

Al Carmines

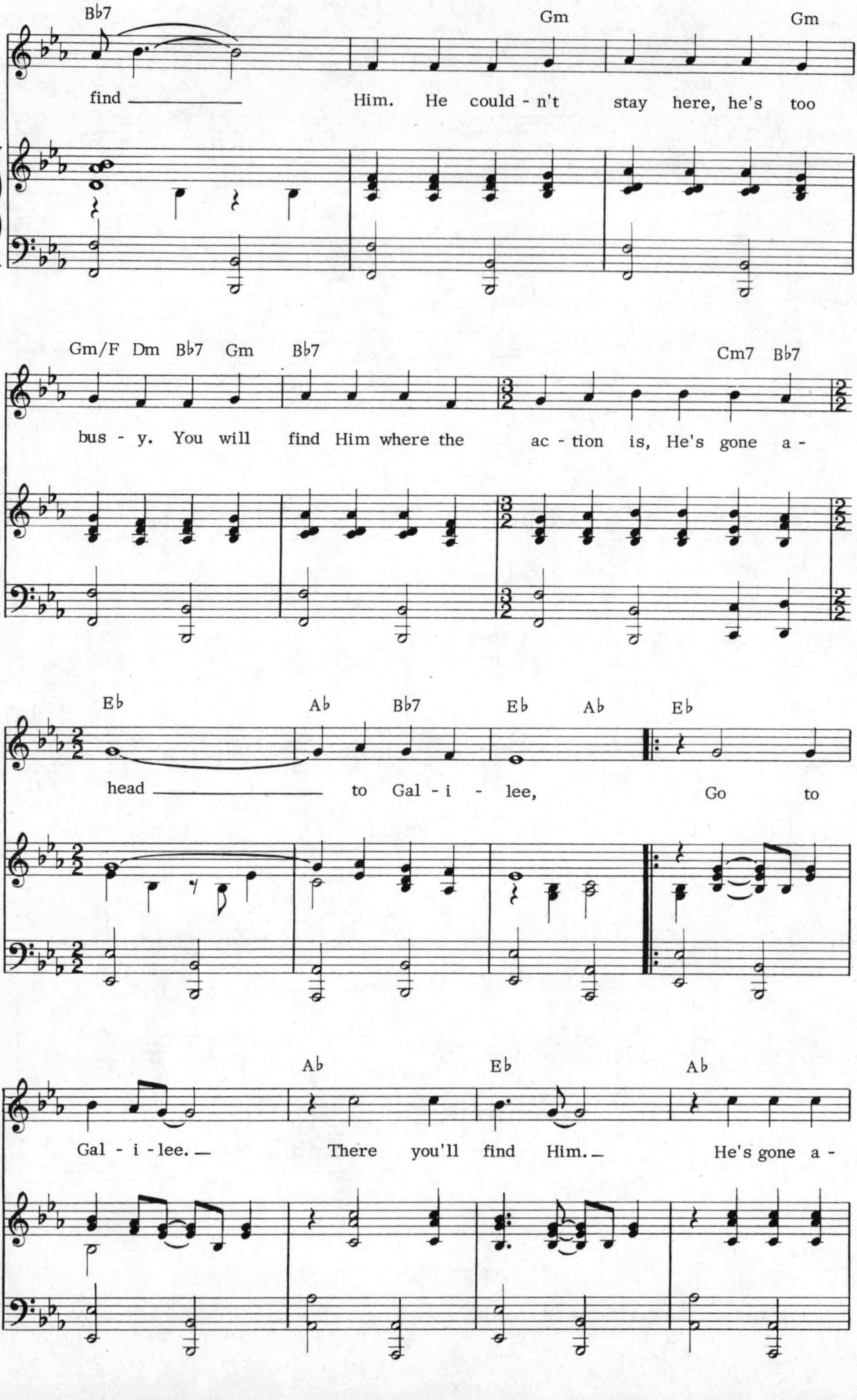
Bb7 Gm Gm
find Him. He could-n't stay here, he's too
Gm/F Dm Bb7 Gm Bb7 Cm7 Bb7
bus-y. You will find Him where the ac-tion is, He's gone a-
Eb Ab Bb7 Eb Ab Eb
head to Gal-i-lee, Go to
Ab Eb Ab
Gal-i-lee. There you'll find Him. He's gone a-

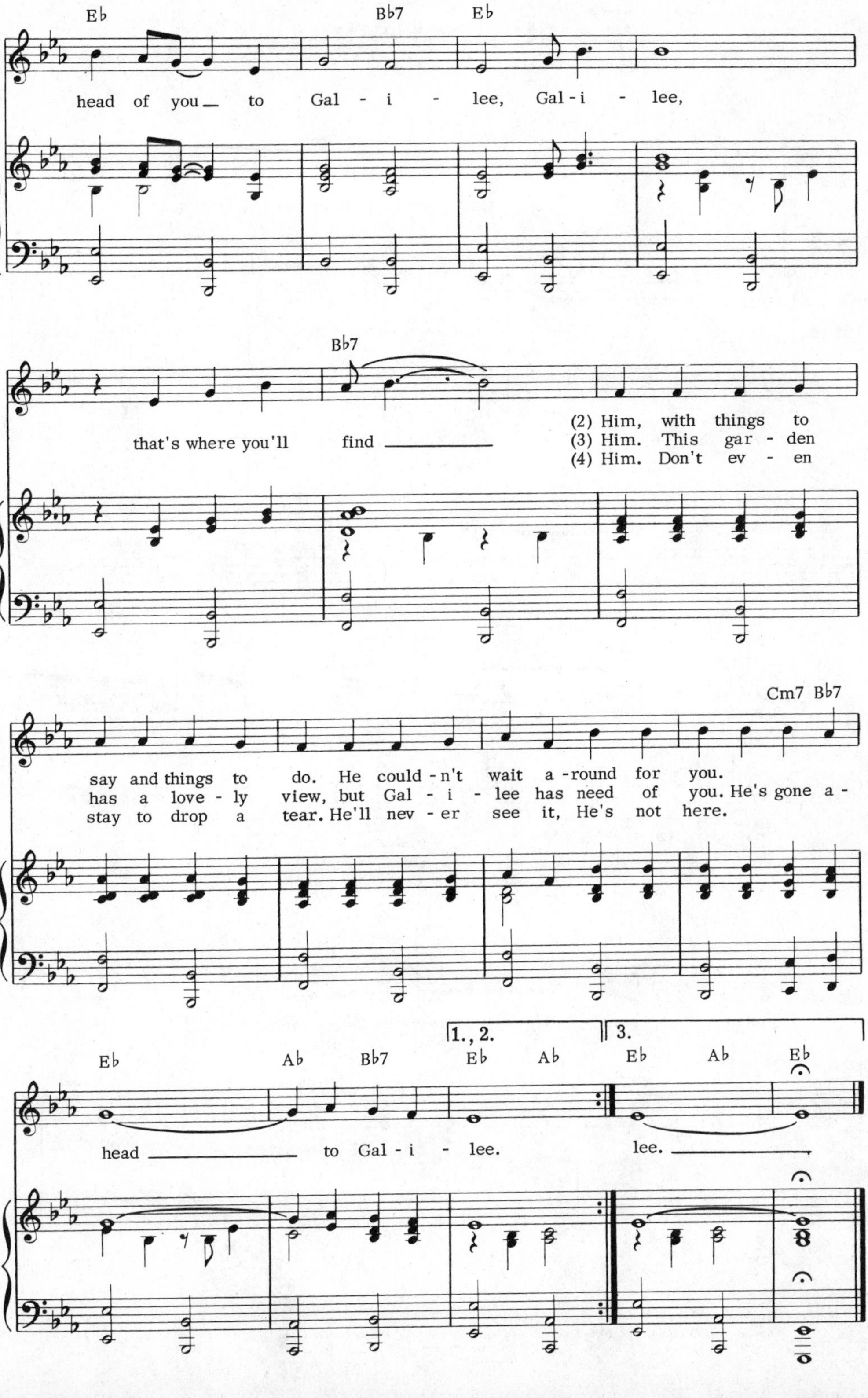
Eb
Bb7
Eb
head of you to Gal - i - lee, Gal - i - lee,
Bb7
that's where you'll find
(2) Him, with things to
(3) Him. This gar - den
(4) Him. Don't ev - en
say and things to do. He could - n't wait a - round for you.
has a love - ly view, but Gal - i - lee has need of you. He's gone a -
stay to drop a tear. He'll nev - er see it, He's not here.
Cm7
Bb7
1., 2.
3.
Eb
Ab
Bb7
Eb
Ab
Eb
Ab
Eb
head to Gal - i - lee.
lee.

Peace Chorus

Al Carmines

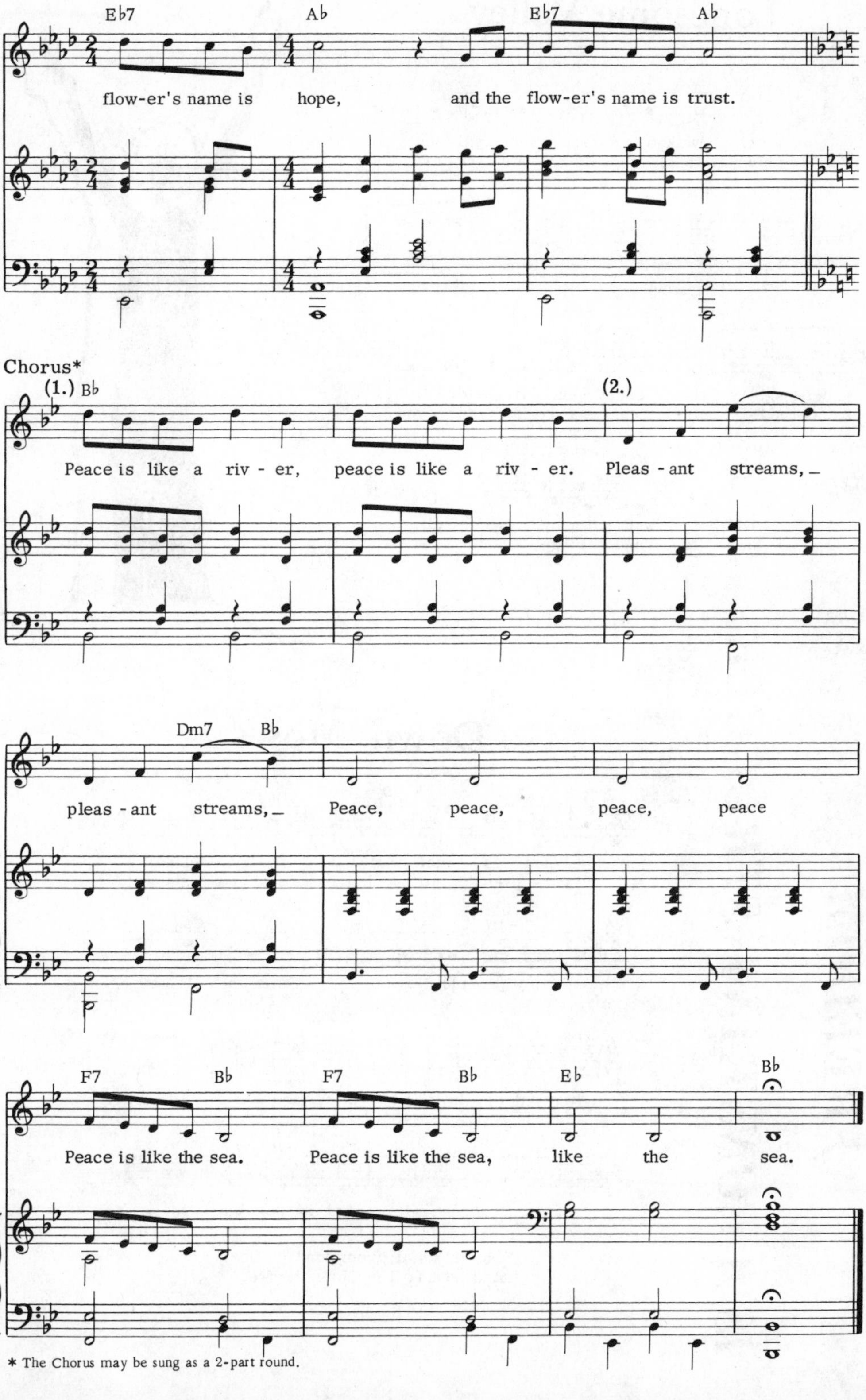

flow-er's name is hope, and the flow-er's name is trust.

Chorus*

(1.) Peace is like a riv-er, peace is like a riv-er. Pleas-ant streams, (2.)

pleas-ant streams, — Peace, peace, peace, peace

Peace is like the sea. Peace is like the sea, like the sea.

* The Chorus may be sung as a 2-part round.

120

Lonesome Valley

American Spiritual

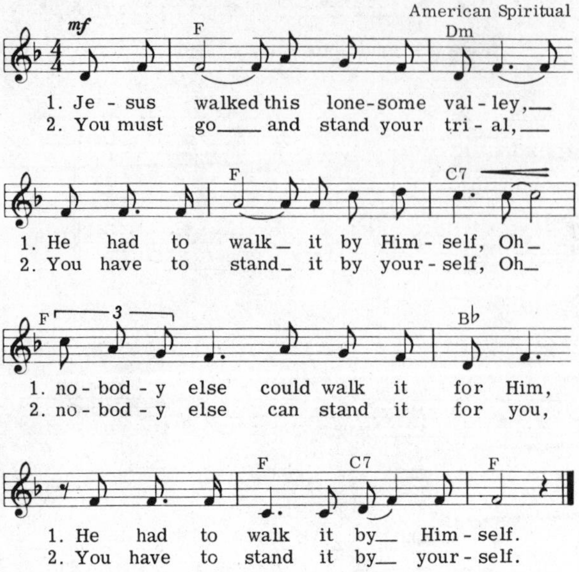

1. Je-sus walked this lone-some val-ley,—
2. You must go— and stand your tri-al,—

1. He had to walk— it by Him-self, Oh—
2. You have to stand— it by your-self, Oh—

1. no-bod-y else could walk it for Him,
2. no-bod-y else can stand it for you,

1. He had to walk it by— Him-self.
2. You have to stand it by— your-self.

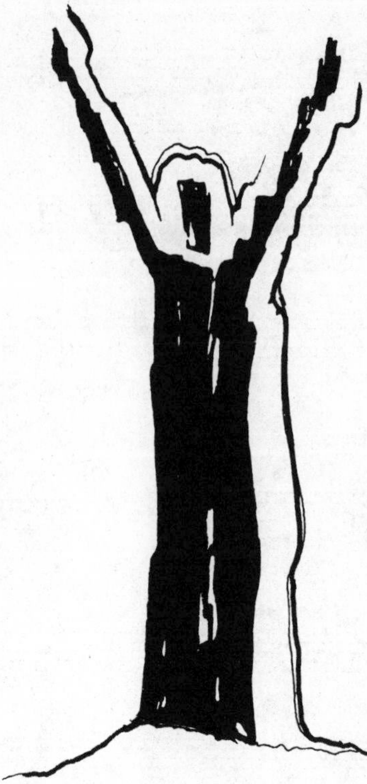

Go Down, Moses

Negro Spiritual

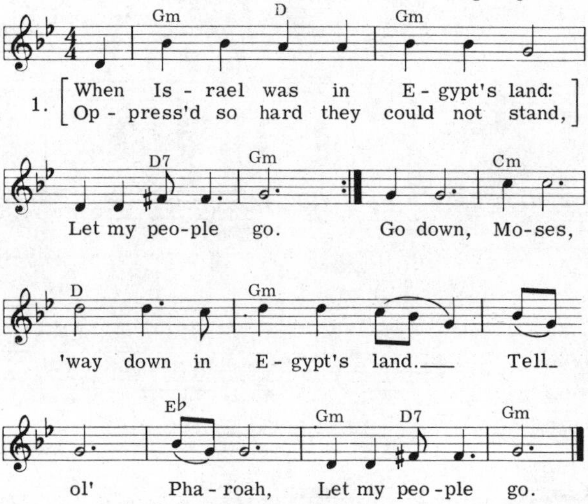

1. When Is-rael was in E-gypt's land:
   Op-press'd so hard they could not stand,

Let my peo-ple go. Go down, Mo-ses,

'way down in E-gypt's land.— Tell—

ol' Pha-roah, Let my peo-ple go.

2. Oh, let us all from bondage flee,
   And let us all in Christ be free!

FREEDOM IS A CONSTANT STRUGGLE

I Have Decided to Follow Jesus

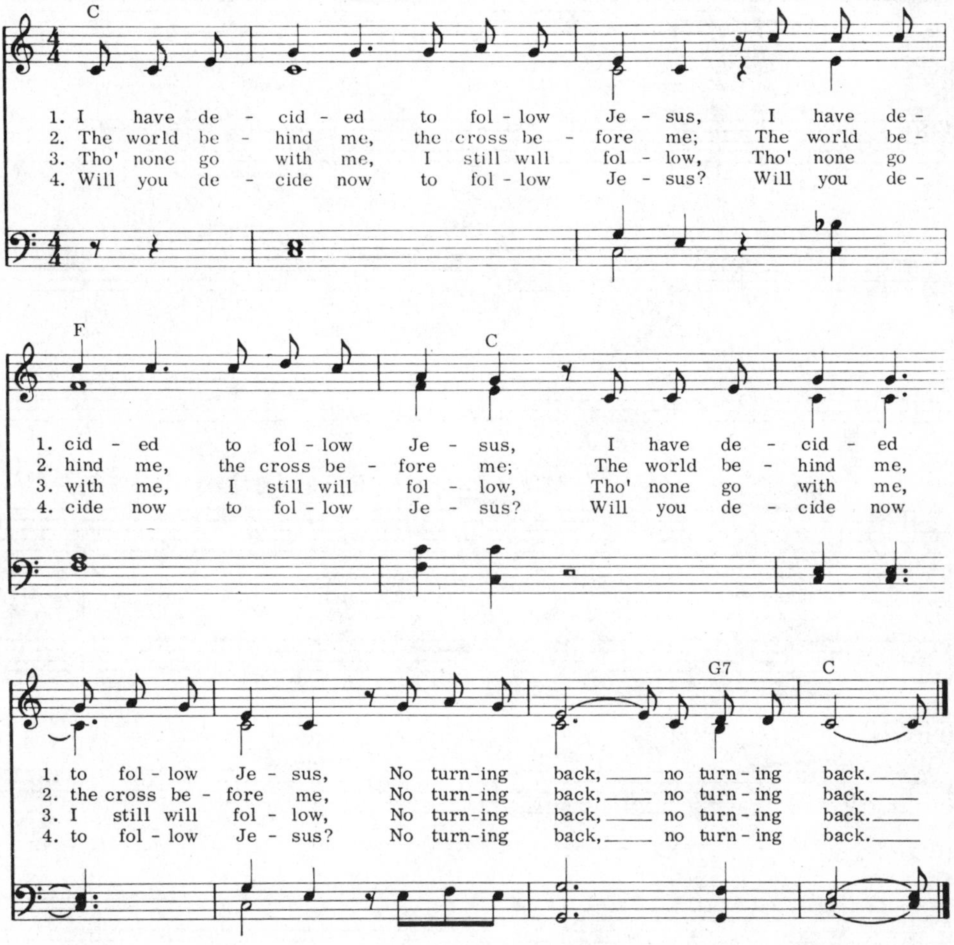

1. I have de - cid - ed to fol - low Je - sus, I have de -
2. The world be - hind me, the cross be - fore me; The world be -
3. Tho' none go with me, I still will fol - low, Tho' none go
4. Will you de - cide now to fol - low Je - sus? Will you de -

1. cid - ed to fol - low Je - sus, I have de - cid - ed
2. hind me, the cross be - fore me; The world be - hind me,
3. with me, I still will fol - low, Tho' none go with me,
4. cide now to fol - low Je - sus? Will you de - cide now

1. to fol - low Je - sus, No turn-ing back, ___ no turn - ing back. ___
2. the cross be - fore me, No turn-ing back, ___ no turn - ing back. ___
3. I still will fol - low, No turn-ing back, ___ no turn - ing back. ___
4. to fol - low Je - sus? No turn-ing back, ___ no turn - ing back. ___

NOT TO DECIDE

IS TO DECIDE

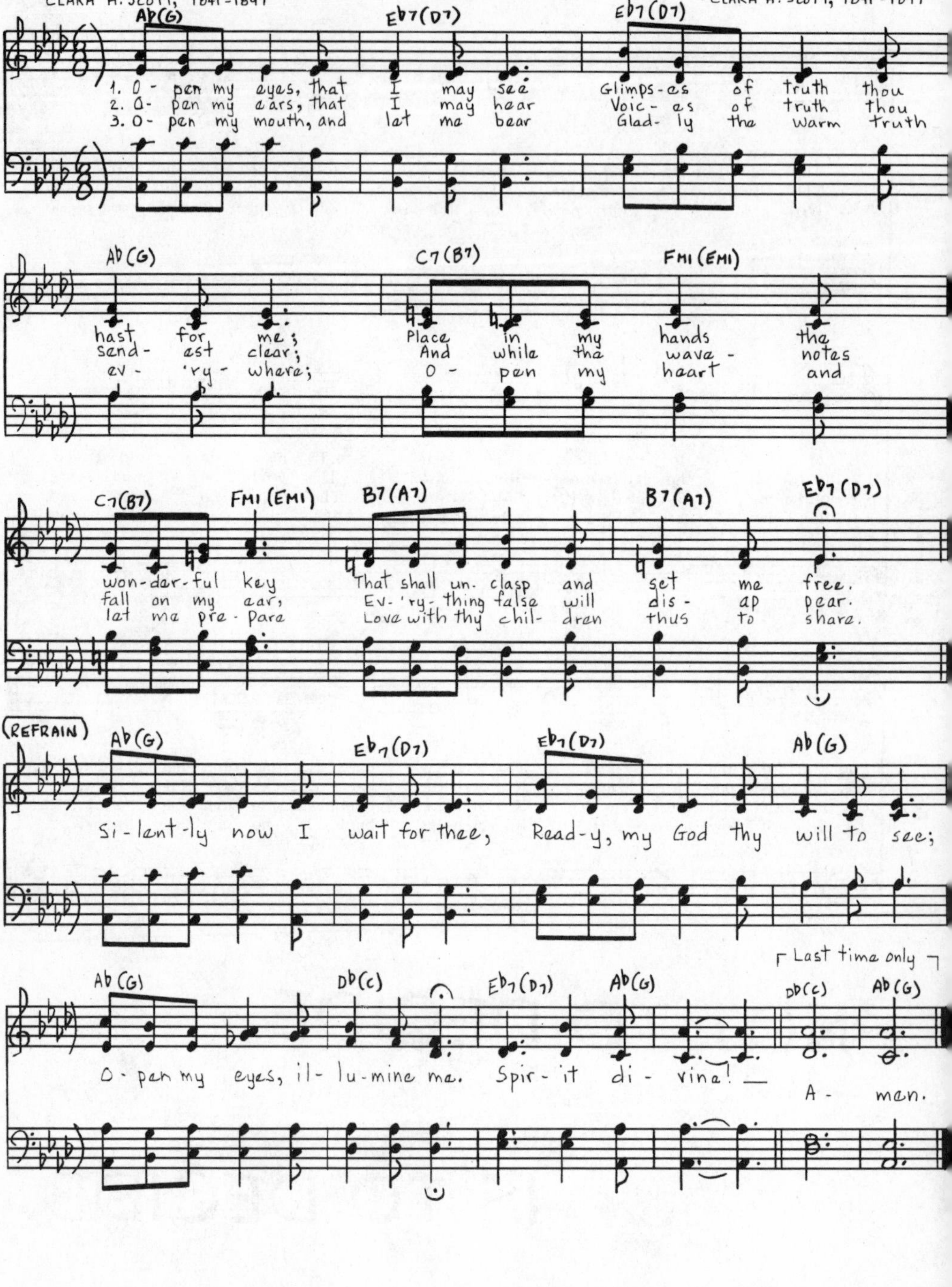

Open My Eyes

122

Capo 1, Play in G
CLARA H. SCOTT, 1841-1897

OPEN MY EYES 88.98. with Refrain
CLARA H. SCOTT, 1841-1897

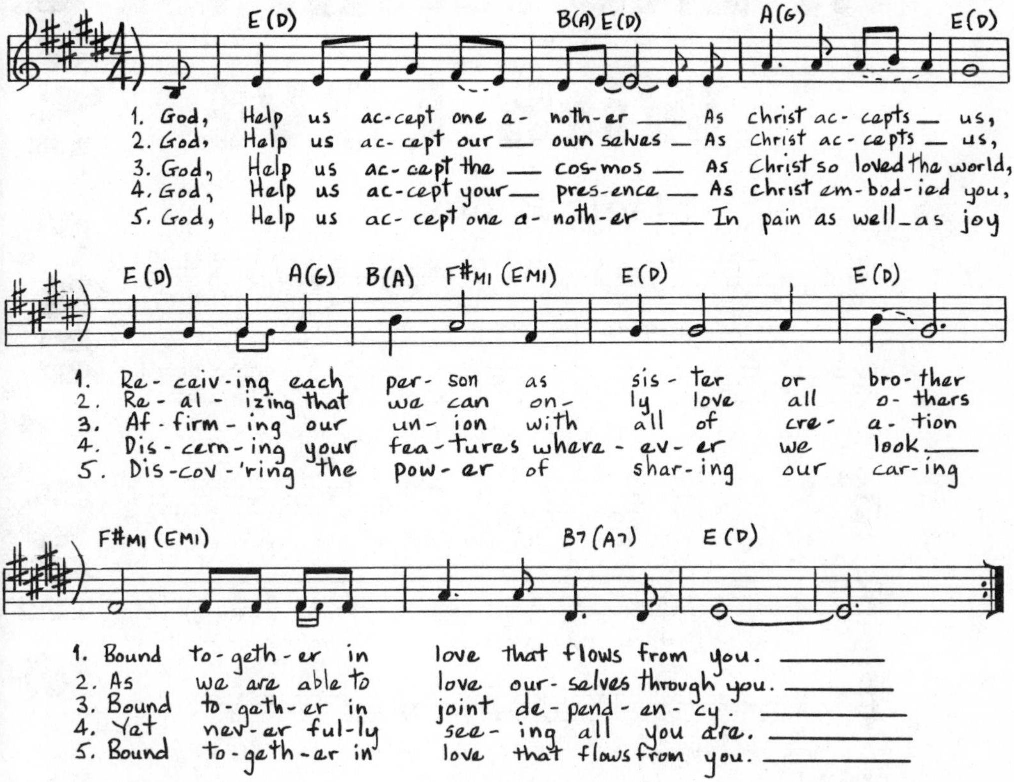

Acceptance

123

Capo 2 (D)

Words and Music by Tom Neufer Emswiler

1. God, Help us ac-cept one a-noth-er ____ As Christ ac-cepts ____ us,
2. God, Help us ac-cept our ____ own selves ____ As Christ ac-cepts ____ us,
3. God, Help us ac-cept the ____ cos-mos ____ As Christ so loved the world,
4. God, Help us ac-cept your ____ pres-ence ____ As Christ em-bod-ied you,
5. God, Help us ac-cept one a-noth-er ____ In pain as well as joy

1. Re-ceiv-ing each per-son as sis-ter or bro-ther
2. Re-al-iz-ing that we can on-ly love all o-thers
3. Af-firm-ing our un-ion with all of cre-a-tion
4. Dis-cern-ing your fea-tures where-ev-er we look ____
5. Dis-cov-'ring the pow-er of shar-ing our car-ing

1. Bound to-geth-er in love that flows from you. ____
2. As we are able to love our-selves through you. ____
3. Bound to-geth-er in joint de-pend-en-cy. ____
4. Yet nev-er ful-ly see-ing all you are. ____
5. Bound to-geth-er in love that flows from you. ____

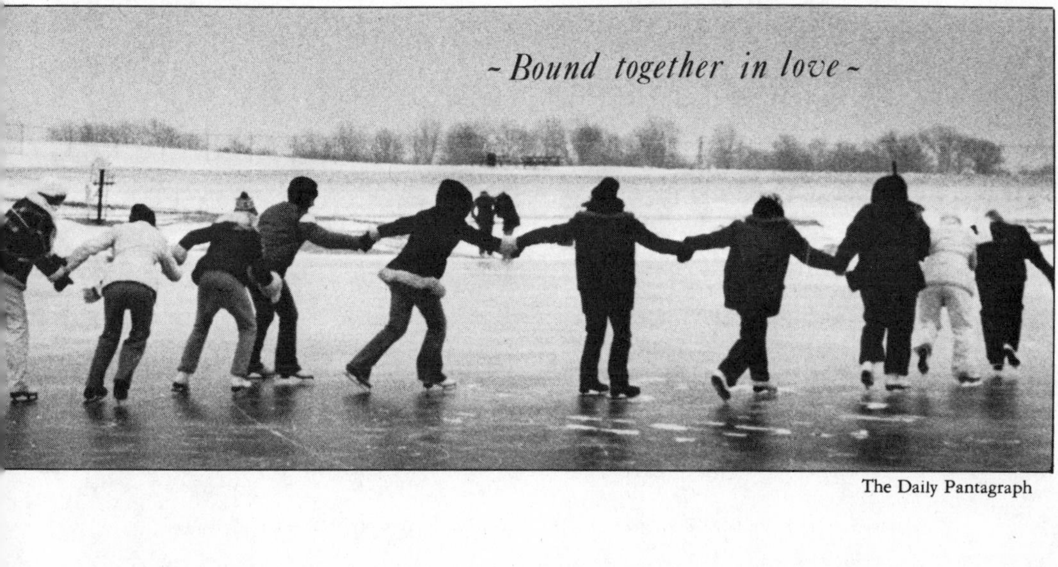

- *Bound together in love* -

The Daily Pantagraph

Be a SPENDTHRIFT With LOVE

Magic Penny

Malvina Reynolds

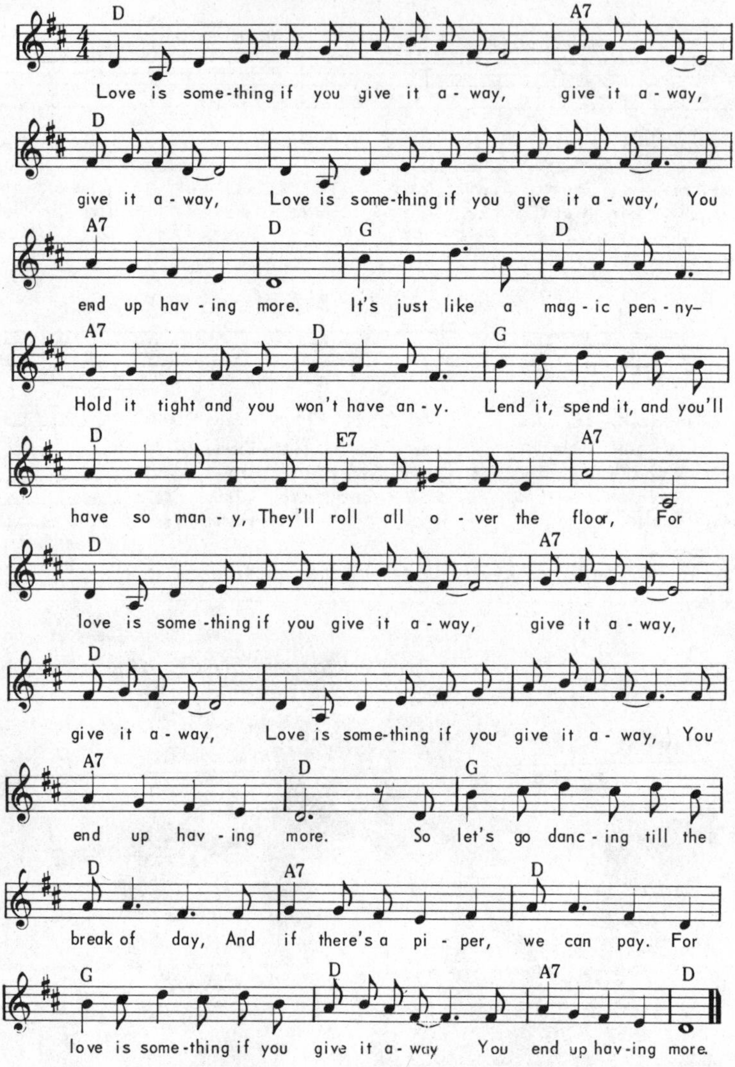

Love is some-thing if you give it a-way, give it a-way, give it a-way, Love is some-thing if you give it a-way, You end up hav-ing more. It's just like a mag-ic pen-ny— Hold it tight and you won't have an-y. Lend it, spend it, and you'll have so man-y, They'll roll all o-ver the floor, For love is some-thing if you give it a-way, give it a-way, give it a-way, Love is some-thing if you give it a-way, You end up hav-ing more. So let's go danc-ing till the break of day, And if there's a pi-per, we can pay. For love is some-thing if you give it a-way You end up hav-ing more.

Hey! Can YOU Spare a HUG?

Oh, When the Saints

Traditional

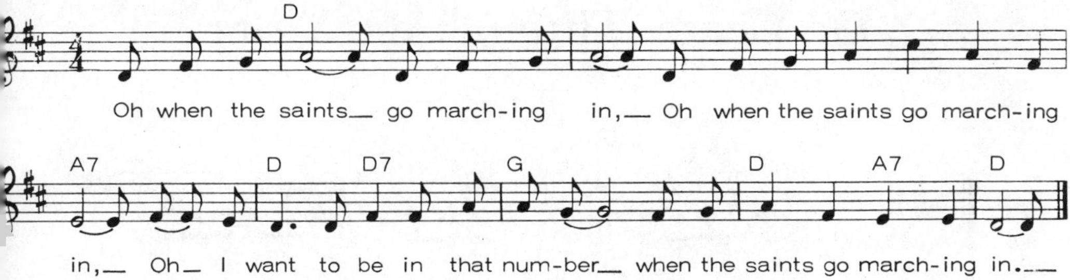

1. Oh when that light begins to shine, etc.
2. Oh when the sun refuse to shine, etc.

Till we meet again

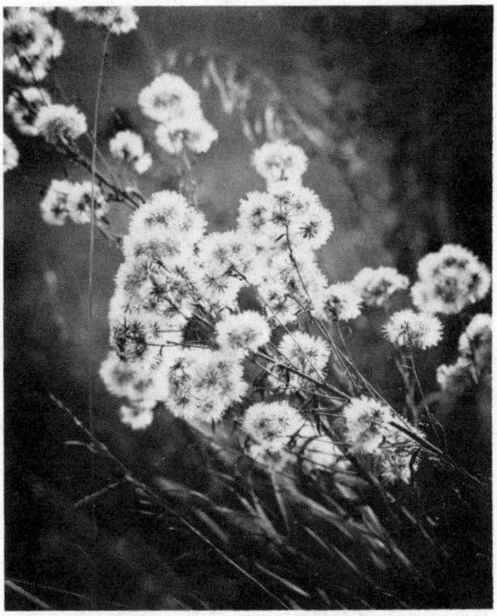

The Daily Pantagraph

Shalom Chaverim

(Farewell Good Friends)

Israeli Round

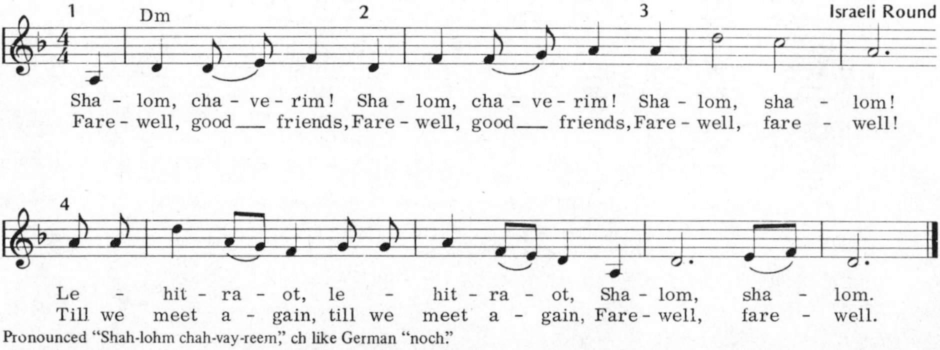

Pronounced "Shah-lohm chah-vay-reem," ch like German "noch."

Go Gently Through the Years

Diane L. Rutledge

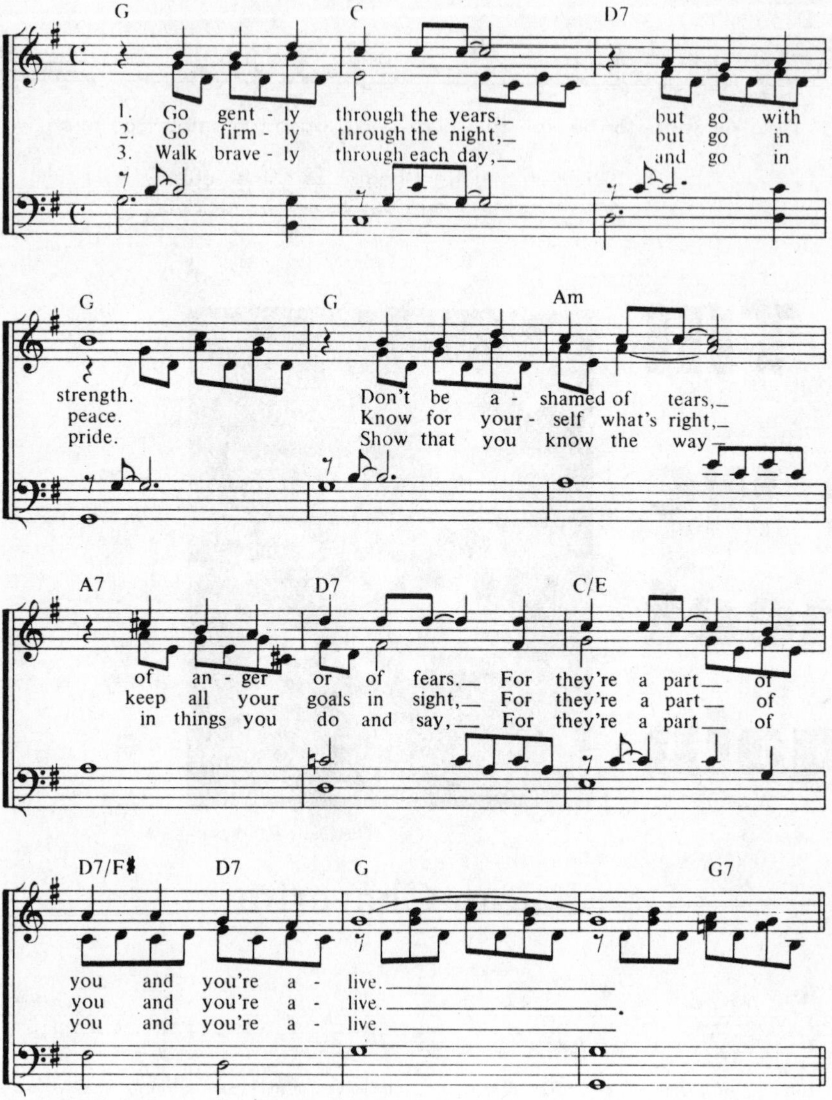

1. Go gent-ly through the years,— but go with
2. Go firm-ly through the night,— but go in
3. Walk brave-ly through each day,— and go in

strength. Don't be a-shamed of tears,—
peace. Know for your-self what's right,—
pride. Show that you know the way—

of an-ger or of fears.— For they're a part— of
keep all your goals in sight,— For they're a part— of
in things you do and say,— For they're a part— of

you and you're a-live.————
you and you're a-live.————.
you and you're a-live.————

LIFE & TIME --
our only real possessions

Climb moun - tains while you may___ and sing your

songs. Start liv - ing ev - ery day,___

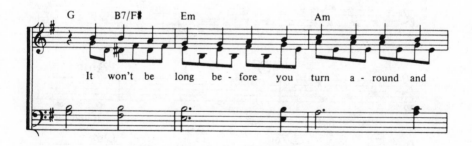

It won't be long be - fore you turn a - round and

won - der where life's gone.___

Go Now In Peace

Joe Wise

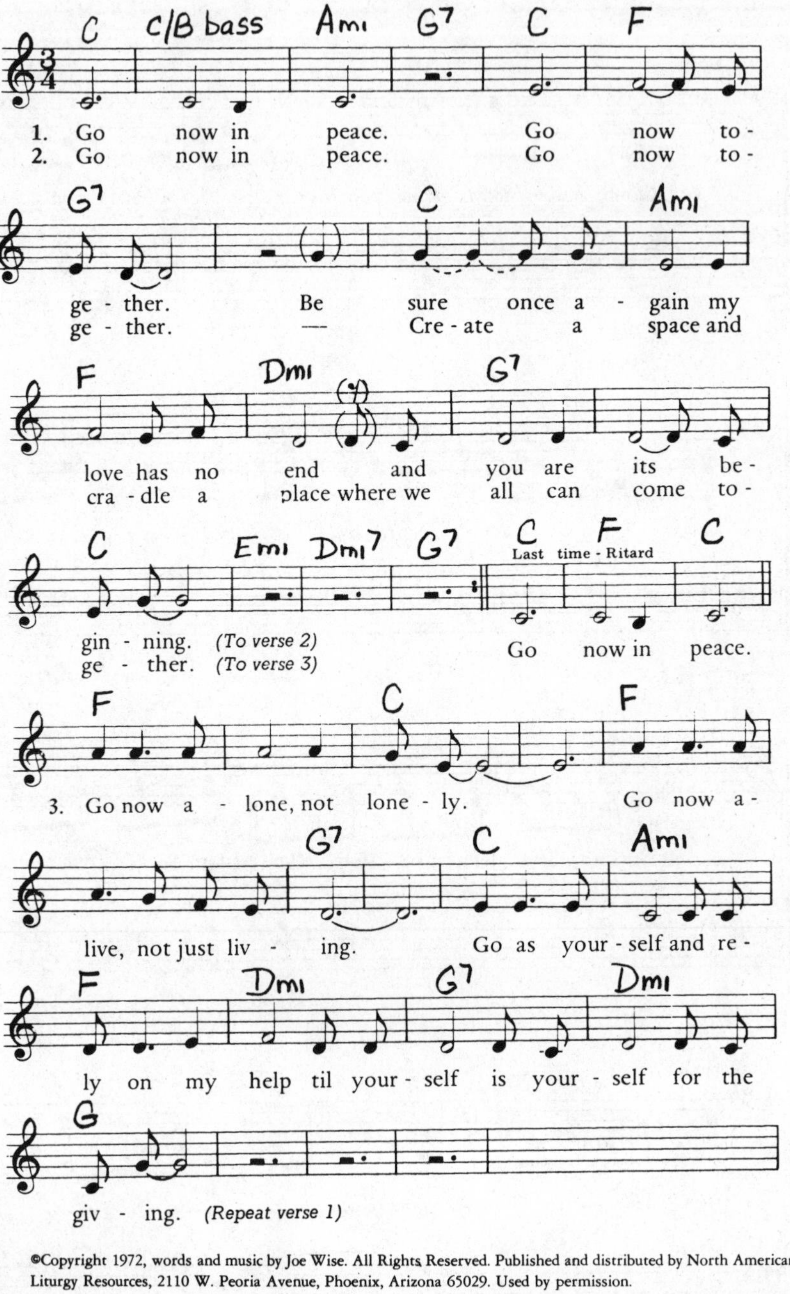

1. Go now in peace. Go now to-ge-ther. Be sure once a-gain my love has no end and you are its be-gin-ning. *(To verse 2)*

2. Go now in peace. Go now to-ge-ther. — Cre-ate a space and cra-dle a place where we all can come to-ge-ther. *(To verse 3)*

Last time - Ritard
Go now in peace.

3. Go now a-lone, not lone-ly. Go now a-live, not just liv-ing. Go as your-self and re-ly on my help til your-self is your-self for the giv-ing. *(Repeat verse 1)*

FOR CHILDREN OF ALL AGES

(from 1-100)

Yeast Song

Capo 5 (c)

Words and Music by ART ALLEN

Take a lit-tle yeast, add it to some dough, and it will grow and grow.
Dough's like you and me, sim-ple as can be, Just plain and com-mon stuff.

Take a lit-tle love, God's own love and the world will change, I know.
When you add the yeast, Pow-er will in-crease till it ris-es o'er the top.

Worries

Words and Music by ART ALLEN

Oh you wor-ry 'bout your clothes, And you wor-ry 'bout your nose, And you
wor-ry 'bout the hair on your head, But God is tak-ing care of the
birds in the air, And will take good care of you. Oh, there
Though the
was a man so rich, He said, "I'm a luck-y man," But
birds up in the sky, Don't have clothes or drive a car, Yet
when he died he had to leave it all be-hind.
hear them sing a joy-ous song as days go by.

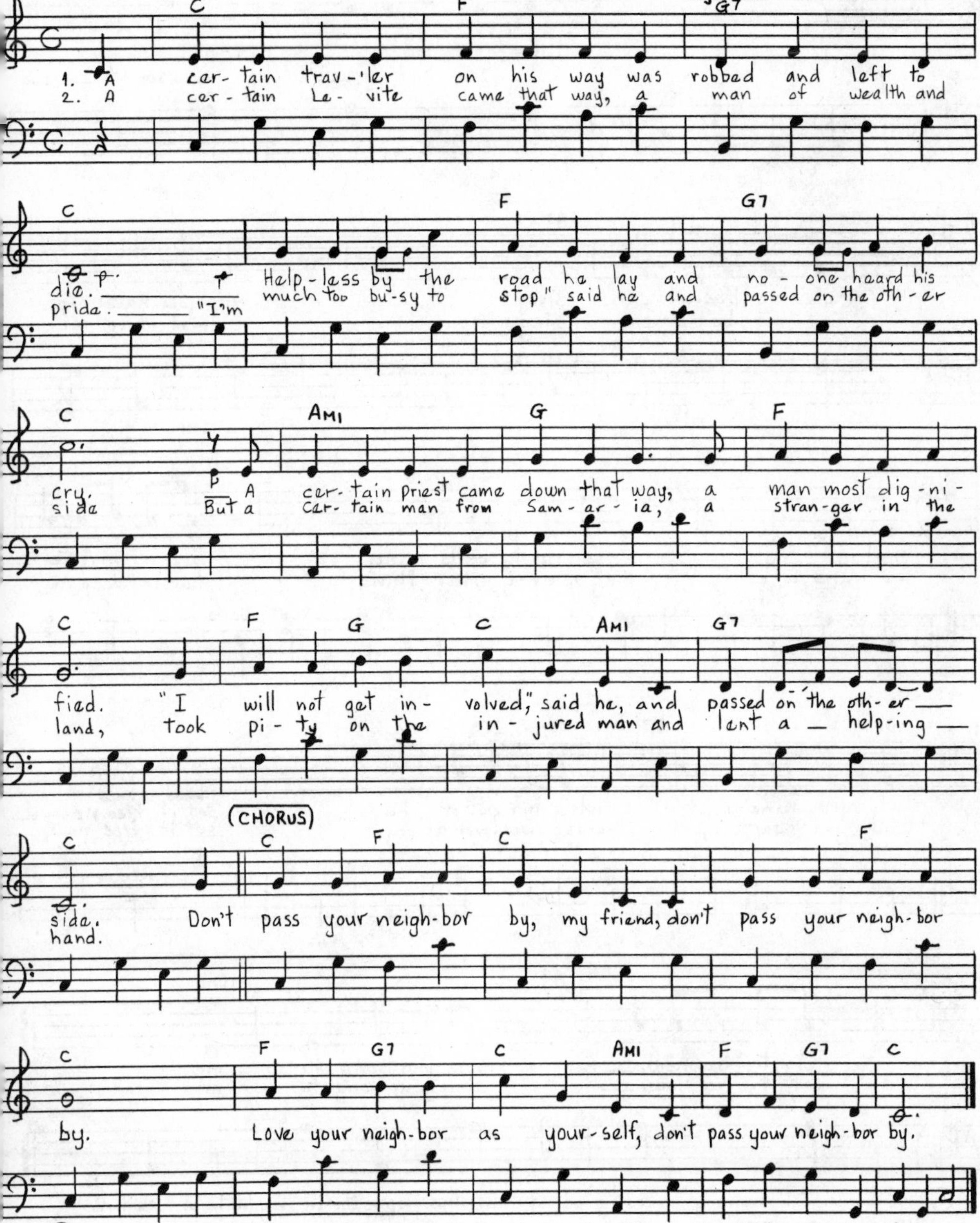

The Good Samaritan

By MARY LU WALKER

1. A certain trav'ler on his way was robbed and left to die.
Helpless by the road he lay and no-one heard his cry.
A certain priest came down that way, a man most dignified.
"I will not get involved," said he, and passed on the other side.

2. A certain Levite came that way, a man of wealth and pride.
"I'm much too busy to stop" said he and passed on the other side.
But a certain man from Samaria, a stranger in the land,
took pity on the injured man and lent a helping hand.

(CHORUS)
Don't pass your neighbor by, my friend, don't pass your neighbor by.
Love your neighbor as yourself, don't pass your neighbor by.

Everybody Has a Song

By Mary Lu Walker

1. Ev-'ry-bod-y — has a song. —
2. Ev-'ry-bod-y — has a song, —

av-'ry-bod-y can sing. All you have to
ev-'ry-bod-y can sing. Sing of hap-pi-

do is try. E-ven rus-ty bells ring; does-n't mat-ter
ness and love. Sing of an-y old thing; bur-ied deep in-

if your tune — sounds a bit out of key, set it free now, —
side your heart, — there's a sweet mel-o- dy, set it free now, —

let it be now, — sing your song to me.
let it be now, — sing your song to me.

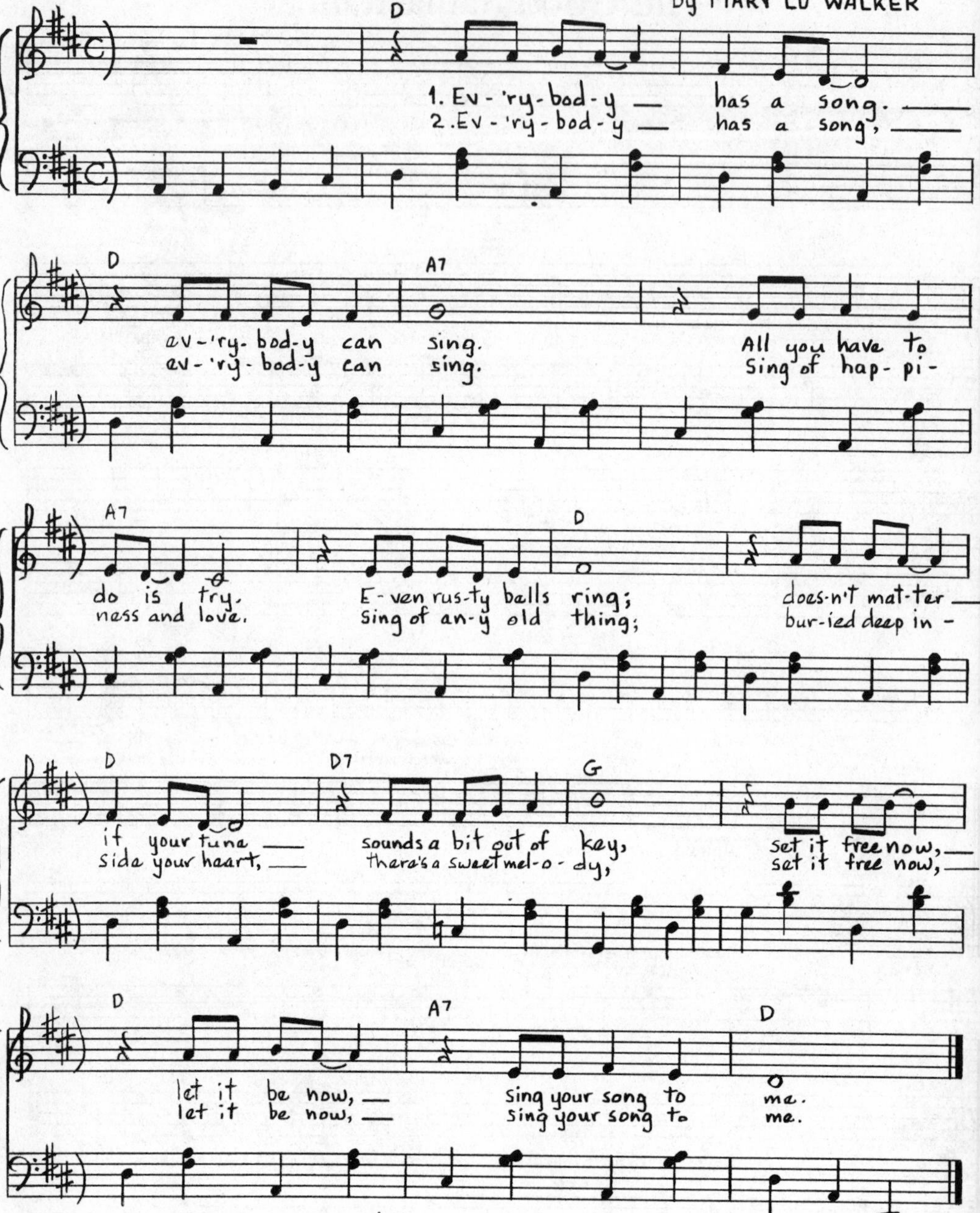

Hide Me

by MARY LU WALKER

Hide me in the sha-dow,___ Hide me in the sha-dow of your wings. Hide me and pro- tact me,___ pro- tact me as the ap-pla of your eye. ___

1. That I may
2. You are my

(TO REFRAIN)

3. eye.

FINE

(REFRAIN)

walk
light,

in your light
I will not fear,

that I'll be
you guida my

free from the dark- ness of sin.
steps in the path- ways of peace.

(D.C. AL FINE - LAST TIME)

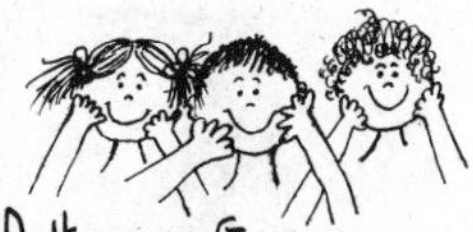

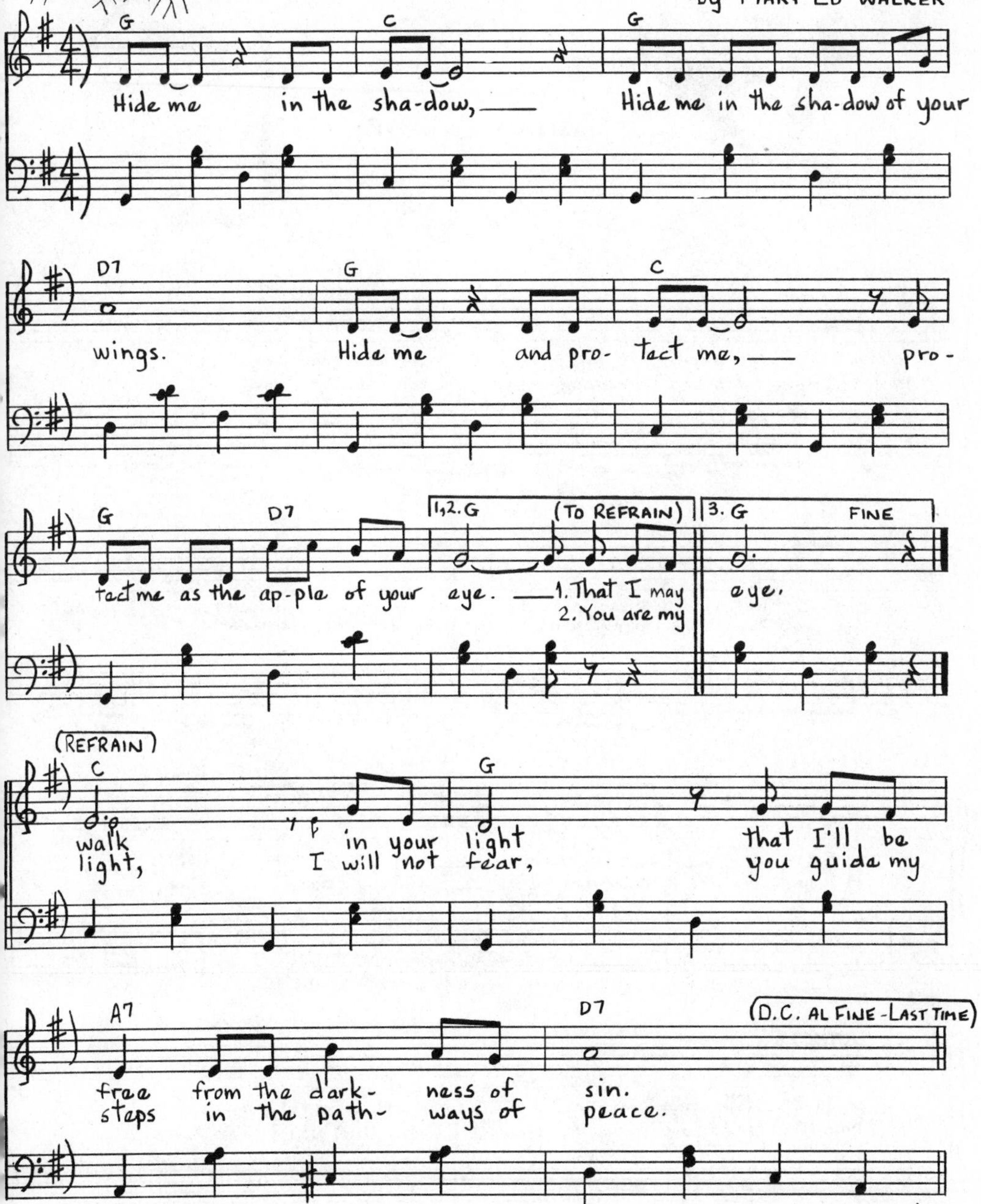

Runaway Song

By Mary Lu Walker

1. If I ran a-way to-day, if I made you cry;
2. If you ran a-way to-day, if you made me cry;

if I tra-veled far and wide and nev-er told you why. But
if you tra-veled far and wide and nev-er told me why. But

if I found the times were hard, ____ and I was all a - lone, ____
if you found the times were hard, ____ and you were all a - lone, ____ I'd

could I still come home to you, __ could I still come home.
hope that you'd come home, my child, I'd hope that you'd come home.

The Runaway Song

could I knock up- on your door _____ and would you let me in? Would
you could knock up- on my door _____ I'd run- to let you in. I'd

you be glad to see me _____ ev- en though I'd been So
be so glad to see you _ no mat- ter where you'd been So

long, so long a- way from home, _____ So
glad, so glad to have you home, _____ So

long, so long a- way from home.
glad, so glad to have you home.

WELCOME HOME!

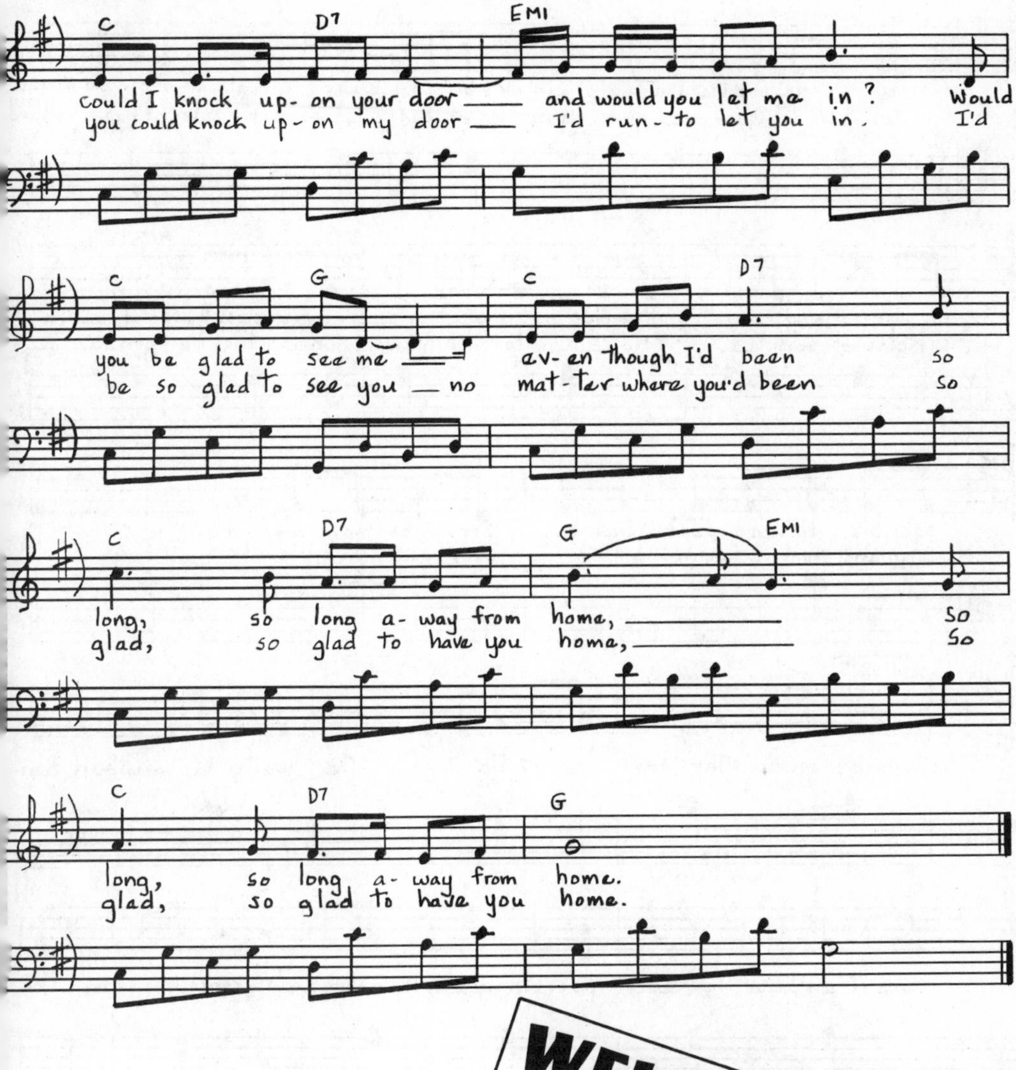

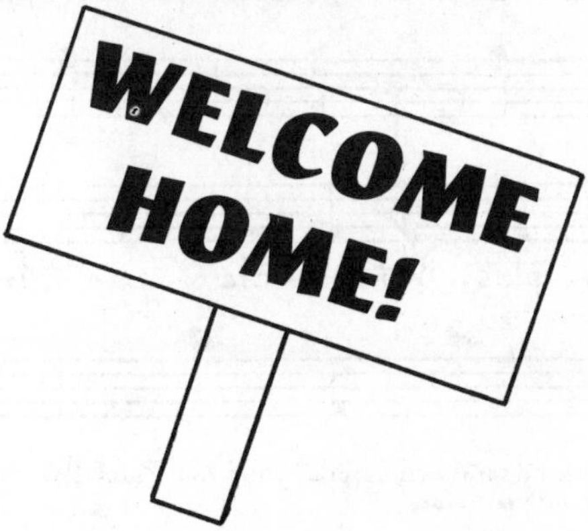

Luke 15:24

Pebbles

Mary Lu Walker

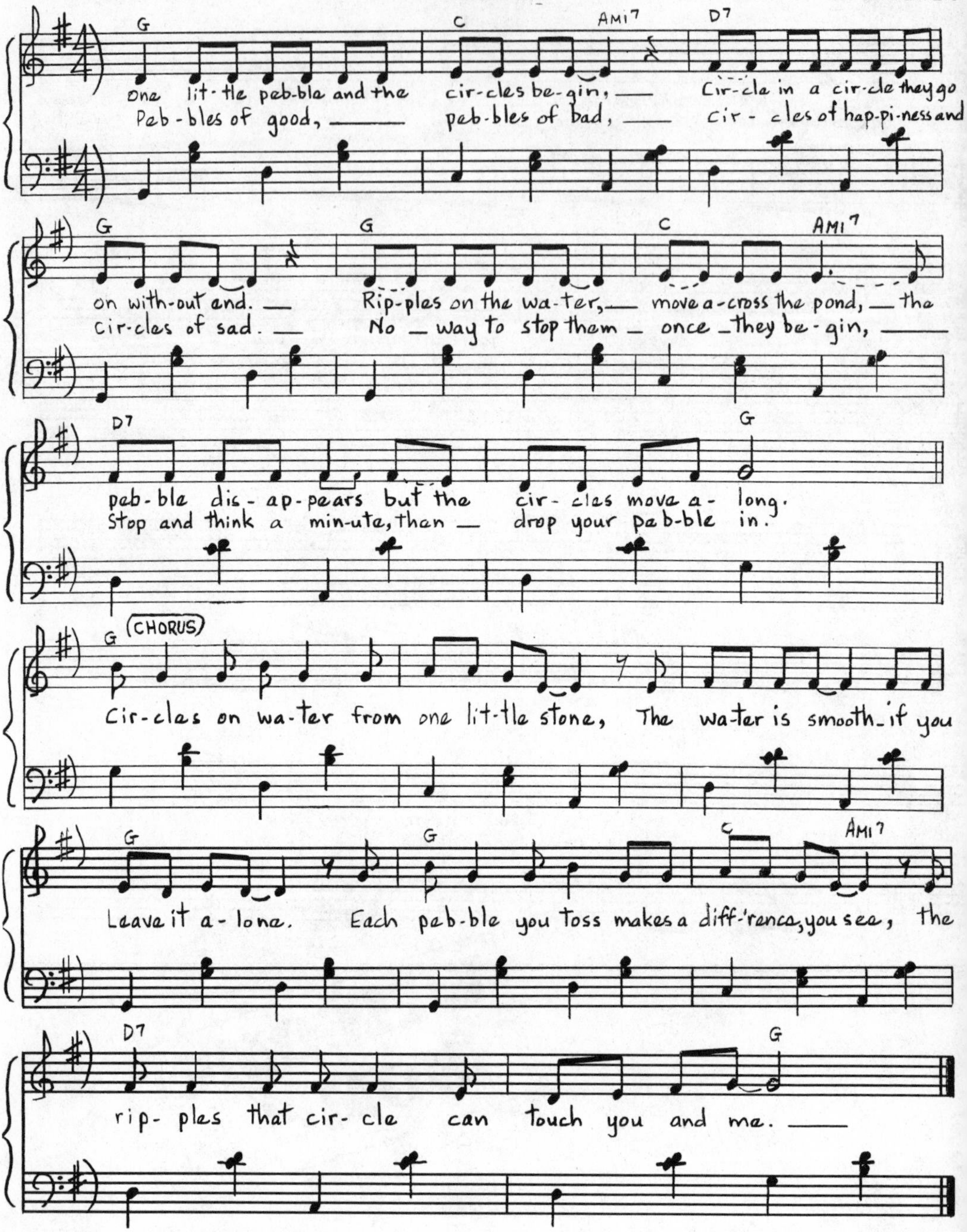

© 1975 by The Missionary Society of St. Paul the Apostle in the State of New York. Used by permission.

Alleluia

By Mary Lu Walker

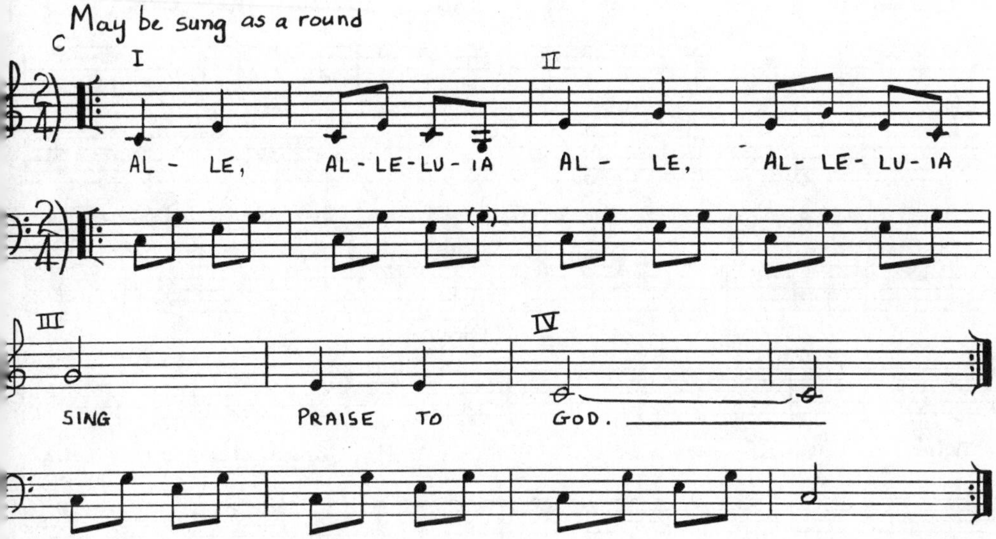

May be sung as a round

AL - LE, AL-LE-LU-IA AL - LE, AL-LE- LU-IA

SING PRAISE TO GOD. _____

Be an

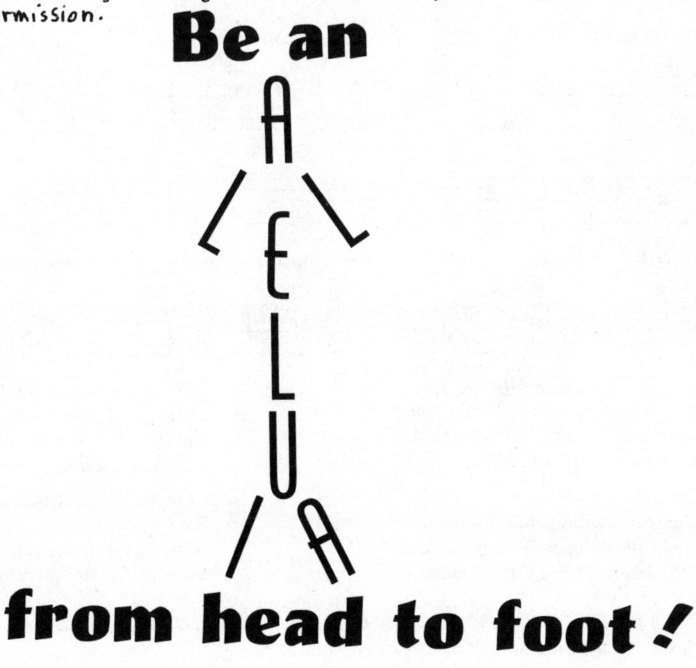

from head to foot!

Advent Song

By MARY LU WALKER

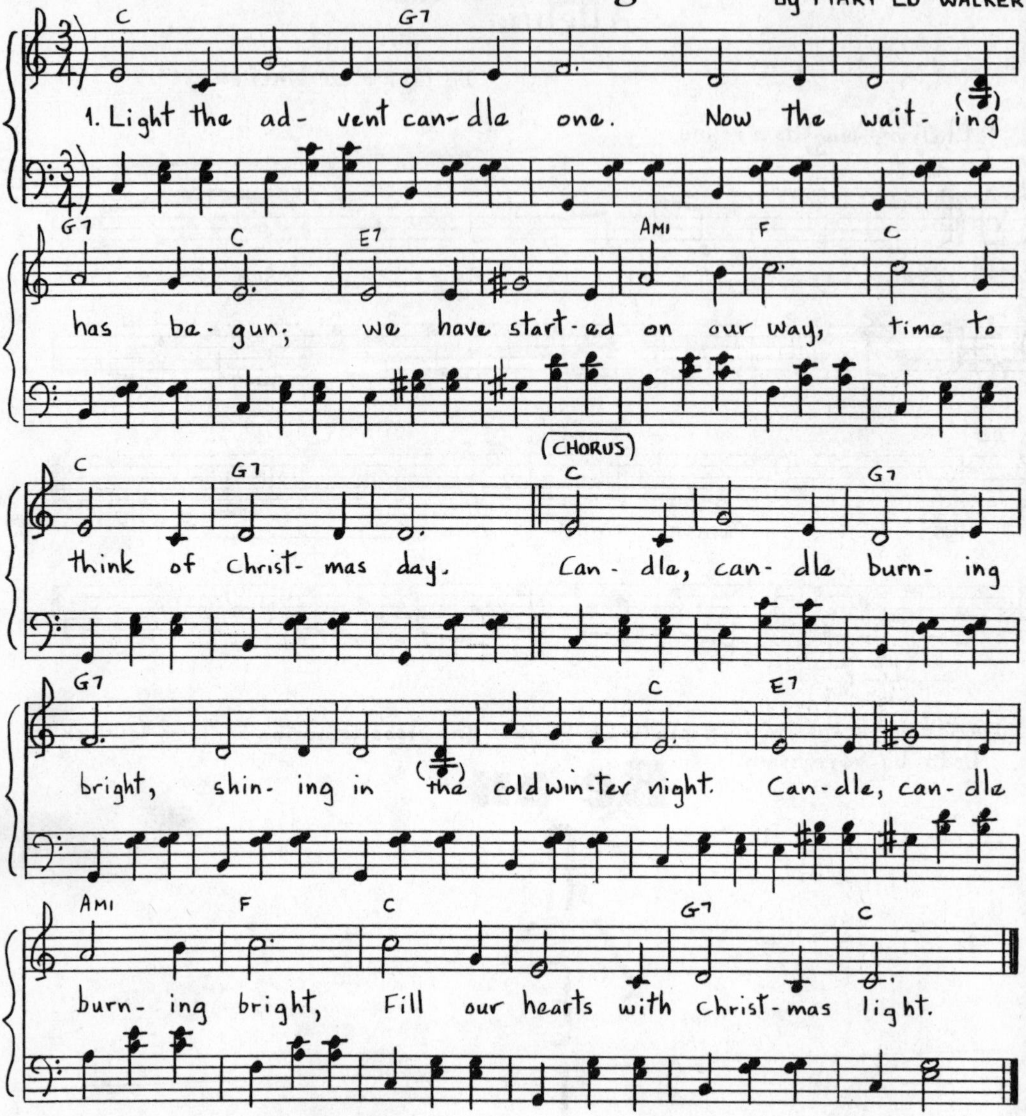

2. Light the Advent candle Two,
   Think of humble shepherds who
   Filled with wonder at the sight
   Of the child on Christmas night.

3. Light the Advent candle Three,
   Think of heavenly harmony
   Angels blessing, "Peace on Earth,"
   At the blessed Savior's birth.

4. Light the Advent candle Four,
   Think of joy forevermore,
   Christchild in a stable born,
   Gift of love that Christmas morn.

5. Light the Christmas candles now,
   Sing of donkey, sheep and cow,
   Birthday candles for the king,
   Let the Alleluias ring.

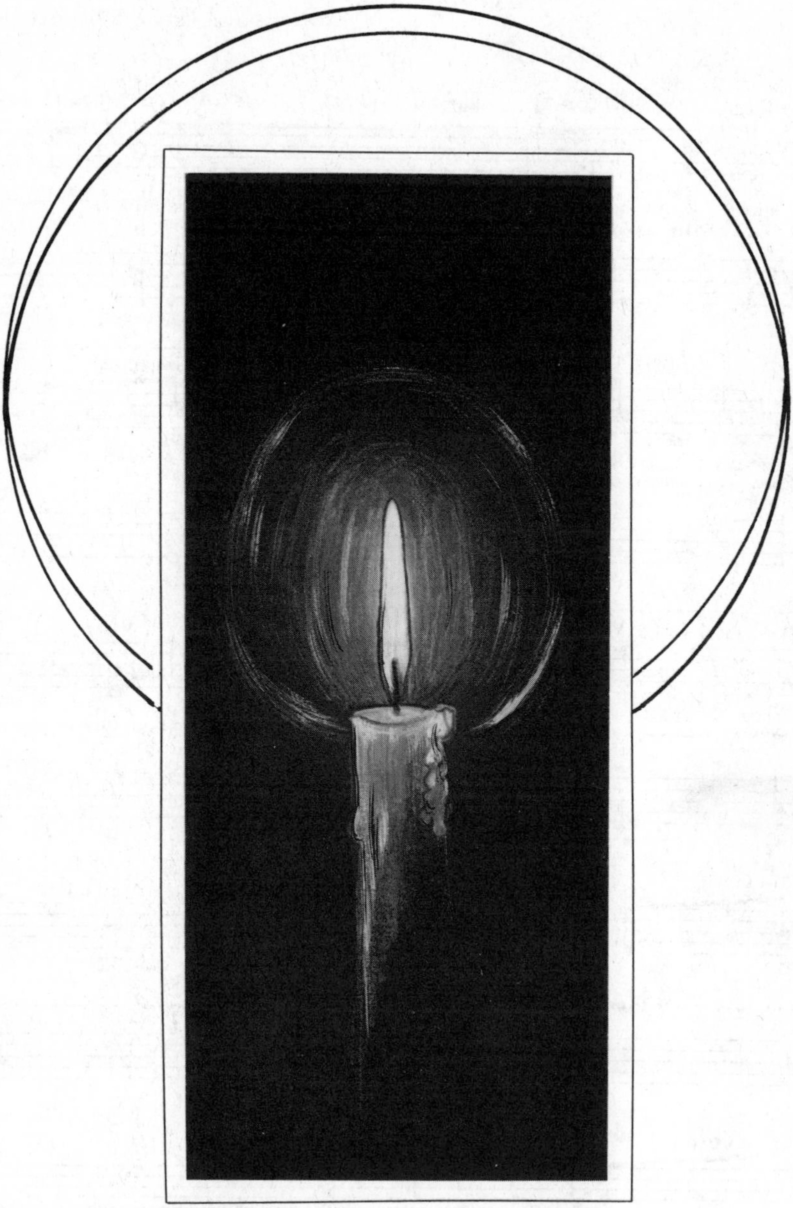

SONGS FOR SPECIAL TIMES

140

Soon Enough
(Mary's Song)

Words and Music by JUDITH MAY NEWTON

1. Sleep to-night, lit-tle one, Till it's bright, lit-tle one, You can't hear how the cold wind blows, ___ You can't see the star that glows. ___ Just soon e-nough the Light that will fill ___ all cre-a-tion liv-ing out God's will, ___

2. Feel the warmth of my breast, Find your joy in ___ rest; Soon e-nough come the storms and chill, ___

Un-til then, my lit-tle one, be still. ___

He's Arrived

Words and Music by ART ALLEN

He's ar- rived! He has come! He was born in Beth-le-hem, No, I
don't know what he weighed. He has come the world to save. It's a
joy- ous day both far and near, the Prom- ised One is here.

1. Come my friends to see him, it's a sight! He is in a cat-tle
2. No, he does-n't have a pur- ple robe. No, he does-n't wear a
3. Did you see the star up in the sky? Did you see the shep-herds

stall. Yes, he's in a man- ger, what a night! You must
crown. Though he's just a ba- by, wait and see— He will
come? Won't you join us in our joy- ous cry,— "God has

Come, both one and all.
turn the world a- round.
sent the Prom- ised One."

D.G. AL CODA

CODA

the Prom- ised One is here! The Prom- ised One is here!

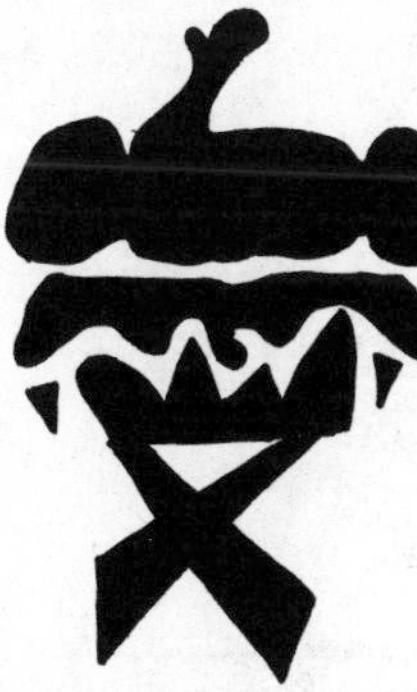

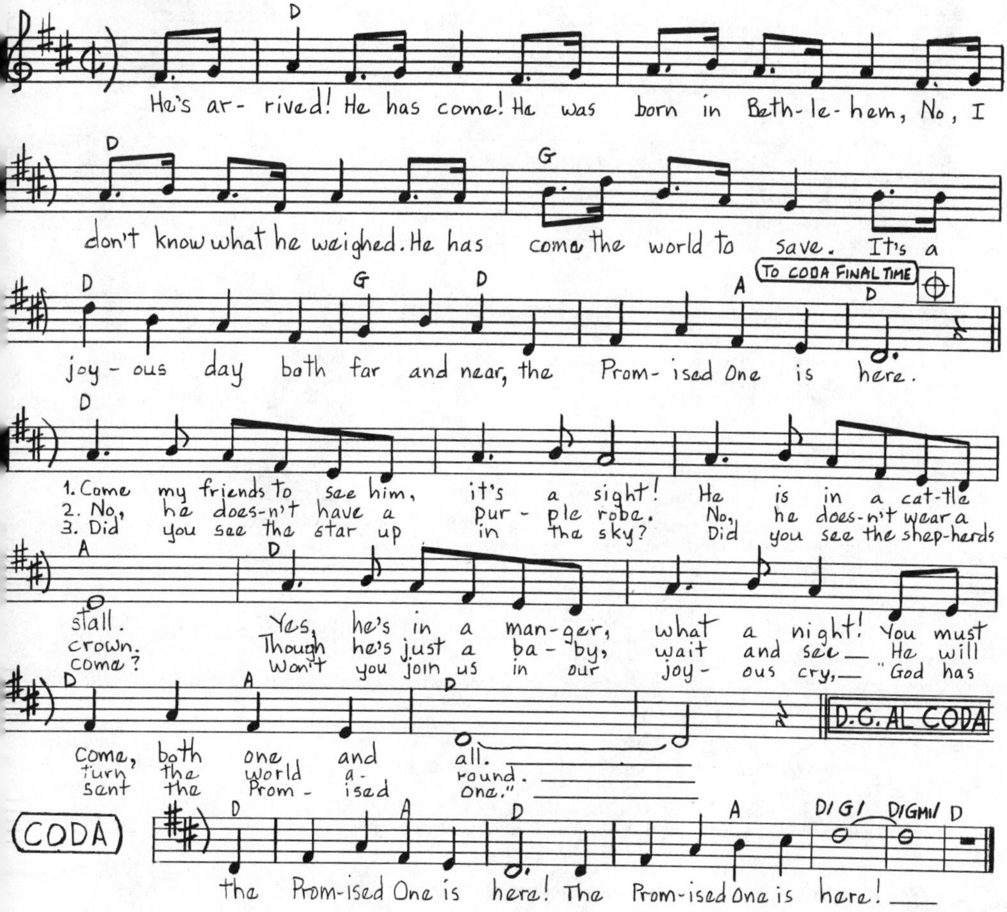

142

Song of Mary

Words by
BOB RUSS

Music by
JOHN YLVISAKER
ASCAP

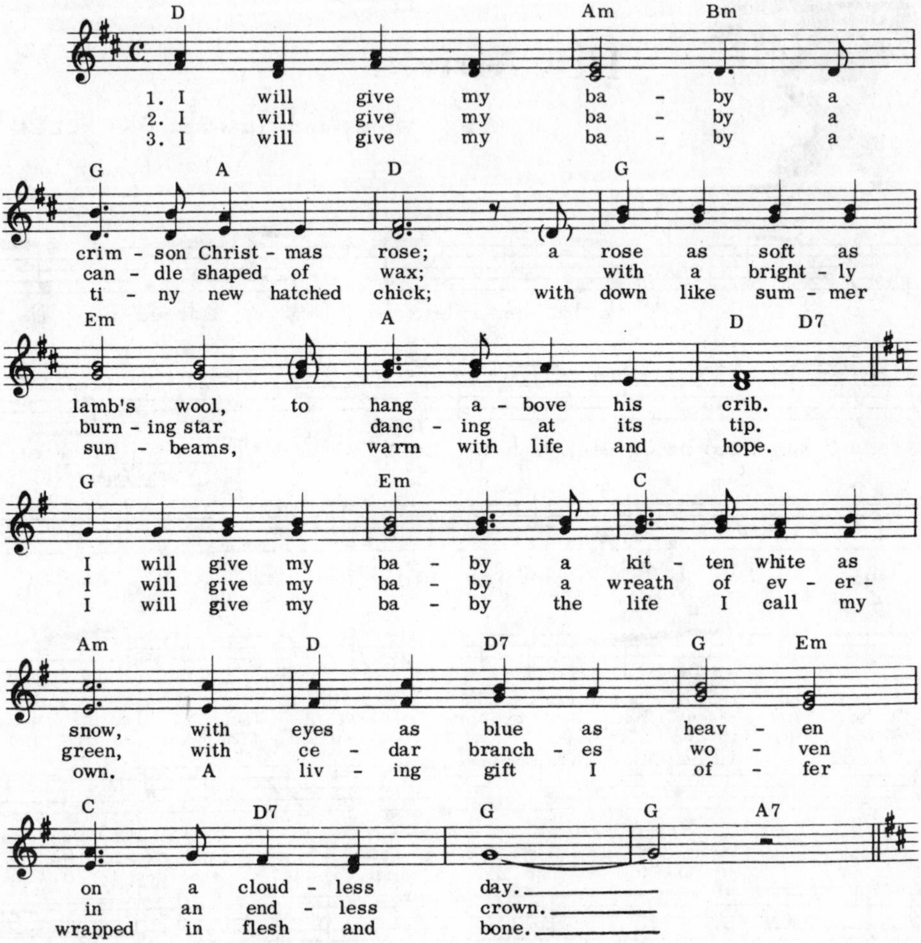

1. I will give my ba - by a
2. I will give my ba - by a
3. I will give my ba - by a

crim - son Christ - mas rose; a rose as soft as
can - dle shaped of wax; with a bright - ly
ti - ny new hatched chick; with down like sum - mer

lamb's wool, to hang a - bove his crib.
burn - ing star danc - ing at its tip.
sun - beams, warm with life and hope.

I will give my ba - by a kit - ten white as
I will give my ba - by a wreath of ev - er -
I will give my ba - by the life I call my

snow, with eyes as blue as heav - en
green, with ce - dar branch - es wo - ven
own. A liv - ing gift I of - fer

on a cloud - less day.
in an end - less crown.
wrapped in flesh and bone.

Bob Russ is a young writer from Blue Earth, Minnesota. Confined to a wheel chair, Bob lives with a ham radio, a tape recorder and the most fascinating library I've ever seen. Some have said that he has the equivalent to a Phd in comparative religions. All I can say is that Bob is a very creative thinker and a wonderful person to know.

and a little child

Song of Joseph

Words by
HJELMAR GULLBERG

Music by
JOHN YLVISAKER
ASCAP

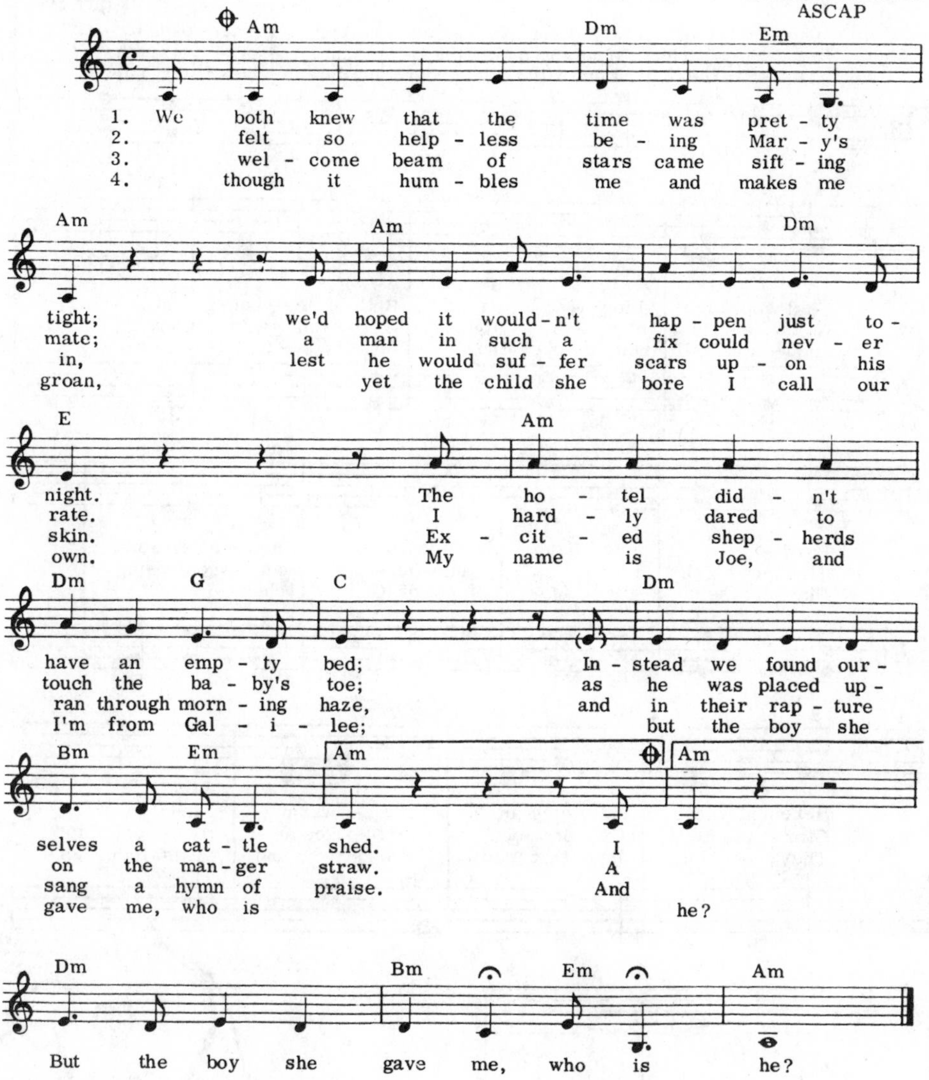

shall lead them

A Winter's Gift

144

Judith May Newton

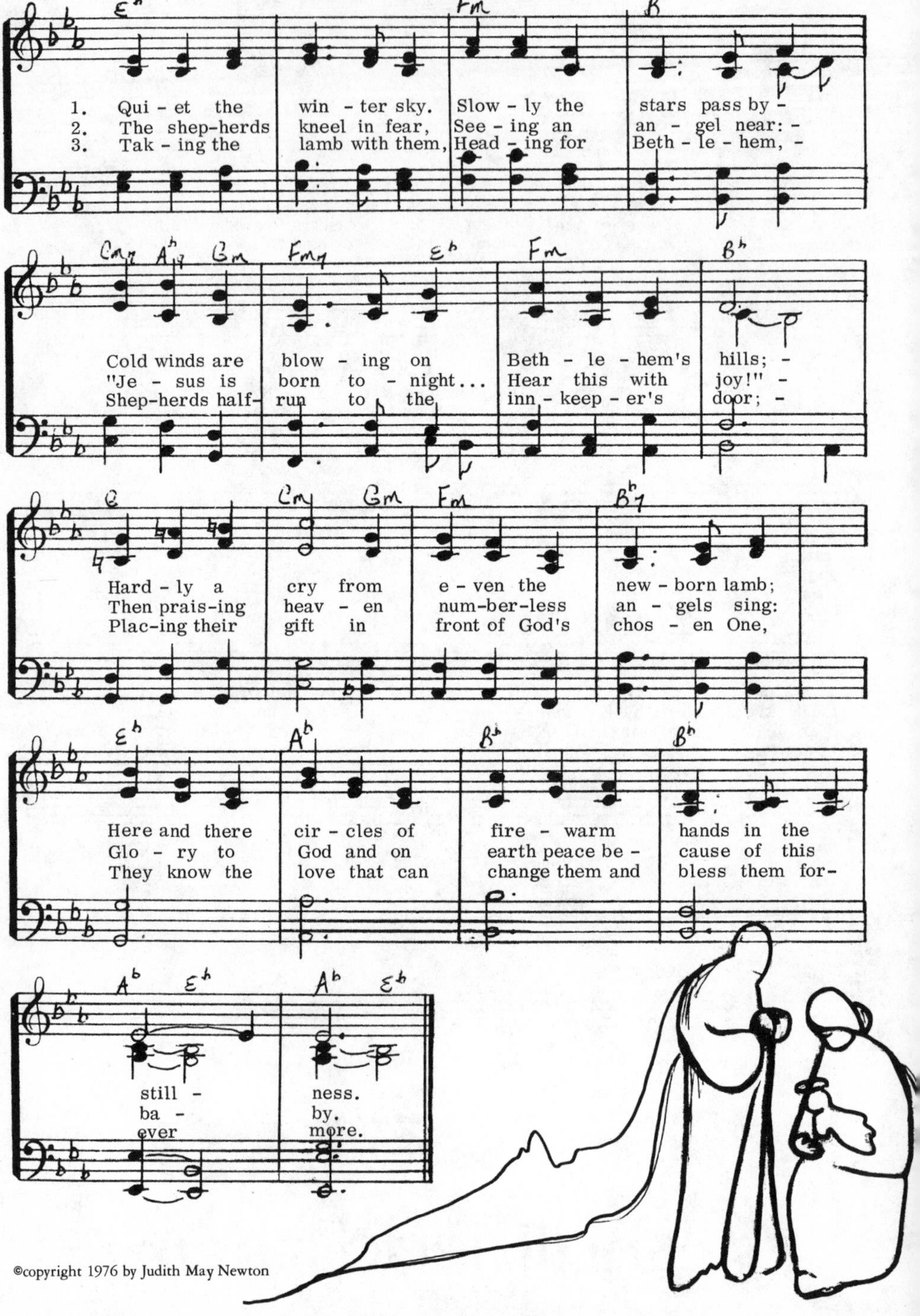

1. Qui - et the win - ter sky. Slow - ly the stars pass by -
2. The shep - herds kneel in fear, See - ing an an - gel near: -
3. Tak - ing the lamb with them, Head - ing for Beth - le - hem, -

Cold winds are blow - ing on Beth - le - hem's hills; -
"Je - sus is born to - night... Hear this with joy!" -
Shep - herds half - run to the inn - keep - er's door; -

Hard - ly a cry from e - ven the new - born lamb;
Then prais - ing heav - en num - ber - less an - gels sing:
Plac - ing their gift in front of God's chos - en One,

Here and there cir - cles of fire - warm hands in the
Glo - ry to God and on earth peace be - cause of this
They know the love that can change them and bless them for-

still - ness.
ba - by.
ever more.

Children Go!

This is a cumulative carol. In verse 2 the children are sent two by two:

'Two for Joseph and Mary
One for the little bitty baby boy
Born in Bethlehem, Bethlehem, Bethlehem.'

Repeat the music ★ . . . ★ as each number is added.

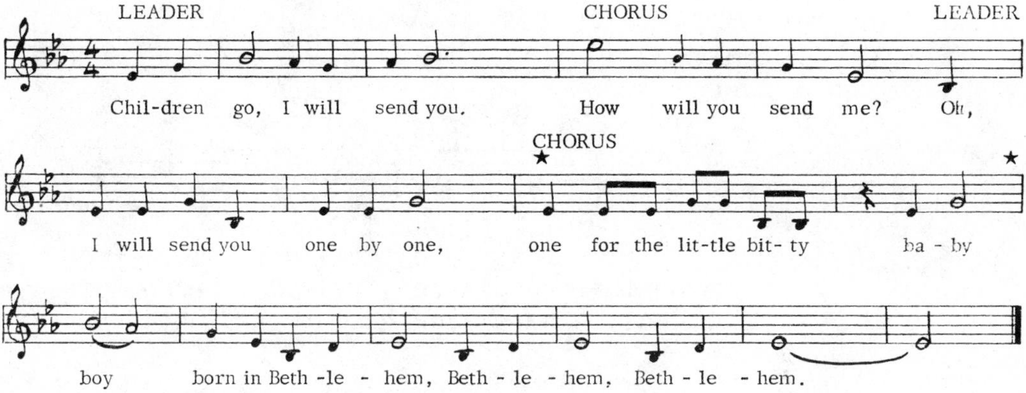

1. Children go, I will send you.
   How will you send me?
   Oh, I will send you one by one,
   One for the little bitty baby boy
   Born in Bethlehem, Bethlehem, Bethlehem.

2. Two for Joseph and Mary.

3. Three for the good old wise men.

4. Four for the oxen that stood in the stall.

5. Five for the snow that lay on the ground.

6. Children go, I will send you.
   How will you send me?
   Oh, I will send you six by six.
   Six for the stars that shone in the sky.
   Five for the snow that lay on the ground.
   Four for the oxen that stood in the stall.
   Three for the good old wise men.
   Two for Joseph and Mary.
   One for the little bitty baby boy
   Born in Bethlehem, Bethlehem, Bethlehem.

The Crowded Stable

Dedicated to Zutzang and Joan Hsu,
and Father and Mother Ko, and all the family

With rhythm, but
not too fast

Richard Avery
Donald Marsh

1. From far a-cross the des--ert sands, From
2. Just see the crowds: red, yel-low, brown And
3. God brings us here to share this sight: A

1. cold and snow---y north-ern lands,
2. black and white all gath-ered round.
3. ba---by's face, a ho---ly light.

1. Steam--ing jung-les, ci----ty streets,
2. Brought to-geth-er by the star,
3. Rage and fear and en---vy cease.

1. In this sta---ble here we meet.
2. From all na-tions here we are.
3. Here we all find love and peace.

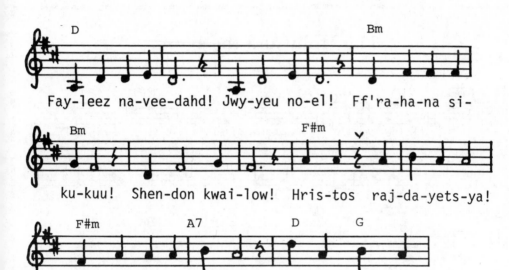

Fay-leez na-vee-dahd! Jwy-yeu no-el! Ff'ra-ha-na si-
ku-kuu! Shen-don kwai-low! Hris-tos raj-da-yets-ya!
Froy-lick-a vai-nock-ten! Mer-ry Christ-mas!
Mer-ry Christ-mas! Je-sus Christ is born!

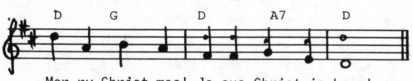

Fayleez navidahd = *FELIZ NAVIDAD, Spanish*
Jwyeu noel = *JOYEUX NOEL, French*
Ff'rahana sikukuu, *Swahili, as in Kenya*
Shendon kwailow, *Taiwanese, a Chinese dialect*
Hristos rajdayetsya, *Russian*
Froylicka vainockten = *FROELICHE WEIHNACHTEN,*
German

To teach this song or lead it in a service without lots of rehearsal, have a
leader or choir call out the language
(the first time through) and sing each
phrase of the chorus with the people
echoing, phrase by phrase. Enjoy the
different sounds! Try the chorus as a
kind of round.

The Holly and the Ivy

Trad.
Capo 5, Play in C

18th Cent.

The holly represents Jesus' crown of thorns; the berries, the drops of blood on his forehead. The ivy stands for everlasting life through faith in Christ.

Hajej, Nynei
(Rocking Song)

Trad. Czech
Capo 5 Play in C

Trad Czech

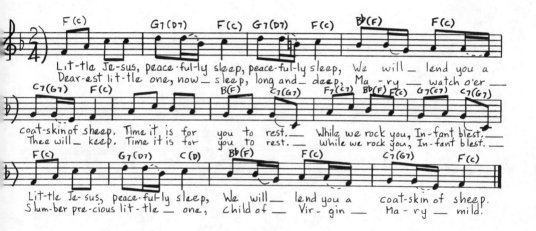

Lit-tle Je-sus, peace-ful-ly sleep, peace-ful-ly sleep, We will lend you a
Dear-est lit-tle one, now sleep, long and deep, Ma-ry watch o'er

coat-skin of sheep. Time it is for you to rest. While we rock you, In-fant blest.
Thee will keep. Time it is for you to rest. While we rock you, In-fant blest.

Lit-tle Je-sus, peace-ful-ly sleep, We will lend you a coat-skin of sheep.
Slum-ber pre-cious lit-tle one, child of Vir-gin Ma-ry mild.

Lulajze, Jezuniu
(Lullaby, Jesus)

Trad.

Trad.

1. Lull-a- by, Je-sus, my ba-by, my trea-sure. Lull-a- by
2. I'll give you tas-ty sweets and can-dies, dear Je-sus. Rai-sins and
3. Lull-a- by, star-ry-eyed In-fant Ho-ly. Lull-a- by

Je-sus, my love with-out meas-ure.
al-monds and oth-er treats, too. Lull-a- by, Je-sus in your
gem of the earth born so low-ly.

lit-tle crib ly-ing. Moth-er- is near-by to calm your cry-ing.

Frederic Chopin used the melody of "Lulajze Jezuniu" in the middle section of his Scherzo
n B minor, opus 20

A Star Is Born

David S. Goodall

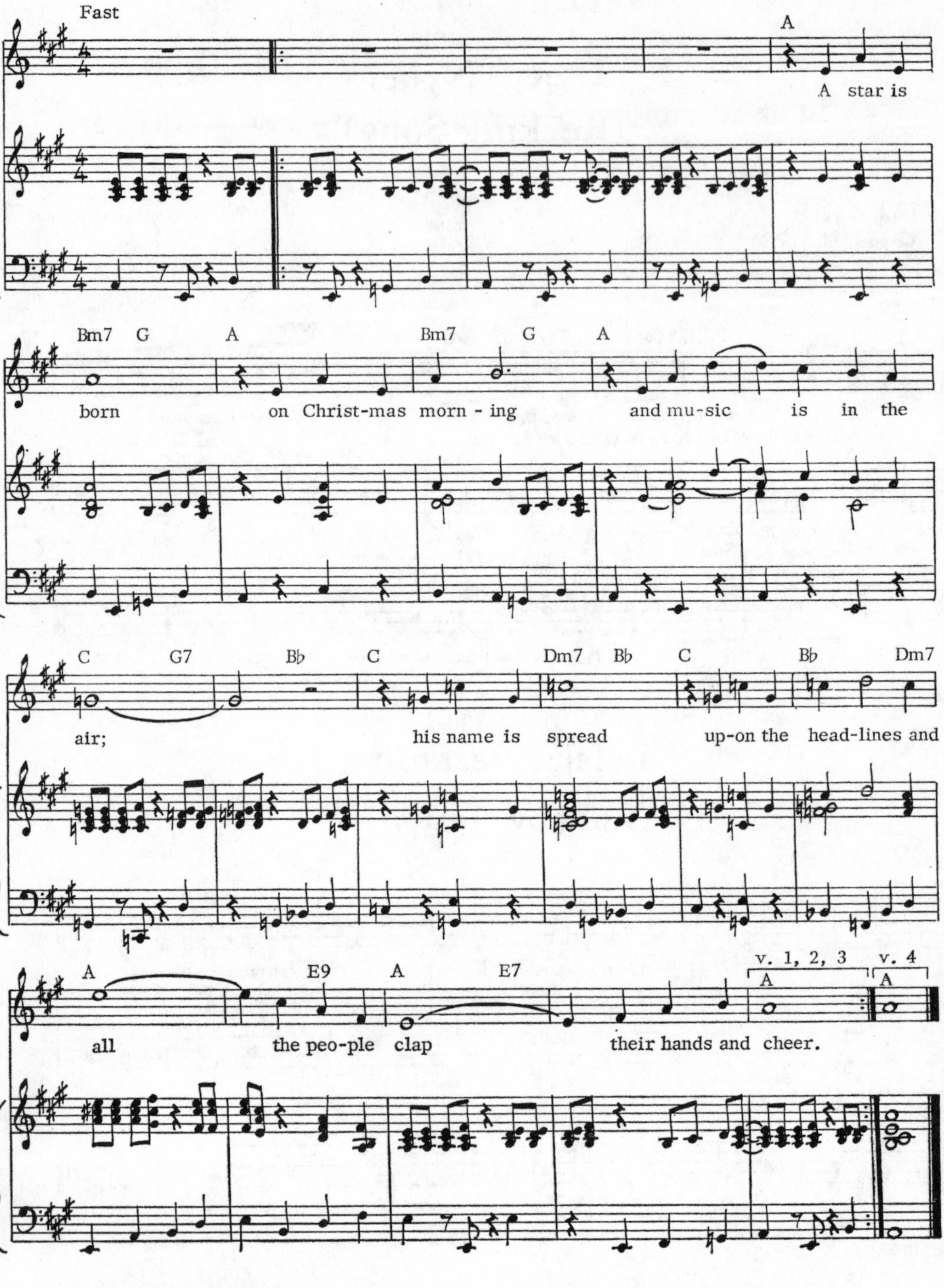

A star is born on Christ-mas morn-ing and mu-sic is in the air; his name is spread up-on the head-lines and all the peo-ple clap their hands and cheer.

A STAR IS BORN

1 A star is born
  on Christmas morning
  and music
  is in the air;
  his name is spread
  upon the headlines
  and all
    the people clap
  their hands and cheer.

2 A star is born
  for grief and mourning
  he chooses
  to die, not live;
  he will not make
  his way by taking
  but on-
  -ly by the will-
  -ingness to give.

3 The stars above
  have ways of loving
  beyond all
  our power to know;
  but on the day
  of our creation
  a star
  dies out the love
  of God to show.

4 A star is born
  on Easter morning,
  There's singing
  in every street;
  where every day
  I serve my neighbour
  the star
  of Bethlehem's sto-
  -ry is complete.

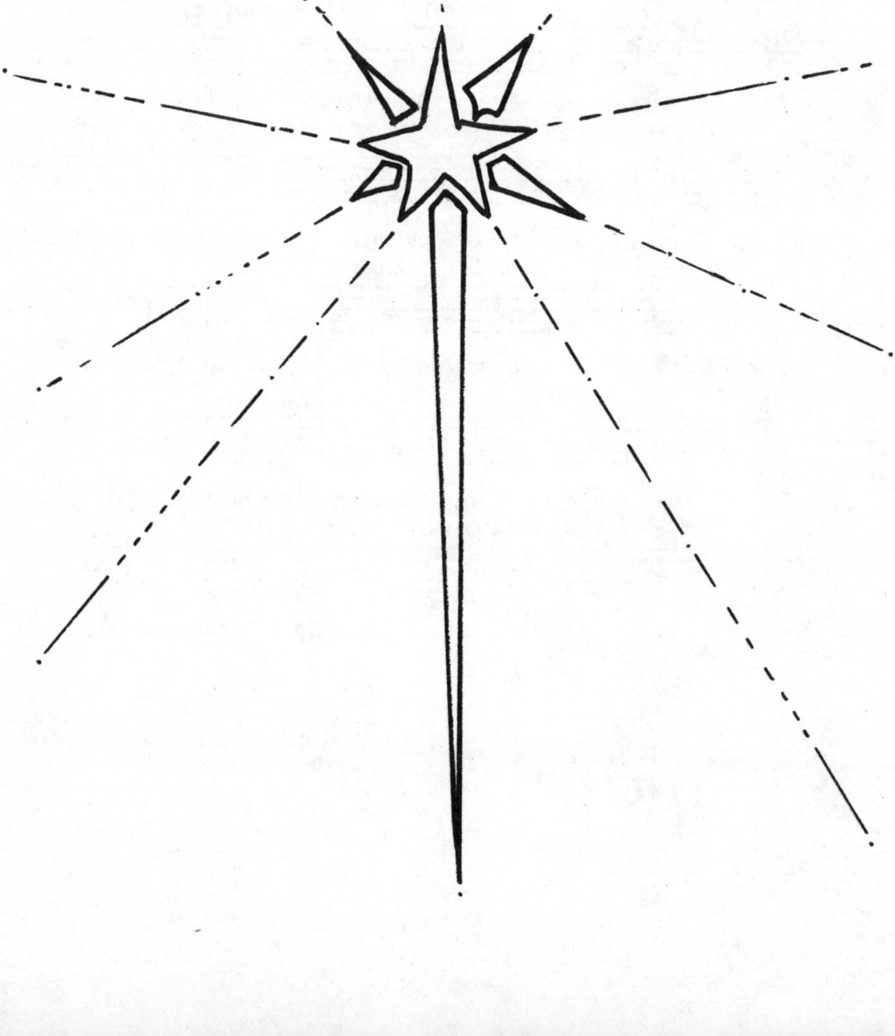

Rise Up Shepherds

Trad.

Capo 5 (G)

Traditional

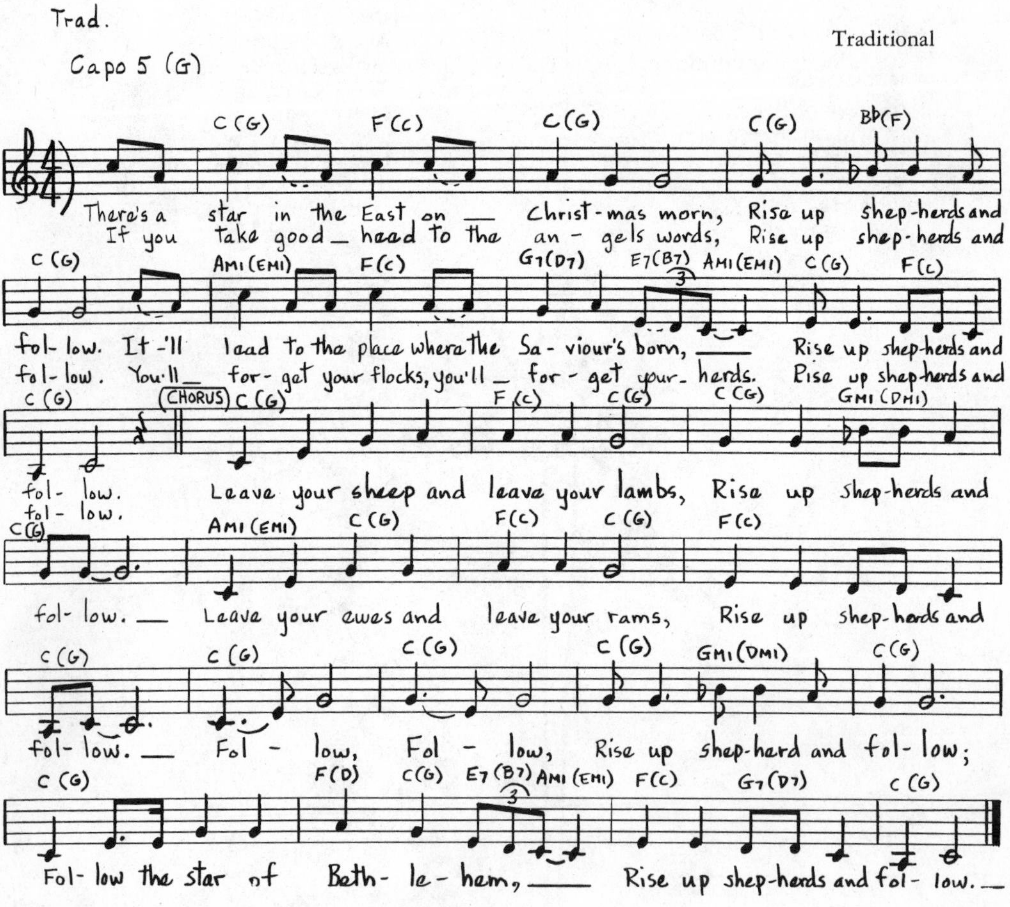

There's a star in the East on ___ Christ-mas morn, Rise up shep-herds and
If you take good ___ heed to the an - gels words, Rise up shep-herds and

fol-low. It -'ll lead to the place where the Sa-viour's born, ___ Rise up shep-herds and
fol-low. You'll for-get your flocks, you'll ___ for - get your_ herds. Rise up shep-herds and

fol-low.
fol-low. (CHORUS) Leave your sheep and leave your lambs, Rise up shep-herds and

fol-low. ___ Leave your ewes and leave your rams, Rise up shep-herds and

fol-low. ___ Fol - low, Fol - low, Rise up shep-herd and fol-low;

Fol-low the star of Beth - le - hem, ___ Rise up shep-herds and fol-low. ___

FOLLOW, FOLLOW

Take Time

AN EPIPHANY CAROL
dedicated specially to Clarence L. Marsh

Richard Avery
Donald Marsh

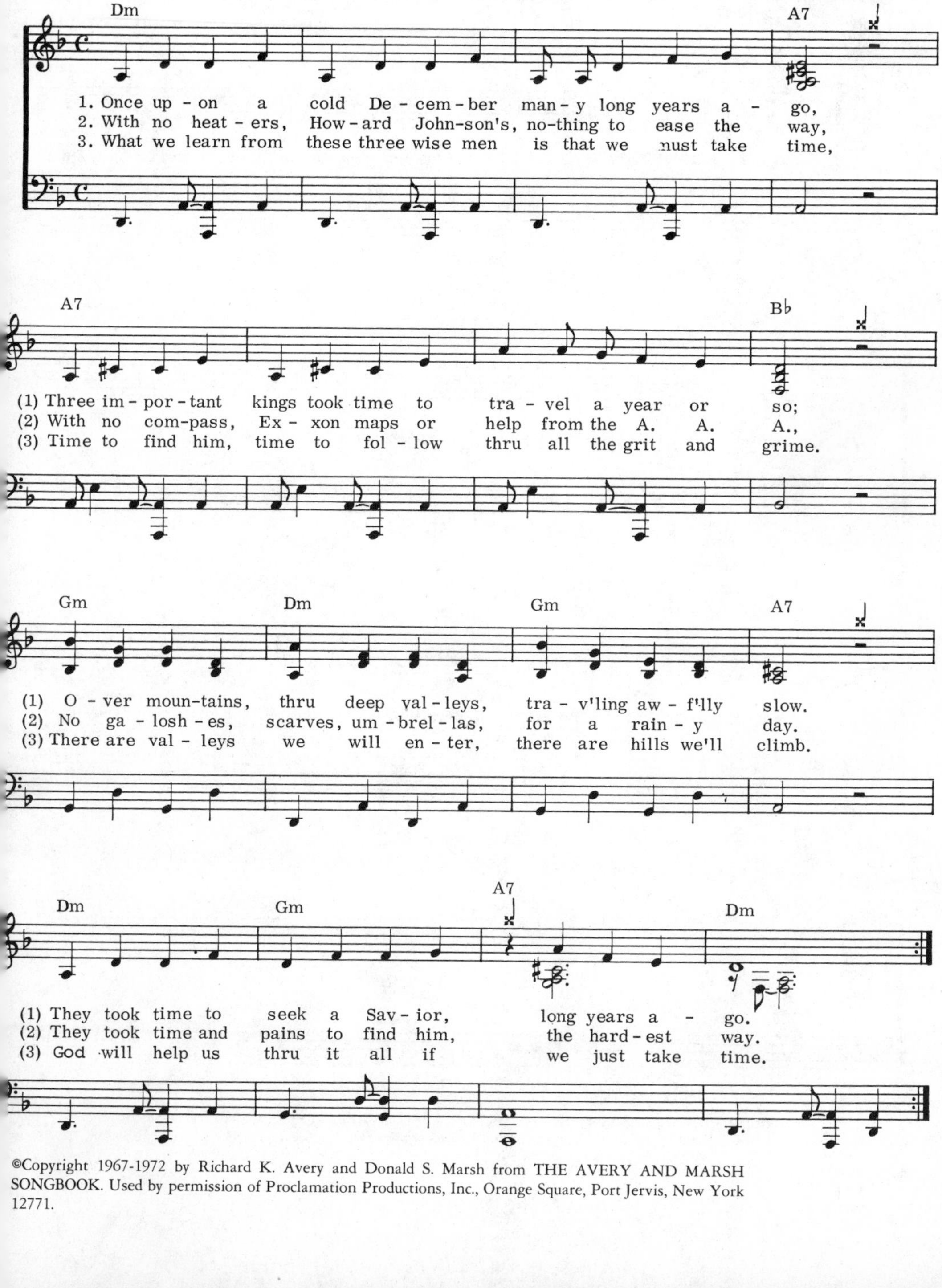

1. Once up-on a cold De-cem-ber man-y long years a-go,
2. With no heat-ers, How-ard John-son's, no-thing to ease the way,
3. What we learn from these three wise men is that we must take time,

(1) Three im-por-tant kings took time to tra-vel a year or so;
(2) With no com-pass, Ex-xon maps or help from the A. A. A.,
(3) Time to find him, time to fol-low thru all the grit and grime.

(1) O-ver moun-tains, thru deep val-leys, tra-v'ling aw-f'lly slow.
(2) No ga-losh-es, scarves, um-brel-las, for a rain-y day.
(3) There are val-leys we will en-ter, there are hills we'll climb.

(1) They took time to seek a Sav-ior, long years a-go.
(2) They took time and pains to find him, the hard-est way.
(3) God will help us thru it all if we just take time.

Let's Go

RICHARD AVERY
DONALD MARSH

Got-ta get rea-dy! Let's go!__ Got-ta get rea-dy! Let's go!__ Get

out the mu-sic, Find a drum, Make a cym-bal out of some-thing.__

__ Play a flute, Blow a trum-pet. We've been told a new world's com-ing

soon, Com-ing soon.

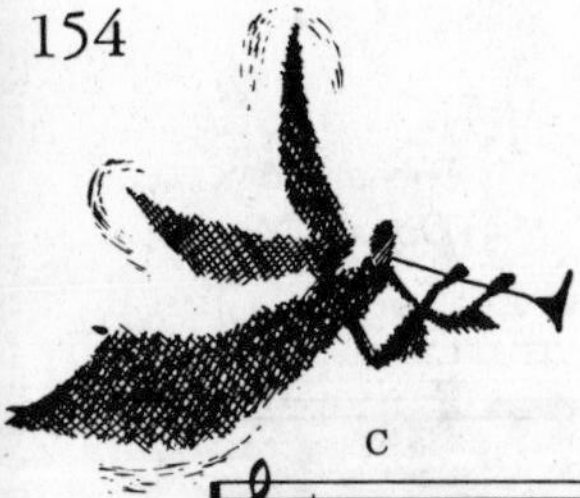

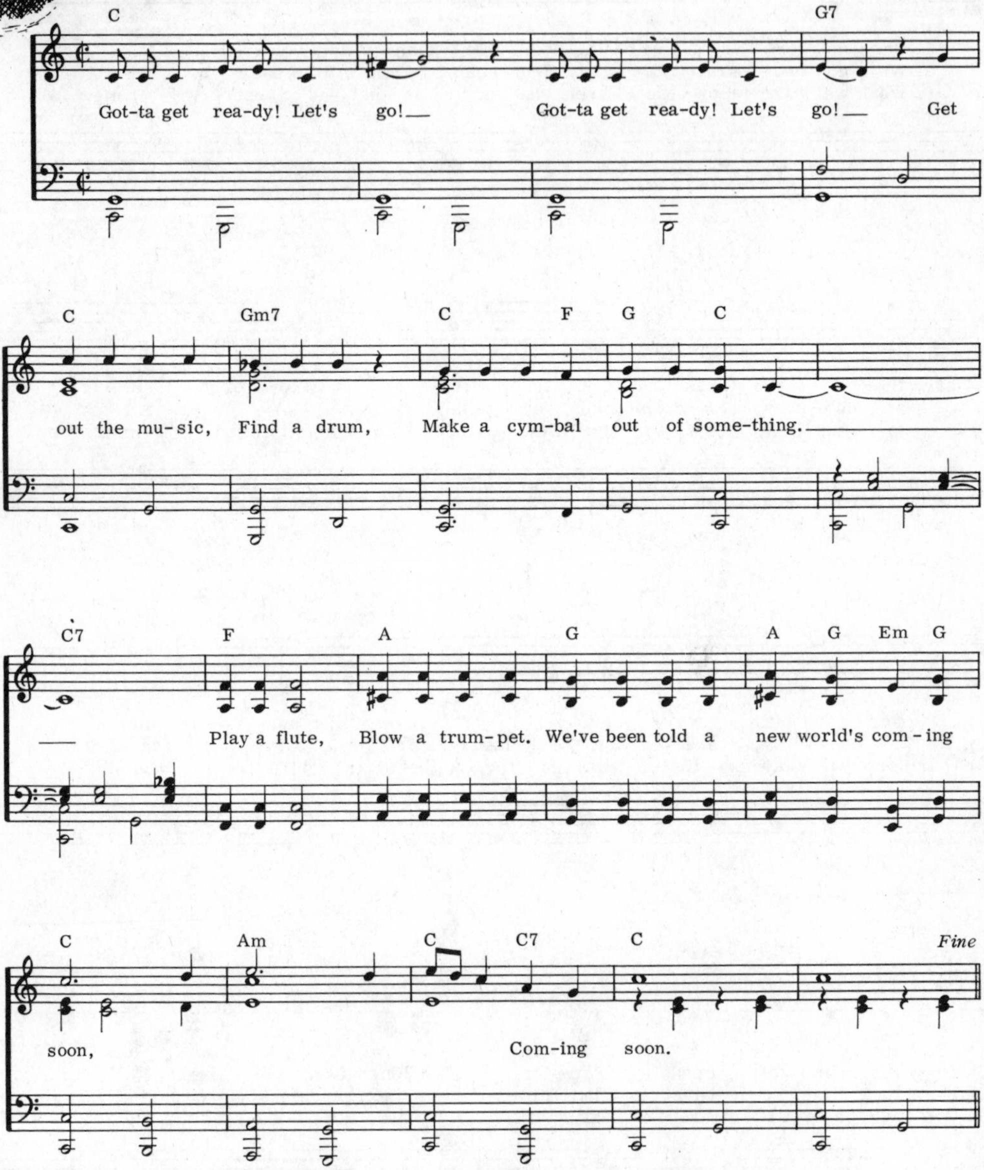

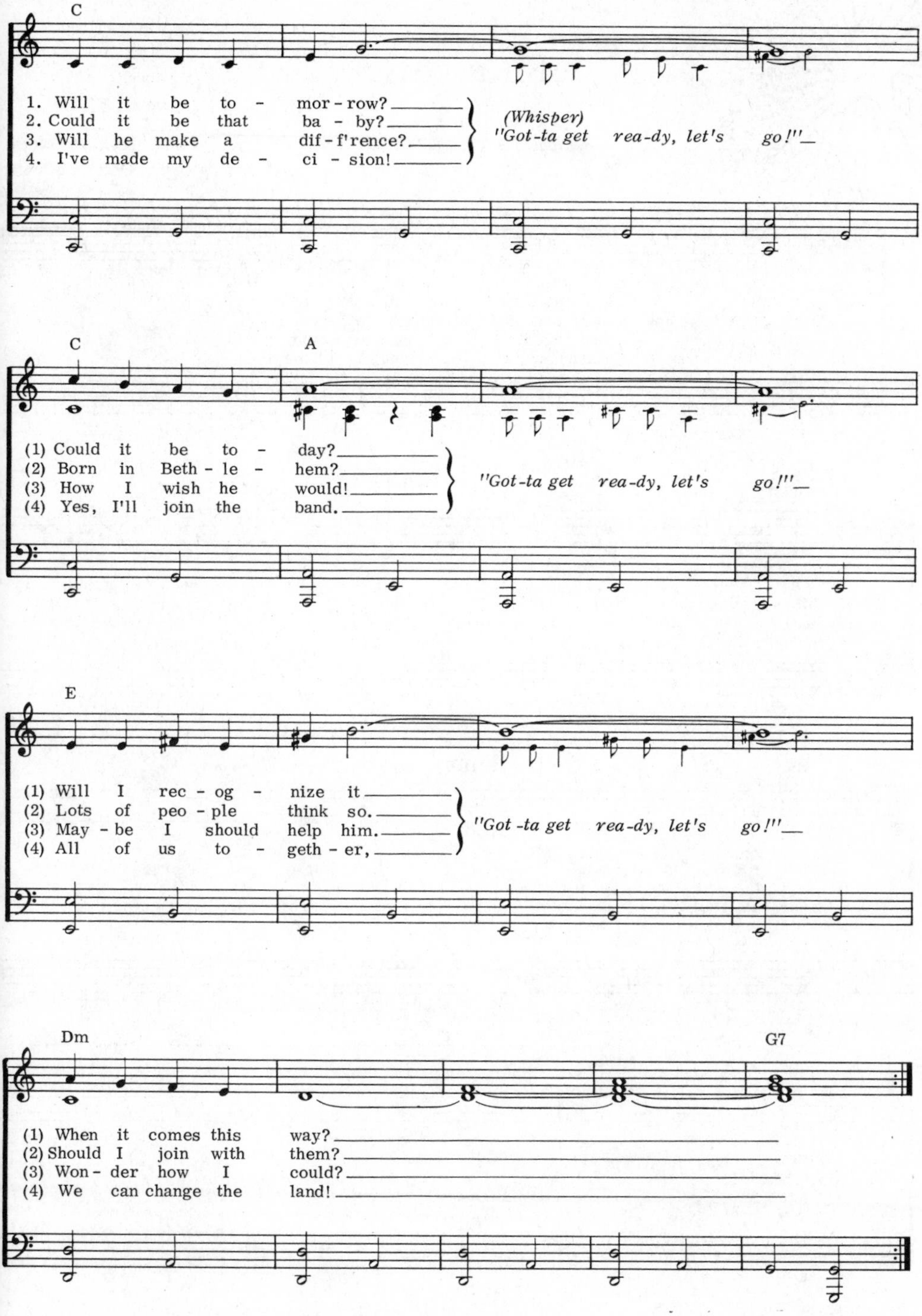

1. Will it be to - mor - row? _____
2. Could it be that ba - by? _____
3. Will he make a dif - f'rence? _____
4. I've made my de - ci - sion! _____

(Whisper)
"Got-ta get rea-dy, let's go!" _____

(1) Could it be to - day? _____
(2) Born in Beth - le - hem? _____
(3) How I wish he would! _____
(4) Yes, I'll join the band. _____

"Got-ta get rea-dy, let's go!" _____

(1) Will I rec - og - nize it _____
(2) Lots of peo - ple think so. _____
(3) May - be I should help him. _____
(4) All of us to - geth - er, _____

"Got-ta get rea-dy, let's go!" _____

(1) When it comes this way? _____
(2) Should I join with them? _____
(3) Won - der how I could? _____
(4) We can change the land! _____

156

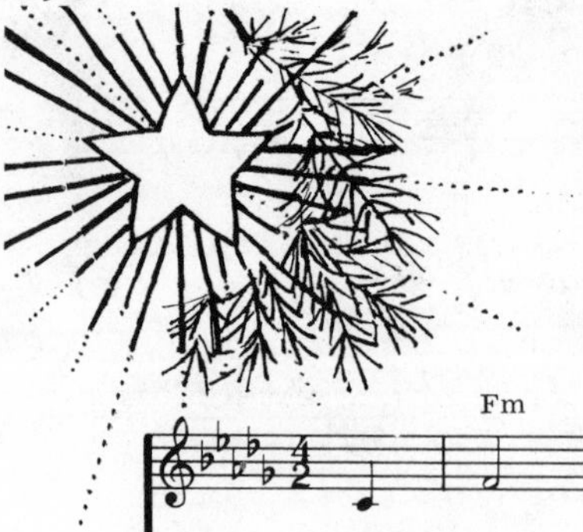

Shine Star

A SONG FOR EPIPHANY
dedicated to Gertrude Schneider

Richard Avery
Donald Marsh

1. When I see no star to light my way
2. Now some choose that star of Beth-le - hem
3. I've cho - sen that star of long a - go
4. With this brand new year a-head of me,

I
That
And
A

(1) go un - pre-pared to meet the day.
(2) shines like a bril - liant di - a - dem.
(3) live in the ho - ly af - ter - glow.
(4) round whose sharp cor - ners I can't see,

I need a guide, like
So clear-ly it re -
And e - ven though some
I need a guide as

(1) some ce - les - tial ray,
(2) veals a way for them
(3) times the star burns low,
(4) clear as it can be.

To lead me so I'll sel - dom
Be - yond the fi - nal re - qui -
It lights the dark-ness that I
So

(1) stray.
(2) em.
(3) know.

(4) shine star, to my des - ti - ny!

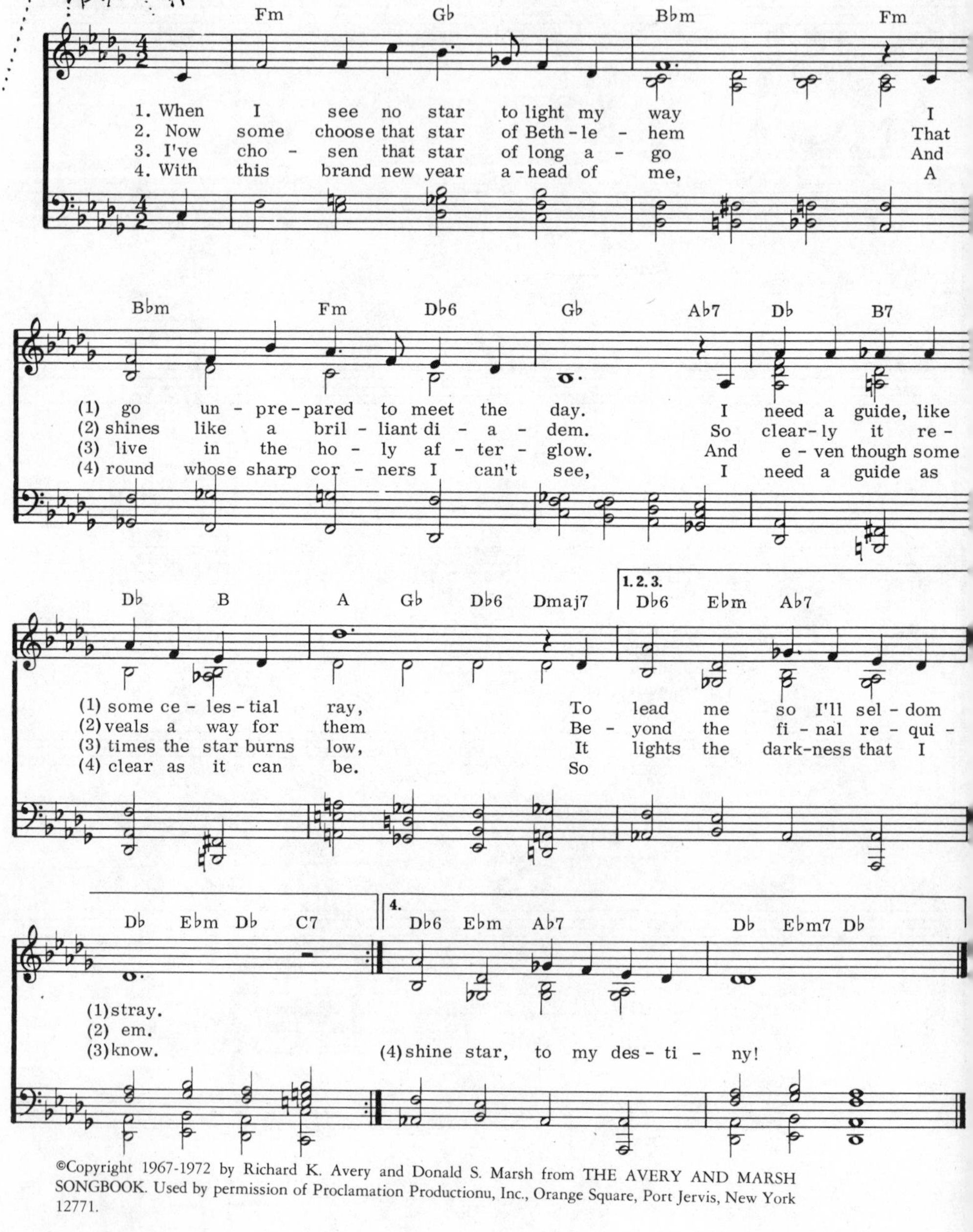

Go, Tell It on the Mountain

Spiritual

Go, tell it on the moun-tain, O-ver the hills and ev-ry-where;

Go, tell it on the moun-tain That Je-sus Christ is born. *Fine*

1. While shep-herds kept their watch-ing O'er si-lent flocks by night, Be-
2. The shep-herds feared and trem-bled When, lo! a-bove the earth, Rang
3. Down in a low-ly man-ger Our hum-ble Christ was born, And

hold, through-out the heav-ens There shone a ho-ly light.____
out the an-gel cho-rus That hailed our Sav-iour's birth.____
God sent us sal-va-tion That bless-ed Christ-mas morn.____ *D.C.*

DO YOU HEAR

WHAT I HEAR?

Passed Through the Waters

RICHARD AVERY
DONALD MARSH

1. Like sur - vi - vors of the Flood, Like walk - ers thru the sea, Like
2. Like small chil - dren washed and clean, Or drowned to live a - gain, Like
3. Do you see the Spir - it's fire? And hear the wind blow free? Do you

(1) walk - ers thru the God di - vi - ded sea:_____ We are
(2) peo - ple drowned and brought to life a - gain:_____ We are
(3) feel the wind and fi - re blow - ing free?_____ We are

Chorus

(1) res - cued, we are claimed, we are loved and we are named, } We are
(2) washed and we are saved, we are ris - en from the grave, } We are
(3) cho - sen each by name, marked by wa - ter, then by flame, } We are

Bap - tized!_____ I am Bap - tized!_____ We have

passed thru the wa - ters And that's all that mat - ters! We have

passed thru the wa - ters! O thanks be to God!

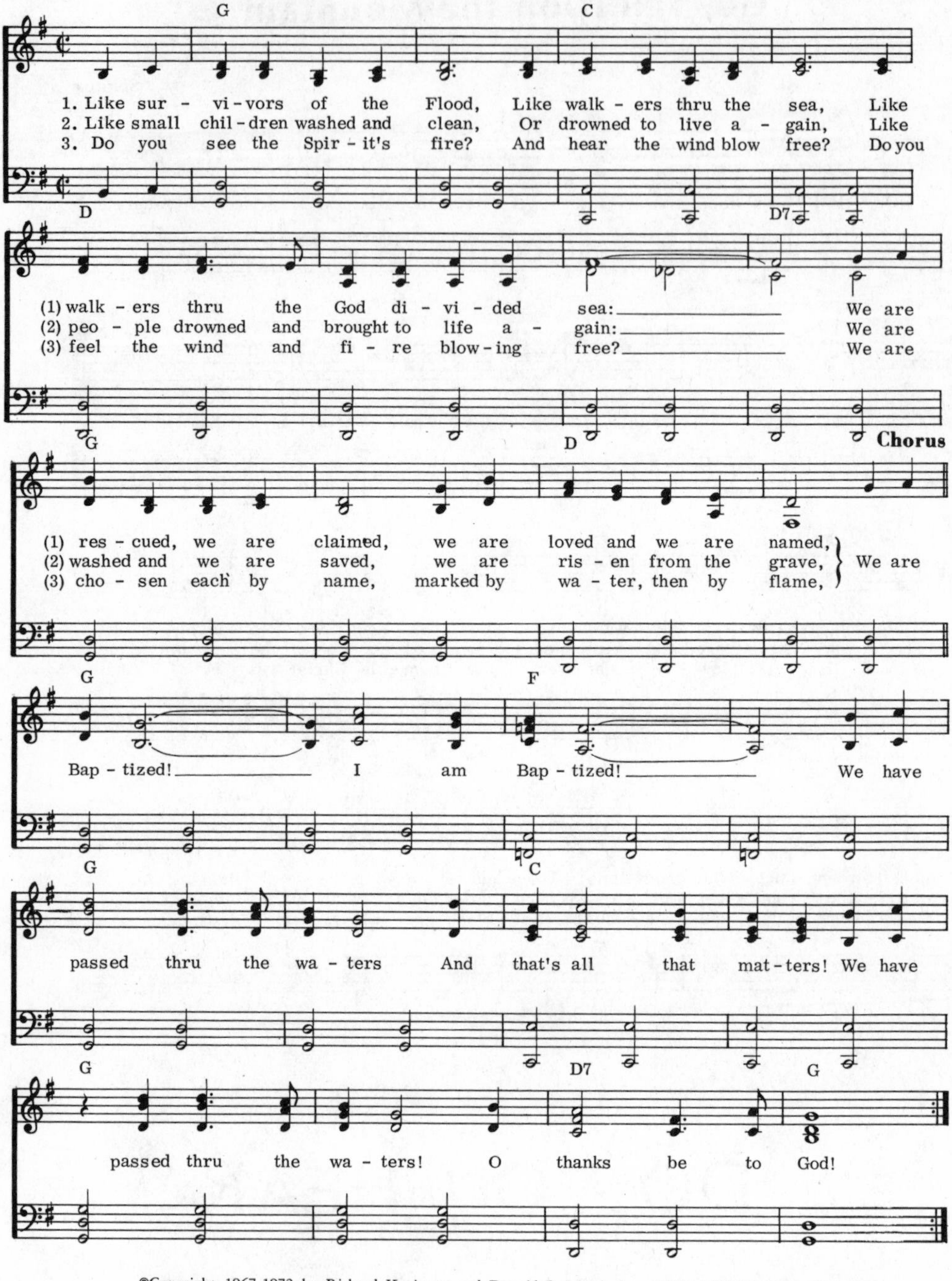

Shepherd, Shepherd

Richard Avery
Donald Marsh

For the Von Ignatiuses in memory of
Olive Brown

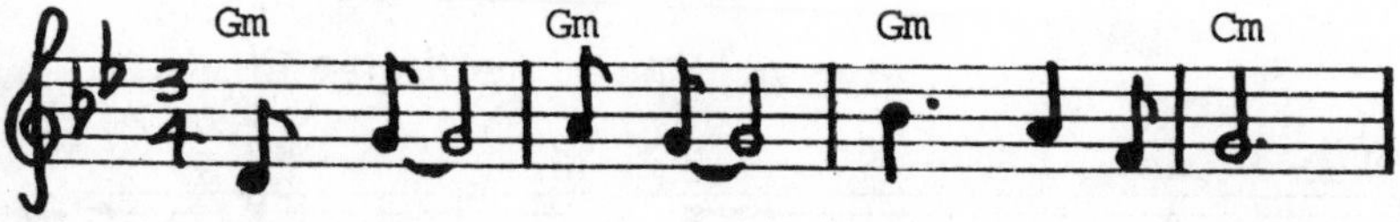

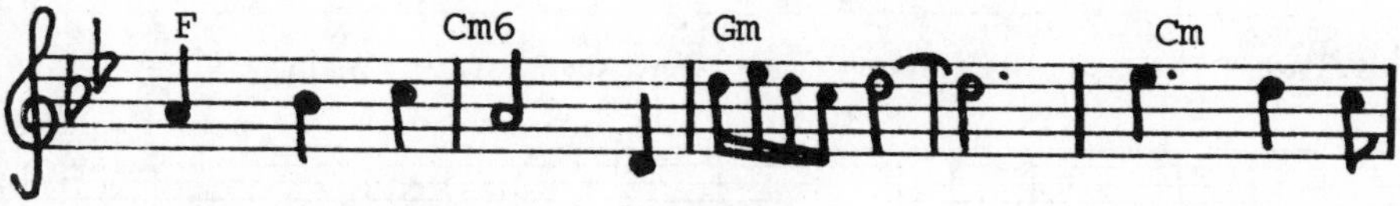

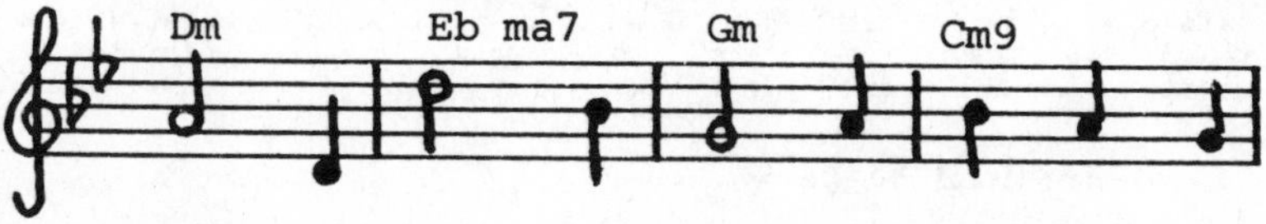

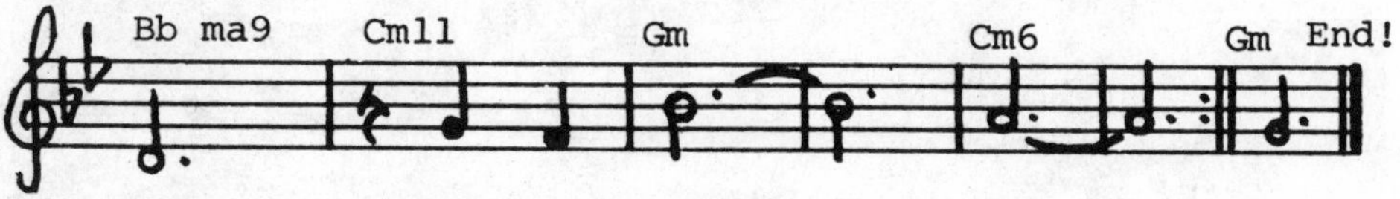

1. Shep-herd, shep-herd, pipe me a song,
2. An---gels, an--gels, come from a-bove,
3. Neigh-bor, neigh-bor, give me your hand,
4. Je----sus, Je----sus, dance me a reel,

1. Lone-some and sweet and high.   I've got to
2. Mys---tic and pure and bright.   Take me from
3. So----lid and warm and strong.   Help me to
4. Rhy-thmic and fast and true.   Teach me the

1. learn to get a--long With-out one I
2. death to life and love And make a new
3. learn how I can stand a--lone, since that
4. tune, the steps, the feel And I'll live and

1. love   who has died.
2. day   from this night.
3. time's   come a---long.
4. dance   here with you.

> This is a song for times of grief, perhaps
> for funerals. Sing it slowly, with passion.
> The last verse should be most exultant.

160

Unless God Builds the House

Based on Ps. 127:1
Mt. 7:24-27

Words and Music by TOM NEUFER EMSWILER

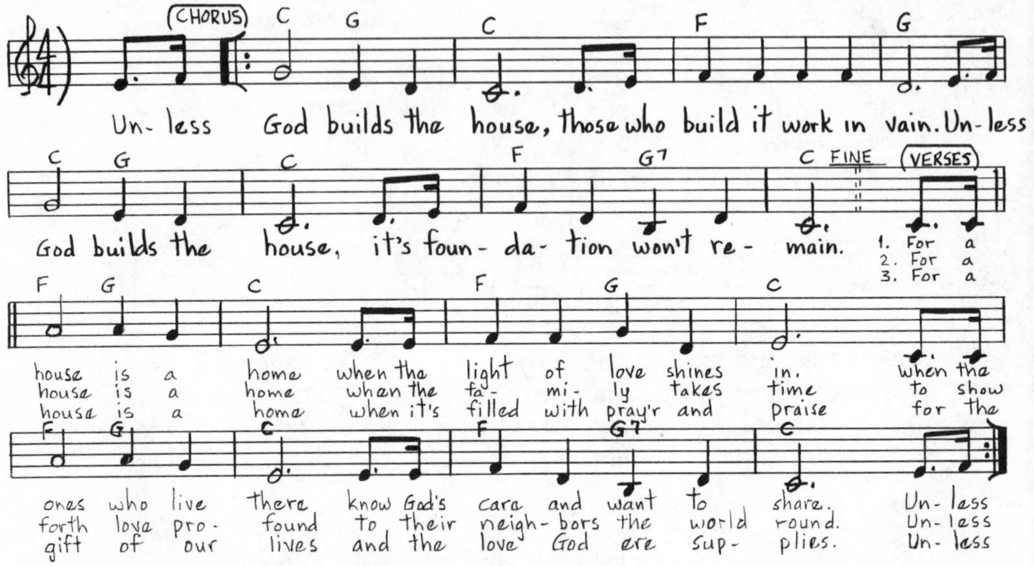

(CHORUS)

Un-less God builds the house, those who build it work in vain. Un-less

God builds the house, it's foun-da-tion won't re-main.

(VERSES)
1. For a
2. For a
3. For a

house is a home when the light of love shines in. when the
house is a home when the fa-mi-ly takes time to show
house is a home when it's filled with pray'r and praise for the

ones who live there know God's care and want to share. Un-less
forth love pro-found to their neigh-bors the world round. Un-less
gift of our lives and the love God ere sup-plies. Un-less

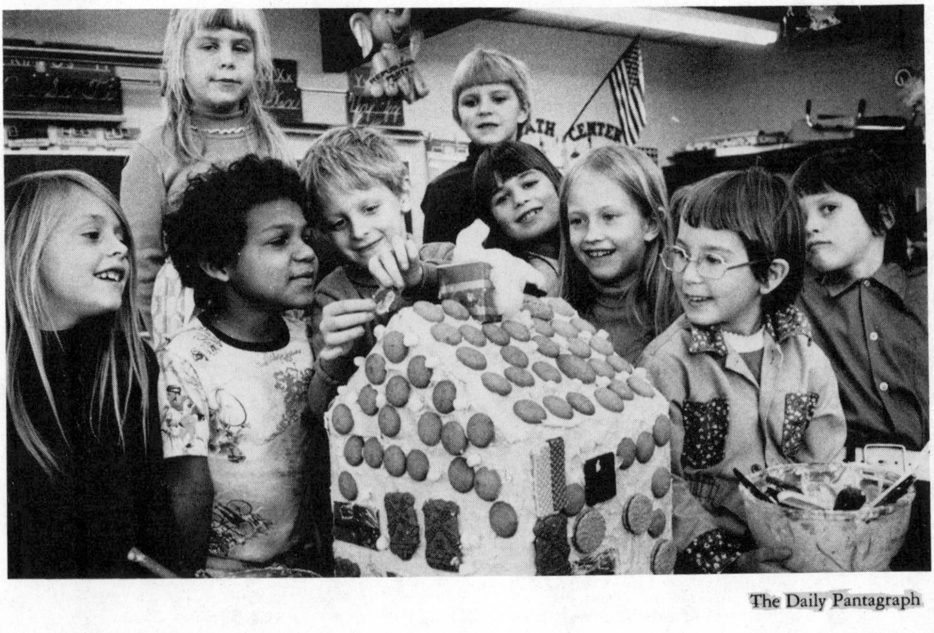

The Daily Pantagraph

Together

Words & Music
by Art Allen

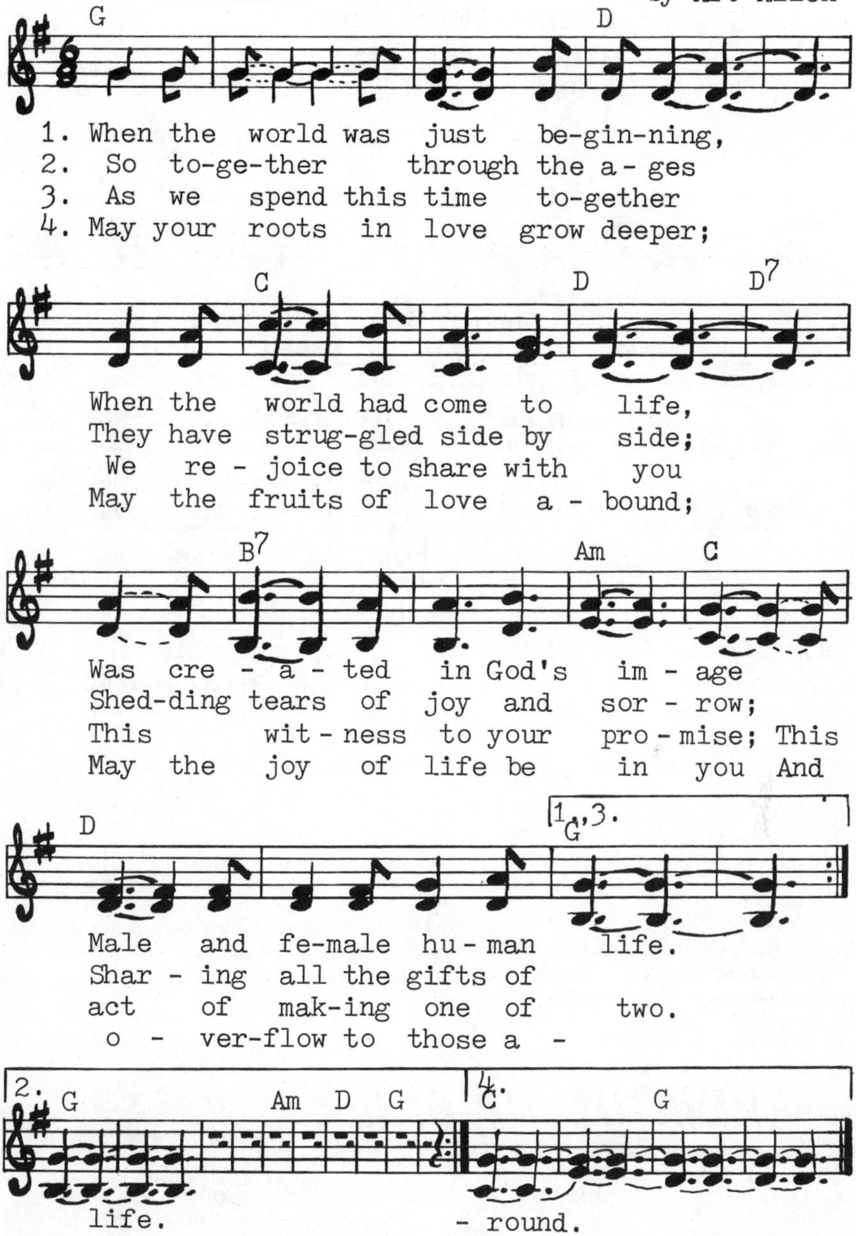

1. When the world was just be-gin-ning,
2. So to-ge-ther through the a-ges
3. As we spend this time to-gether
4. May your roots in love grow deeper;

When the world had come to life,
They have strug-gled side by side;
We re-joice to share with you
May the fruits of love a-bound;

Was cre-a-ted in God's im-age
Shed-ding tears of joy and sor-row;
This wit-ness to your pro-mise; This
May the joy of life be in you And

Male and fe-male hu-man life.
Shar-ing all the gifts of
act of mak-ing one of two.
o-ver-flow to those a-

life.
- round.

162

For Those Who Eat

Words and Music by ART ALLEN, A.S.C.A.P.

Capo 2, Play in C

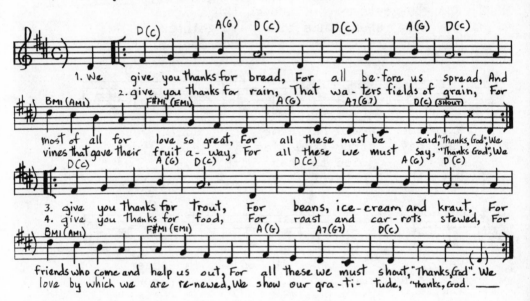

1. We give you thanks for bread, For all be-fore us spread, And most of all for love so great, For all these must be said, "Thanks, God". We
2. give you thanks for rain, That wa-ters fields of grain, For vines that gave their fruit a-way, For all these we must say, "Thanks God", We

3. give you thanks for Trout, For beans, ice-cream and kraut, For friends who come and help us out, For all these we must shout, "Thanks, God". We
4. give you Thanks for food, For roast and car-rots stewed, For love by which we are re-newed, We show our gra-ti-tude, "thanks, God.

PRAYER BEFORE MEALS

Thank you, God, for sustaining us; whether it is through this food, or through your children gathered here at your table, or through any other gift from your hand. Thank you, God, for sustaining us. Amen. (by Harvey Estes. Used by permission.)

BRING US TOGETHER

OTHER
WORSHIP RESOURCES

What follows are some other worship resources that we have found meaningful in public worship. Unless otherwise noted, they were written by the editors, but always out of the context of community with many people sharing ideas and wordings with us. We have intentionally tried to limit these resources to those in which the congregation could take an active part. Although we have provided suggestions on using these resources with a congregation, feel free to adapt them to your community and their needs. We hope that this section, like the rest of the hymnal, is only a beginning; and that your congregation can build on it to produce their own non-sexist worship resources.

CALLS TO WORSHIP
AND
INVOCATIONS

L=leader
C=congregation

*1. L: In the beginning there was the energy of creation . . . and it moved. And God said, - "Light!"

C: AND THERE IS LIGHT. AND THE ENERGY CONTINUED TO MOVE. . . AND GOD SAID, "SPACE!"

L: And there IS space. And the energy continued to move . . . and God said, "Earth!"

C: AND THERE IS EARTH. AND THE ENERGY KEPT MOVING. . . AND GOD SAID, "MALE AND FEMALE!"

L: And there IS male and female . . . and we are here. And now the earth is ours to inherit, and the gifts of the earth.

C: AND SO WE COME TO WORSHIP TO CELEBRATE THESE GIFTS AND TO LEARN AGAIN WHAT IT MEANS TO BE ENTRUSTED WITH THEM.

+ + + + + + + +

* See last page of Other Worship Resources

164

2. L: There are times when we need to stand on a mountain top and look
      around.
   C: WORSHIP CAN BE SUCH A TIME.
   L: There are times when we should examine the complex wonder of a
      single snowflake.
   C: WORSHIP CAN BE SUCH A TIME.
   L: There are times when we need to stand close to another and drink
      in the universe that is in that person's eyes.
   C: WORSHIP CAN BE SUCH A TIME.
 ALL: IN WORSHIP WE STAND AMAZED AT THE RUGGED EXPANSE OF THE
       UNIVERSE; WE STAND IN SILENT AWE BEFORE THE COMPLEX
       WONDER OF A SNOWFLAKE; AND WE ARE OVERWHELMED BY THE
       DEPTH AND BEAUTY IN ANOTHER'S EYES. AS WE CELEBRATE
       THIS WONDER WE BECOME NEW PERSONS WHO ARE REVOLUTION-
       IZED BY GOD'S LOVE!

+ + + + + + + +

*3. L: Why are we gathered at this time and place?
    C: WE ARE GATHERED AS THE PEOPLE OF GOD - TO HOLD BEFORE US
       THE MIRROR OF THE WORLD, AND THE MIRROR THAT IS JESUS
       CHRIST OUR SAVIOR. AND WITH THESE MIRRORS TO SEE OURSELVES
       AS WE ARE AND SHOULD BE.
    L: Then let us praise the Christ of us all - before whom we eternally stand.

+ + + + + + + +

*4. L: "I am the door. Come in. Do not be afraid." This is what Jesus says
       to those who stand half-secure behind half-shut doors.
    C: THIS IS JESUS' SAYING TO ALL THE CHILDREN OF THE EARTH WHO
       CLING TO THEIR BLANKETS OF SIN LIKE SILENT CRUTCHES.
    L: There are those moments when in the name of Jesus bold and certain
       people on earth must say: "Come in. Do not be afraid. It is I."
    C: CHRIST WAITS. THERE IS ROOM FOR ALL TO COME IN, EVEN
       THROUGH THE HALF-OPEN DOOR. SISTER AND BROTHER, COME
       NOW. COME AND LEARN AND LIVE.

+ + + + + + + +

*5. L: Now is the time to live; to come to the God who creates us, to sing
       to the Redeemer who frees us.
    C: NOW IS THE TIME TO COME ALIVE, TO INVITE THE WHOLE WORLD
       TO JOIN IN PRAISING GOD.
    L: Yes, now is the time to invite the sky to thunder God's word, the earth
       to rumble in praise.
    C: WE INVITE ALL TO CELEBRATE WITH US, TO GLORIFY GOD'S NAME,
       TO DANCE WITH GOD'S SPIRIT, WHICH FILLS US.

+ + + + + + + +

* See last page of Other Worship Resources

(Calls to Worship cont. L=leader; C=congregation)

*6. L: To worship is to heighten our awareness of the poetry of our
      existence.
    C: IT IS TO OPEN ALL THE WINDOWS OF OUR BEING TO THE
      INDWELLING POWER OF GOD'S LOVE.
    L: It is to join the mighty chorus of praise and thanksgiving that has
      boomed out since the beginning of creation.
    C: TO WORSHIP IS JOY. IT'S GREAT TO BE HERE!

                    + + + + + + + +

7. L: God was in love with the world and could not keep the secret.
   C: THE TELLING OF IT WAS CREATION!
   L: God has made the sun and the moon and the stars of heaven.
   C: GOD HAS MADE THE GREAT WATERS AND THE GREEN LAND
      AND ALL KINDS OF CREATURES TO LIVE IN THE WATER AND
      ON THE LAND.
   L: God has breathed CARE into every atom of creation.
   C: THAT CARE WAS POURED OUT ON US AS WE WERE FASHIONED
      BY OUR CREATOR AND AS GOD CONTINUES TO GO ON CREATING
      WITH US EACH DAY.
   L: We gather to celebrate this partnership in creation.
   C: ALLELUIA! AMEN!

                    + + + + + + + +

8. L: To worship God is to celebrate the mystery and miracle at the heart
      of life.
   C: THERE IS SO MUCH WE DON'T UNDERSTAND, LIKE BIRTH AND
      DEATH AND LIFE.
   L: All mystery. All miracle.
   C: OR AN ACORN BECOMING AN OAK TREE.
   L: Mystery, miracle.
   C: CLOUDS OF GAS BECOMING A STAR.
   L: Mystery, miracle.
   C: AND ME BECOMING MYSELF.
   L: Somehow we become more nearly who we are meant to be as we share
      God's loving presence.
   C: AND SO WE WORSHIP, BOWING BEFORE THE MYSTERY AND MIRACLE
      OF GOD.

                    + + + + + + + +

* See last page of Other Worship Resources

166

(Calls to Worship cont.   L=leader; C=congregation)

9.   L: We have come here in worship to LISTEN.
     C: WHAT DID YOU SAY?
     L: I said we have come here in worship to LISTEN. We want to be
        open to the in-rushing presence of the Spirit of God.
     C: HELP US, GOD, TO HEAR NOT ONLY WITH OUR EARS BUT WITH
        OUR EYES, NOT ONLY WITH OUR MINDS BUT WITH OUR HEARTS.

                    + + + + + + + +

10. L: God's love is poured out upon us, not because we are worthy, but
        because we are needy.
     C: OUR COMING TOGETHER HERE TODAY IS A RECOGNITION OF
        THIS NEED.
     L: And it is an affirmation of our faith in God's love.
     C: HELP US TO BE LIKE PAUL "ON TIPTOE WITH EXPECTANCY,"
        WAITING TO KNOW THE POWER OF GOD FOR OUR FRAIL LIVES.
     L: Such anticipation would truly bring worship alive.
     C: AND IT CAN ENLIVEN US. LET US STAND ON TIPTOE FOR THE
        SPIRIT OF GOD IN THIS HOUR.
                    + + + + + + + +

                        INVOCATIONS

                (To be prayed together in unison)

1.   O God, we know that you are present everywhere like the air around
     us. But we ask that at this hour you grant to us a special experience
     of your presence. Put your arms around us, O God. Help us to know
     that we are one family in you. Amen.*

2.   O God, we ask you now for the gift of worship. Put the strength in our
     arms that we may lift them up to praise you. Put the song on our lips
     that we may share your joy among all people. Put the power in our lives
     that they may be lived as worship of you. Amen.*

3.   O God, who was in the beginning as the Word, who spoke the creation into
     being, who comes to us through the scripture: be present in our words of
     praise and thanksgiving today. Amen.*

4.   We thank you, O God, for inviting us to your table. Teach us to receive
     the bitter herbs of your judgment as well as the honey of your forgiveness.
     Teach us to share this community with those outside who are hungry as
     well as among ourselves who have the privilege of feasting with you.
     Amen. *
                    + + + + + + + +

*Written by Harvey Estes, used by permission.

CONFESSIONS

*1. O God, we admit that too often we live on the surface of life. We
     are afraid of the depths, though we try to hide many things deep
     within us. We are haunted by the knowledge that we have hurt
     others by our own selfish acts. We are harassed by the realization
     that our sense of priorities and laziness have prevented us from
     responding to situations where we might have made a creative
     difference. What gets into us,God, to make us miss the mark of our
     Christian love time after time? Help us, O God, we pray. Amen.

+ + + + + + + +

*2. O God, we admit that too often we see our lives as a burden to be
     borne rather than as a joy to be celebrated. Forgive us for getting
     bogged down in all our problems and heartaches. Help us to realize
     the joyous miracle of your love, even in the midst of discouragement
     and despair. In Christ's name we pray. Amen.

+ + + + + + + +

3. God, we come before you today ashamed of our life-denying actions
    and attitudes. We admit that too often our thinking is negative and
    self-defeating both toward ourselves and toward others. We re-
    cognize that sometimes we allow our emotions to rule us in ways
    that bring hurt and embarrassment. We do not treat our bodies
    with the love and respect you want from us, and we bring this same
    death-dealing lack of respect to your earth and all its precious re-
    sources. Help us to be awakened to these faults so that we can
    become celebrants of life rather than harbingers of death. In
    Christ's name we pray. Amen.

+ + + + + + + +

4. God, we confess that sometimes our songs come out all wrong. Often
    our hearts are filled with jealousies and hatreds. We sometimes feel
    like a warped record unable to play at the right speed. Our songs
    which start out with so much hope and joy sometimes end up sounding
    like dirges. We know you can bring melody back into our lives. Help
    us when things go wrong to hear the tune of your love loud and clear.
    In Christ's name we pray. Amen.

+ + + + + + + +

* See last page of Other Worship Resources

5. O God, we admit that often we do not fully hear each other. We
get preoccupied with our own worries and miss chances to share
love and concern with others in need. Sometimes we fail to
listen to another because we are frightened that we will hear a
word of judgment from them. We read your Word half-heartedly,
not daring to open ourselves to its application for our own lives.
Help us to discover that the first step of love is listening and that
when we really open ourselves to you we can discover your grace
which truly is amazing. In Christ's name we pray. Amen.

+ + + + + + + + + +

6. God,

I saw someone today I should have spoken to, but I was scared of
involvement so I kept quiet.
I heard of some hungry people I could help, but I saved my money
for Baskin-Robbins.
I smelled fear in my friend, but I talked about trivialities until it
was time to leave.
I touched one I love, but my touch was filled with lustful selfishness
instead of giving care.
I tasted a friend's cooking, and I was so jealous of what this person
could do I left without comment.
What gets into me God that makes me hurt those I love and fail to
respond even when I know I can?
Help me to come alive with Christ's love so that I can be the caring
person I so desparately want to be.
                                        Amen.

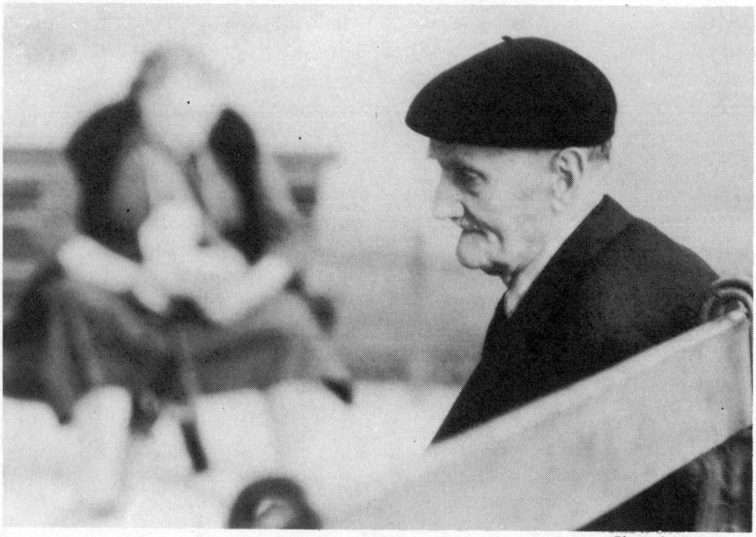

Cheryl Munn

(Confessions cont. L=leader; C=congregation)

7. O God, we admit that we often tie ourselves up in knots instead of rejoicing in your love. We twist and turn, tightening the hold on the things that bind us and keep us from your peace. Help us to become aware of our self-centeredness, insecurity, and fear that prevent us from being freed. Help us to see Christ's releasing power for our lives and to become the new beings you want us to be. In the name of Jesus the Christ who frees us. Amen.

+ + + + + + + +

8. L: God, you send us prophets like Jeremiah and Jesus.
   C: AND WE THROW THEM IN WELLS OR NAIL THEM TO CROSSES. HAVE MERCY.
   L: God, you send us prophets.
   C: AND WE CLAIM THEY ARE EXTREMISTS OR MEDDLERS IN OTHER PEOPLE'S BUSINESS. HAVE MERCY.
   L: God, you send us prophets.
   C: AND WE TURN UP OUR STEREO OR TV OR TALK ABOUT MODERATION SO WE WON'T BE DISTURBED. HAVE MERCY.
   L: God, you send us prophets.
   C: AND WE HATE THEM BECAUSE THEY REMIND US THAT OFTEN WE ARE COMFORTABLE BECAUSE OTHERS ARE POOR. HAVE MERCY.
   L: God, you send us prophets.
   C: WE PUT THEM IN PRISON AND MAKE THEM SAINTS AFTER THEY DIE. HAVE MERCY.

+ + + + + + + +

9. God, I so want to be an instrument of your peace
       But instead I am a weapon for war.
   Forgive me.
       My hatred, jealousy, anger and resentment fester
       And the powers that lead to war are increased.
   God, I so want to be a beacon of your hope
       But instead I am a fog of despair.
   Forgive me.
       My insecurity, fear, and depression erupt
       And my hope is quenched in sadness.
   God, I so want to be your person
       But instead I let other forces control me.
   Help me I pray. Amen.

+ + + + + + + +

CARE

170

10. Almost 2000 years ago John the Baptist confessed that he did not
recognize the Christ. We must confess the same. In the hungry
of the world, in the homeless and jobless, in all who long for love
and ache for justice, we have not recognized the Christ. For the
past we ask your pardon, God. And for the future we ask your
help - that we may see Jesus' face and touch his body in our
sisters and brothers. Amen.

+ + + + + + + +

11. O God, we confess that while we like to believe ourselves to be modern
people who are "with it," we are often afraid of change. We know that
Christ calls us to be transformers of the world and yet too often in our
insecurity we are merely protectors of the status quo. Help us to
understand that the process of salvation only takes place in our lives
and in the world as we allow ourselves to be open to creative change.
Amen.

+ + + + + + + +

12. O God, we admit that often we allow our fear of freedom to overpower
our desire for freedom. It is usually so easy to choose the safe and
secure even if this may shrivel our lives and shrink our conscience.
We admit, too, that even when we seek after freedom we often misunder-
stand what it is. We confuse it with license and think that to be free is
to be wildly irresponsible. Help us, God, to discover the reality of
freedom in you. In the name of the Christ we pray. Amen.

+ + + + + + + +

13. God, we come before you as people who have often been afraid to risk
ourselves in full-fledged obedience to your Word. We have heard your
call to love unconditionally but have preferred to interpret that call to
include only certain persons at convenient times. We have heard your
call to lose our lives for others, but have preferred to interpret this
call as requiring only an occasional symbolic gesture of concern for
someone in need. We confess before you today that we have failed in
our vocation as Christians and that we desperately need your help if we
are to be faithful to your Word. In Jesus' name we pray. Amen.

+ + + + + + + +

14. God, we sometimes get discouraged. Our tasks seem so huge and
our resources so small. We get weary. We wonder if our lives
really make any difference. Help us to understand that even you
get disheartened and that Jesus faced profound disappointments in
his ministry. Give us the power to keep on in the midst of depression.
Amen.

+ + + + + + + +

WORDS OF ASSURANCE

L=leader
C=congregation

*1. L: There is no sin so terrible that God's love cannot forgive.
In the name of Jesus Christ your sins are forgiven.
C: THERE IS NO SIN SO TERRIBLE THAT GOD'S LOVE CANNOT
FORGIVE. IN THE NAME OF JESUS CHRIST YOUR SINS ARE
FORGIVEN.

+ + + + + + + +

*2. L: Jesus said, "Neither do I condemn you; go and do not sin again"
(John 8:11b). Our life is given back to us with hope.
C: EVERY DAY IS AN OPPORTUNITY TO DECIDE AGAIN THAT THIS
DAY SHALL NOT BE LIKE THE OTHERS.
L: That a new person is being created at this moment, free from the
past, with the future open.
C: WE HAVE BEEN FREED TO LIVE FULLY IN THE PRESENT;
THAT'S THE GOOD NEWS OF THE GOSPEL.

+ + + + + + + +

*3. L: A sparrow falters.
C: LIFE GOES ON.
L: A sparrow falls.
C: CREATION'S CASTOFFS.
L: Yet forever received and affirmed.
C: EVEN THE SPARROW FINDS A HOME.
L: You are accepted.
C: ACCEPTED BY THAT WHICH IS GREATER THAN OURSELVES.
L: Do not ask for the name now.
C: DO NOT TRY TO DO ANYTHING NOW.
L: Do not seek for anything, perform anything, intend anything.
C: SIMPLY ACCEPT THE FACT THAT WE ARE ACCEPTED.
L: Forever received and affirmed.
C: EVEN THE SPARROW FINDS A HOME.

+ + + + + + + +

*4. L: Listen! Here is good news: Jesus said, "I will never turn away
anyone who comes to me" (John 6:37B TEV). He has come to
forgive you in your failure.
Women: To accept you as you are,
Men: To set you free,
ALL: AND TO MAKE YOU WHAT YOU WERE MEANT TO BE.

+ + + + + + + +

172

*5. L: I am commissioned to proclaim to you the most glorious fact
       of the universe.
    C: WE'RE ALL EARS. LET US HEAR IT.
    L: The Creator of the universe loves you no matter what.
    C: NO MATTER WHAT?
    L: No matter what, God still loves you in fullness and splendor.
    C: WITH THIS GREAT GOOD NEWS, WE ARE INSPIRED TO BEGIN
       AGAIN. WHATEVER HAS BEEN WRONG IN OUR LIVES, WE NOW
       HAVE A CHANCE TO BEGIN TO MAKE IT RIGHT. ALLELUIA!

+ + + + + + + +

6. L: God says, "There is nothing you can do to make me stop loving you."
   C: WHEN THE TRUTH OF THOSE WORDS BREAKS THROUGH, WE
      ARE TRANSFORMED.
   L: You are accepted and loved as you are. You don't have to carry around
      the guilty burdens of the past.
   C: WE ARE A NEW CREATION THROUGH THE POWERFUL PRESENCE
      OF GOD'S CONSTANT LOVE.

+ + + + + + + +

7. L: To "own up" to our problems and mistakes means we are opening
      ourselves to new possibilities in our lives.
   C: THE DOOR IS THERE. WE MUST WALK THROUGH.
   L: The one who says "I am the door" now says "Come in."
   C: WE TOOK THE FIRST STEP WITH OUR CONFESSION. OUR SECOND
      STEP IS LISTENING WITH OUR WHOLE BEINGS TO THE FACT OF
      OUR FORGIVENESS.
   L: "Neither do I condemn you. Go and sin no more."

+ + + + + + + +

8. Women: The music of forgiveness is our lifesong.
   Men: Without it our lives would be doused in despair.
   Women: They are words we need to hear over and over again.
   Men: Because we forget, because our lives go wrong, because we
          become so easily discouraged.
   Women: God never gives up on you. God's love for you is eternal.
   Men: God never gives up on you. God's love for you is eternal.
   ALL: ALLELUIA!

+ + + + + + + +

9. L: We only appreciate the miracle of a sunrise when we have waited in
      darkness.
   C: WE HAVE JUST CONFESSED SOME OF THE DARKNESS OF OUR LIVES.
   L: And now the sunrise - God loves you no matter what.
   C: DAYBREAK. ALLELUIA!

+ + + + + + + +

SCRIPTURE READINGS

Old Testament

L=left
R=right

*1. Psalm 8   (a paraphrase) (to be read in unison)
O God, our God,
Your greatness is seen in all the world!
Your glory reaches to the heavens,
Even children and babies sing your praise.
You have built a fortress because of your foes,
to still the enemy and the revengeful.

When I look at the sky, the work of your fingers,
at the moon and the stars, which you have made–
What are we, that you think of us;
And our children, that you should care for them?

Yet you made us but a little less than you yourself;
And you crowned us with glory and honor!
You made us rulers over all you have made;
You gave us responsibility for all things:
sheep and cattle, and wild animals too;
the birds and the fish,
and all the creatures in the seas.
God, our God,
your greatness is seen in all the world.

+ + + + + + + +

2. Psalm 23   (a paraphrase)
L: God, you are my shepherd;
I have everything I need.
R: You let me rest in the green meadows
and lead me to the refreshing waters.
L: You give me new strength
and guide me in the right paths.
Your name is thus held in honor.
R: Even if I go through the darkest valley
I will not be afraid, for you are with me.
Your shepherd's rod and staff comfort me.
L: You prepare a table for me
in the very presence of my enemies.
R: You anoint my head with oil;
My cup overflows.
ALL: GOODNESS AND KINDNESS SHALL PURSUE ME
EVERY DAY OF MY LIFE:
AND I SHALL LIVE IN YOUR HOUSE TILL THE END OF MY DAYS.

+ + + + + + + +

174

(Old Testament cont. L=leader; C=congregation)

3. Psalm 103:1-12   (a paraphrase)
   L: My soul blesses God;
   C: MY WHOLE BEING CRIES OUT, "BLESS YOUR HOLY NAME!"
   L: My soul blesses God;
   C: AND REMEMBERS ALL GOD'S MARVELOUS GRACE:
   L: in forgiving all my sins,
   C: IN HEALING ALL MY DISEASES,
   L: in rescuing me from the pit of death,
   C: AND IN SURROUNDING ME WITH STEADFAST LOVE,
   L: in filling my years with goodness,
   C: IN RENEWING MY YOUTH LIKE AN EAGLE'S.
   L: God, who does what is right,
   C: IS ALWAYS ON THE SIDE OF THE OPPRESSED:
   L: God showed tender love to Moses,
   C: AND GOD'S ACTS WERE REVEALED TO THE PEOPLE OF ISRAEL.
   L: God is tender and caring,
   C: SLOW TO BECOME ANGRY, AND FULL OF CONSTANT LOVE.
   L: God does not keep on reprimanding.
   C: GOD'S ANGER EXISTS ONLY FOR A SHORT TIME,
   L: God has not treated us as our sins deserve
   C: OR PUNISHED US AS OUR MISDEEDS SUGGEST.
   L: For as high as the sky is above the earth,
   C: SO GOD'S STRONG LOVE ARCHES HIGH OVER ALL WHO STAND
      IN AWE OF THEIR CREATOR.
   L: As far as the east is from the west
   C: SO FAR HAS GOD REMOVED OUR SINS FROM US.

+ + + + + + + +

4. Psalm 142   (a paraphrase)
   L: Help, God, I need you!
   C: I MUST POUR OUT MY TROUBLES BEFORE YOU.
   L: I know that when I am ready to quit
   C: YOU KNOW WHAT I SHOULD DO.
   L: I feel trapped by my enemies.
   C: NOBODY SEEMS TO CARE ABOUT ME,
   L: But you, God, are my refuge,
   C: YOU ARE ALL I HAVE IN THE LAND OF THE LIVING.
   L: Hear my cry for I am sunk in despair.
   C: RESCUE ME FROM MY ENEMIES.
   L: They are too strong for me,
   C: SET ME FREE FROM MY PRISONS
   L: that I may shout thanks to your name!
   C: LOVING AND RIGHTEOUS PEOPLE WILL SURROUND ME
   L: As you help me through this terrible time.

+ + + + + + + +

(Old Testament cont. L=left; R=right)

5.   Psalm 150 (a paraphrase) (to be read in joyous unison)
    Praise God everywhere! Praise God in churches, in heaven and
earth, for God's mighty deeds and marvelous greatness! Praise God
with trumpets, harps, lyres, drums, dancing, flutes, cymbals, and
all things that express joy. Let everything that breathes praise God.
PRAISE BE TO GOD!!!

+ + + + + + + +

6.   Isaiah 35:1-10 (a paraphrase)
   L: The wilderness and the dry land shall be glad,
      the desert shall rejoice and bloom,
   R: It shall bloom forth with wild flowers,
      with bright jonquils.
   L: It shall sing and shout for joy.
   R: The desert will be as glorious as Lebanon,
      its splendor like the fertile fields
      of Carmel and Sharon.
   L: Everyone shall see God's glory,
      the splendor of our Creator.

   R: Give strength to tired hands,
      steady all trembling knees,
   L: Tell those who are downhearted,
      "Have courage! Don't be afraid.
   R: God is coming to your rescue
      and your enemies will not overtake you."

   L: Then the eyes of the blind will see
      and the ears of the deaf will hear.
   R: The lame will leap like the deer
      and those who can't speak will
      sing for joy.
   L: Rivers of water will flow through the desert;
      The burning sand will become a great lake,
      and the dry land will gush forth with water.
   R: Where jackals used to live
      will grow reeds and rushes.

   L: Through the desert will run a highway,
      called "The Road of Holiness,"
   R: And on it shall no sinner walk
      nor fools stray along it.
   L: No lions shall be there;
      no fierce animals roam upon it.
   R: But the redeemed will travel down that way,
      those rescued by God shall return on that road.
ALL: THEY WILL COME TO ZION WITH SINGING,
    AND WITH EVERLASTING JOY ON THEIR FACES;
    GLADNESS AND JOY WILL GO WITH THEM,
    AND THEY WILL BE FOREVER FREE FROM SORROW AND GRIEF.

+ + + + + + + +

176

(Old Testament cont. L=leader; C=congregation)

7. Isaiah 40:28-31 (a paraphrase)
   L: Don't you know? Haven't you heard?
   Our God is everlasting
   The Creator of all the world.
   C: OUR GOD NEVER GROWS TIRED OR WEARY;
   THE THOUGHTS OF THE CREATOR ARE SO DEEP
   THAT NO ONE CAN FATHOM THEM.
   L: In God the weak and tired find power and strength.
   C: EVEN THE YOUNG MAY BECOME WEAK AND STUMBLE.
   L: But those who trust in the Creator
   will find their weakness turned to strength.
   ALL: THEY SHALL RISE ON WINGS LIKE EAGLES;
   THEY SHALL RUN AND NOT BE WEARY;
   THEY SHALL WALK AND NEVER TIRE.

+ + + + + + + +

SCRIPTURE READINGS

New Testament

1. The Beautitudes (Matthew 5:3-11, a paraphrase)
   L: Joy-filled are those who know their need of God;
   C: FOR HEAVEN IS THEIRS.
   L: Joy-filled are those who are sorrowful for their sins;
   C: FOR THEY SHALL BE COMFORTED.
   L: Joy-filled are those of gentle, caring spirit;
   C: FOR THE WHOLE EARTH IS THEIRS.
   L: Joy-filled are those who actively long for justice;
   C: FOR THEY SHALL BE SATISFIED.
   L: Joy-filled are the merciful;
   C: FOR THEY SHALL HAVE MERCY SHOWN TO THEM.
   L: Joy-filled are those who have integrity;
   C: FOR THEY SHALL SEE GOD.
   L: Joy-filled are those who strive for just peace;
   C: FOR THEY SHALL BE CALLED THE SONS AND DAUGHTERS
   OF GOD.
   L: Joy-filled are those who are persecuted in the cause of right.
   C: FOR GOD'S REIGN IS THEIRS.

+ + + + + + + +

(New Testament cont.   L=leader; C=congregation)

2. Matthew 6:9-13   (a paraphrase)   (to be prayed in unison)
    Our God in heaven,
    Holy be your name.
    May your reign come,
        and your will be done on earth
        as it is in heaven.
    Give us today the food we need.
    Forgive us the wrongs we have done
        as we forgive those who
        have wronged us.
    And do not put us to the test
        but save us from the evil one.
    Amen.

                    + + + + + + + +

3. Recognizing Christ (Luke 7:18-23) (a paraphrase)
    L: John sent two of his disciples to ask Jesus,
        "Are you the expected one, or are we to look for
        someone else?"
    C: THERE AND THEN JESUS CURED MANY SUFFERERS OF
        DISEASES, PLAGUES, AND EVIL SPIRITS. AND HE GAVE
        THE GIFT OF SIGHT TO MANY WHO WERE BLIND.
    L: Then Jesus answered John's disciples,
        "Go back and tell John what you have seen and heard --
    C: THE BLIND SEE AGAIN,
    L: the lame walk,
    C: LEPERS ARE CLEANSED,
    L: the deaf hear,
    C: THE DEAD ARE RAISED TO LIFE,
    L: the poor are hearing the good news.
    C: HAPPY IS THE ONE WHO DOES NOT LOSE FAITH IN ME.

                    + + + + + + + +

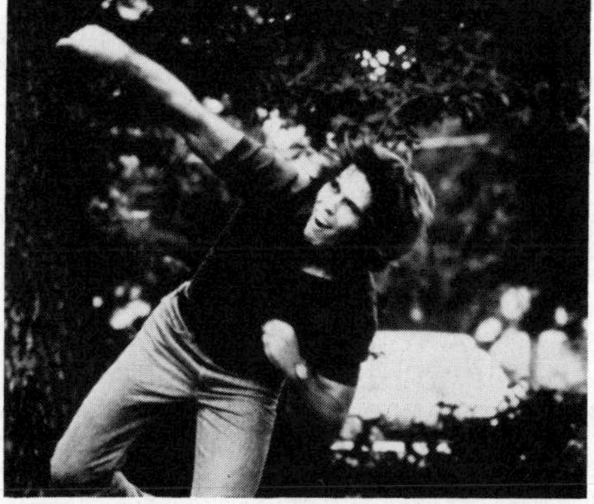

Brian Braye

(New Testament cont.)

4. Jesus' encounter with a Samaritan Woman (Selections from John 4:1-42)
(a paraphrase)

L: (Jesus left Judea and headed for Galilee, which meant he had to pass
through a Samaritan town. When Jesus reached the well of this town
it was about midday. He was tired and sat down beside the well. Soon
a Samaritan woman arrived to draw some water. Jesus asked her,)

Men: Would you give me a drink?

Women: What! You, a Jew, ask a drink of me, a Samaritan woman?

Men: If you only knew the gift God has for you and who I am, you would
have asked me for living water.

Women: You don't even have a bucket and this well is deep. How can you
give me "living water?" Are you greater than our ancestor Jacob,
who gave us this well?

Men: Everyone who drinks the water from this well gets thirsty again.
But those who drink the water that I give will never thirst because
the water that I give will be like an inner spring always welling up
to eternal life.

Women: Sir, give me this water so that I may stop being thirsty and not have
to come all this way to get water any more.

L: (Jesus shows the woman that he knows her present and past history.
She has been married five times and is now living with a sixth man.
The woman is struck by Jesus' knowledge of her and by his authori-
tative yet caring way of speaking. She senses the worship dimension
of their encounter, but she is puzzled because she has learned that
Jews such as Jesus believe that people should worship in Jerusalem,
not in a Samaritan town. She asks Jesus about this and he responds,)

Men: Believe me, woman, the time is coming when you will worship God
neither on this mountain nor in Jerusalem. You Samaritans worship
what you do not know; we Jews worship what we do know for it is from
the Jews that salvation comes. But the time is coming, in fact it is
already here, when true worshippers will worship God in spirit and in
truth. God wants such worshippers for God is spirit and those who
worship must worship in spirit and in truth.

Women: I know that the Messiah, the Christ, is coming and will tell us
everything.

Men: I am Christ speaking to you now.

L: (At this point his disciples return and are surprised to find him talk-
ing to a woman. The woman leaves her water jar and excitedly
hurries back to town to tell the people,)

Women: Come and see someone who has told me everything I ever did.
Could this be the Christ?

L: (Many Samaritans came to believe in Jesus because of this woman's
testimony. Although they came to see him because of her, they left
saying to her,)

C: IT IS NO LONGER BECAUSE OF WHAT YOU SAID THAT WE
BELIEVE, BECAUSE WE HAVE HEARD JESUS OURSELVES AND
WE KNOW THAT HE IS IN TRUTH THE SAVIOUR OF THE WORLD!

(New Testament cont.   L=leader; C=congregation)

5.   Romans 8:31b–32, 35, 37–39 (a paraphrase)
L: If God is for us, who can finally be against us?
C: GOD DID NOT EVEN SPARE JESUS, BUT GAVE HIM UP FOR
US ALL.   SUCH AN ACT OF PROFOUND UNSELFISHNESS IS
A SIGN OF GOD'S LAVISH LOVE THAT PROVIDES US WITH
ALL THAT WE NEED.
L: Nothing, therefore, can separate us from the love of Christ;
not troubles or pain or persecution, not even lack of clothes
or food, not even threats of violence or death.
C: FOR I AM ABSOLUTELY CONVINCED OF THIS: NEITHER DEATH
NOR LIFE, NEITHER SUPERNATURAL NOR GOVERNMENTAL
POWER, NOTHING THAT EXISTS AND NOTHING STILL TO COME,
NO POWER, NO HEIGHT OR DEPTH OR ANY CREATED THING
CAN EVER COME BETWEEN US AND THE LOVE GOD MADE
VISIBLE IN CHRIST JESUS.

+ + + + + + + +

6.   Advice to Christians (Romans 12:9–18, 21 a paraphrase)
L: Don't pretend to love others, really love them!
C: HATE WHAT IS EVIL AND HAVE REAL DEVOTION FOR WHAT
IS GOOD.
L: Love each other as part of the same family.
C: HAVE A PROFOUND RESPECT FOR ONE ANOTHER.
L: Don't let yourself get exhausted working for God. Be aglow with
the Spirit.
C: HOPE CAN KEEP YOU JOYFUL.
L: When you are in trouble you can stand firm as you persist in
prayer. If any of God's people are in need,
C: SHARE WITH THEM, MAKING HOSPITALITY YOUR SPECIAL
CARE.
L: Bless those who persecute you.
C: LAUGH WITH THOSE WHO REJOICE AND BE SORROWFUL
WITH THOSE WHO WEEP.
L: Treat everyone with equal kindness.
C: THIS MEANS YOU CAN'T BE CONDESCENDING; BE REAL
FRIENDS WITH THE POOR.
L: Don't become set in your own opinions.
C: NEVER REPAY EVIL FOR EVIL BUT LET EVERYONE SEE
THAT YOU ARE COMMITTED TO THE HIGHEST IDEALS.
DO ALL YOU CAN TO LIVE AT PEACE WITH EVERYONE.
L: Or in summary,
C: INSTEAD OF LETTING EVIL CONQUER YOU, CONQUER
EVIL WITH GOOD.

+ + + + + + + +

(New Testament cont. L=leader; C=congregation)

7.   Ephesians 2:14-19 (a paraphrase by Peggy Ruth Scharff, used by permission)

   ALL: CHRIST IS THE PERMANENT PEACE TREATY BETWEEN
        ALL PEOPLE.
   L: God's sacrifice of Jesus Christ has made peace possible between
       the advantaged and the disadvantaged people, thus tearing down
       the wall of hatred in one dramatic act.
   C: NOW ANYONE, ANYWHERE, CAN BE A PART OF GOD'S FANTASTIC
       REIGN WHETHER HE OR SHE IS BLACK OR WHITE, DEMOCRAT
       OR REPUBLICAN, MALE OR FEMALE, UGLY OR BEAUTIFUL,
       RUSSIAN OR AMERICAN, SICK OR WELL, YOUNG OR OLD, FOR
       IT MAKES NO DIFFERENCE TO THE MAKER.
   L: It is not important what one's origin or nationality or human form
       is, for the Creator does not care.
   C: EACH ONE OF US CAN BE A CHILD OF GOD AND BE AN
       INTRICATE AND SPECIAL PART OF THE HEAVENLY PARENT'S
       HUGE AND LOVING FAMILY. A PASSPORT IS NO LONGER
       NEEDED, NOR FOR THAT MATTER CAN IT EVEN BE USED,
       TO ENTER GOD'S MAGNIFICENT REIGN.
   ALL: JESUS CHRIST HAS SHOWED US ONCE AND FOR ALL THAT
        GOD'S LOVE WELCOMES EVERYONE AND BINDS US TOGETHER
        IN A UNITY OF LOVE. ALLELUIA! AMEN.

+ + + + + + + +

8.   Ephesians 4:11-16 (a paraphrase to be read together in unison)

   And Christ's gifts were that some should be apostles, some
prophets, some evangelists, some pastors and teachers so that
the saints together make a unity in the work of service, building
up the body of Christ. Thus all of us are to come to unity in our
faith and knowledge of Christ until we reach full personhood, the
maturity of Christ. We are not meant to be children tossed about
with every wind of doctrine, by the cunning of deceitful persons.
Rather, speaking the truth in love, we are called to grow up in
every way into the one who is the head, into Christ, from whom
the whole body, every joint adding its own particular strength,
grows until it has built itself up in love.

+ + + + + + + +

BUILD UP THE BODY IN LOVE

(New Testament cont. L=leader; C=congregation)

9. I John 4:7-12, 16b-21 (a paraphrase)
    L: Dear friends, let us love one another for love comes straight
        from God.
    C: FOR THOSE WHO LOVE ARE GOD'S CHILDREN AND KNOW GOD.
    L: God's love was manifested among us when God sent Jesus into
        the world so that we might discover the meaning of life through
        Christ.
    C: GOD'S LOVE IS PRIMARY. ALL LOVE FLOWS FROM THE
        TRUTH OF GOD'S LOVE IN CHRIST. THIS LOVE HAS THE
        POWER TO BRING FORGIVENESS TO US ALL.
    L: Friends, if this is how God loved us, then we should love one
        another in the same way.
    C: NO ONE HAS EVER SEEN GOD, BUT IF WE LOVE ONE ANOTHER,
        GOD LIVES IN US AND CHRIST'S LOVE IS MADE PERFECT IN US.
    L: God is love; those who live in love live in God and God lives in
        them.
    C: THUS WE HAVE COURAGE AS WE FACE THE JUDGEMENT BECAUSE
        OUR LIFE IN THIS WORLD IS STRENGTHENED BY CHRIST.
    L: There is no fear in love; perfect love drives out all fear. Fear is
        brought about by punishment, but if we are perfected in love, we
        no longer worry about punishment.
    C: WE LOVE BECAUSE GOD FIRST LOVED US.
    L: If any one says, "I love God," but hates sister or brother,
        that person is a liar.
    C: IF WE DO NOT LOVE OUR SISTER OR BROTHER WHOM WE SEE,
        WE CANNOT LOVE GOD WHOM WE DO NOT SEE. THIS,THEN,IS
        THE COMMANDMENT CHRIST GAVE US: WE WHO LOVE GOD
        MUST LOVE OUR SISTERS AND BROTHERS TOO.

+ + + + + + + +

10. I Peter 2:9-10 (a paraphrase)
    L: You are a chosen race, a royal priesthood, a holy nation,
        God's "peculiar people." All the old titles of God's people
        now belong to you. Yours also is the responsibility to sing
        the praises of God who has called you out of darkness into
        the light of the Spirit.
    C: ONCE WE WERE NOT A PEOPLE AT ALL, BUT NOW WE
        ARE THE PEOPLE OF GOD; ONCE WE HAD NO EXPERIENCE
        OF GOD'S MERCY, BUT NOW IT IS INTIMATELY OURS.

+ + + + + + + +

CHOSEN FOR SERVICE

182

AFFIRMATIONS OF FAITH

L=Leader
C=Congregation

*1.   We believe that God was in love with the world and could not keep
        the secret.
      The telling of it was CREATION.
      We believe that God's love is constantly being shown as creation and
        continues and continues and continues every moment of every day.
      We believe that Jesus is our window to divinity and our mirror of
        humanity. Through Jesus we find God's love for us fully revealed
        and we discover that God's will for us is that we love one another
        in full humanness.
      We find God's presence of love with us in the Holy Spirit which often
        speaks to us in voices of other people. Therefore we affirm that
        openness to God and openness to other humans are two sides of the
        same coin and that really listening to others can help us hear God.
      We believe that God never gives up on us and that nothing can separate
        us from God's love.
      Alleluia! Amen.

+ + + + + + + +

*2.   L: Let us affirm together why we worship, for in saying this we will
         also be affirming our faith.
      C: WE WORSHIP TO REVEAL OURSELVES TO GOD AND TO EACH
         OTHER, TO LOOK FOR WHAT WE HAVE LOST, TO GLUE TO-
         GETHER BROKEN PIECES OF LIFE, TO REFIT THE SCATTERED
         JIGSAW PUZZLES OF OUR LIVES AND THE WORLD'S LIFE, TO
         RENEW OUR VISION OF THE LIFE OF JESUS CHRIST, THAT WE
         MIGHT KNOW MORE SHARPLY AND UNMISTAKABLY WHAT CHRIST'S
         WAY REALLY MEANS, TO SEEK TO GET THE POINT OF THE
         GREATEST DRAMA ON EARTH, TO FIND OUR OWN ROLES AND
         LEARN OUR OWN LINES FROM THE DIRECTOR OF ALL HISTORY.

+ + + + + + + +

*3.   We believe that God never gives up on us.
      We believe that Jesus was God in human form who showed us the
        astounding steadfastness of God's love for us.
      We believe God's Holy Spirit is always with us
        even in times of deep suffering and sorrow.
      We know that God's love for us continues
        and continues
                    and continues.

+ + + + + + + +

(Affirmations cont. L=leader; C=congregation)

*4. We believe that God still is creating and that we are called to
   join in this creation.
  We believe that God does not love us because Christ died for us,
   but that Christ died for us because God loved us. And Christ
   continues to die for us today.
  We believe that God's Holy Spirit of love still sets undeserving people
   free and that God calls us to help in this task of liberation.
  We believe that "the Church" is a chosen people, not chosen for its
   own sake, but to be servants of God for the sake of the world.
  We believe that God's love is something that will never give up on
   us, and so we approach the future with confidence.

+ + + + + + + +

*5.   We believe in the infinite worth of every human being. We believe
   that our worth is ultimately derived not by what others think of us or
   even by what we think of ourselves, but by what God thinks of us. We
   affirm that God loves each of us with a richness and depth that is beyond
   our wildest imaginings.
     We believe that every human being falters and fails at times and needs
   the forgiving love of God to keep going. We know that each of us becomes
   deadened to our world and our brothers and sisters, and so we need the
   enlivening power of God's Holy Spirit to be with us bringing us alive inside.
     Each of us faces the terrifying unknown we call death. And that is why
   God's promise of eternal life sealed in Jesus holds out so much hope to us.
   We know that even though our lives may be filled with great trouble and
   sorrow that God never deserts us, never gives up on us. With this faith
   firm in our hearts we can shout with the saints of all the ages. Alleluia!

+ + + + + + + +

*6. L: We are the people of God.
    C: OUR LIVES ARE ETERNALLY SIGNIFICANT.
    L: We are the people of the resurrection.
    C: WE ARE FREE TO LIVE TO LIFE, AND NOT TO DEATH.
    L: We are the people of the covenant.
    C: WE LIVE OUR LIVES IN COMMITMENT.
    L: We are a people of koinonia.
    C: WE LIVE IN MUTUAL LOVE AND SUPPORT.
    L: We are the sons and daughters of God.
    C: WE LIVE AS A FAMILY WITH ALL BOYS AND GIRLS, MEN
       AND WOMEN EVERYWHERE.

+ + + + + + + +

184

(Affirmations cont. L=leader; C=congregation

*7. I believe in the love of God revealed in Jesus Christ.
I believe that behind the clouds of life shines the love of God.
I believe that God has a purpose for the world and a purpose for me.
I believe that God wills the blessedness of all lives and of every single
life.
I believe that Jesus Christ saves life from the power of sin and sorrow
and death.
I believe in the life-giving power and grace of the Holy Spirit.
I believe that through faith and prayer and sacrament I can live the
life which is life indeed.
I believe that God calls me to love and service.
I believe that through Christ, life leads at last to the fullness of
goodness, truth, and beauty.
I believe in the grace of Jesus Christ and the love of God and the
communion of the Holy Spirit.

+ + + + + + + +

8. We believe in God the Creator and Deliverer,
who made and continues to make the heavens and the earth,
who kept the promise to Abraham and Sarah that they would
parent the community of faith,
who delivered Israel from slavery in Egypt to the promised land,
who protected Jerusalem under the line of David,
who chastised the people in captivity in Babylon,
who delivered them again to rebuild the Temple and look for
the Messiah.

We believe in Jesus Christ the Redeemer and the Word,
who was in the beginning with God.
who was born in a human being,
who preached the good news, forgave sins, fed the hungry,
and healed the sick,
who suffered death on a cross and was laid in the tomb,
who arose from the grave and ascended into heaven,
who has brought and will bring the New Age.

We believe in the Holy Spirit the Sanctifier and Sustainer,
who moved on the waters at creation and continues as the
Giver and Nourisher of life,
who guided Israel through the wilderness and under the judges,
who spoke judgment and promise through the prophets,
who descended on Jesus at his baptism,
who empowered the Apostles at Pentecost,
who guides the universal church as we look for the
world to come. Amen.

(by Harvey Estes, used by permission)

+ + + + + + + +

(Affirmations cont.)

9. Declaration of Interdependence

Let it be declared, announced,
   and hereby celebrated...
That all people everywhere
   are dependent upon one another.
That everyone needs everyone else
   for freedom, life, love, and happiness.
That all things in the natural order
   are dependent upon everything else.
That our little planet and all the planets
   and stars in all the solar systems
   are in a state of mutual dependence
   upon one another.
That this universally shared dependence
   comes from God and is of God.
And that each individual part
   of this great relationship
   has its own part to play-
   its own destiny to fulfill
   in God's plan.

© 1976 Gerald M. Knoll
Reprinted with permission from
Abbey Press, St. Meinrad, Indiana

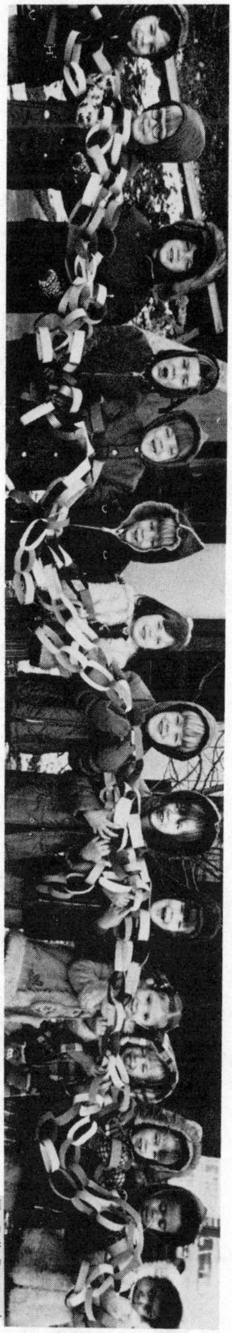

The Daily Pantagraph

ACTS OF DEDICATION

(L=leader; C=congregation)

*1.   L: Our message is that God was reconciling all persons through
        Christ, not counting their trespasses against them.
      C: AND ENTRUSTING TO US THE MESSAGE OF RECONCILIATION.
        SO WE ARE AMBASSADORS FOR CHRIST; GOD APPEALING TO
        NEEDY HUMANITY THROUGH US (II Corinthians 5:19, 20 adapted).
        IN A BROKEN WORLD WHERE WE HAVE NOTHING TO LOSE BUT
        EVERYTHING, WE ACCEPT WITH HUMILITY AND AWE THIS
        INVITATION TO BE AGENTS OF CHRIST'S RECONCILING LOVE
        IN THE WORLD.

+ + + + + + + + +

*2.   L: There is so much to be done. "Dedication" means deciding to
        be the one to do it.
      C: BECAUSE GOD LOVES US, WE CAN KNOW WHAT IT IS TO LOVE
        OTHERS. LET US GO FORTH BOLDLY INTO THE WORLD,
        OBEDIENTLY, DECISIVELY, LOVINGLY, JOYFULLY, TO
        BRING GOD'S PEACE AND LIFE TO ALL.

+ + + + + + + + +

*3.   L: The God of all history needs and calls us to be agents of love.
        We are sent into the world to be concerned and caring people.
      C: SEND US, GOD. SEND US NEXT DOOR, INTO THE NEXT ROOM,
        TO SPEAK SOMEHOW TO A HUMAN HEART BEATING ALONG-
        SIDE OURS. SEND US TO BE BEARERS OF DIGNITY IN A SUB-
        HUMAN, HOPELESS SITUATION. SEND US TO SHOW JOY IN A
        MOMENT AND A PLACE WHERE THERE HAS BEEN NO JOY
        BUT ONLY THE WILL TO DIE.
        SEND US TO REFLECT YOUR LIGHT IN THE DARKNESS OF
        FUTILITY, HOPELESSNESS, AND THE HORROR OF HUMAN
        CRUELTY. BUT GIVE US YOUR LIGHT, TOO, GOD, IN OUR
        OWN DARKNESS AND NEED. AMEN.

+ + + + + + + +

WE ARE AMBASSADORS FOR CHRIST

187

(Acts of Dedication cont. L=Leader; C=Congregation; R=Right; L=Left)

*4. L: "People who need people are the luckiest people in the world."
     C: WE NEED PEOPLE AND PEOPLE NEED US.
     L: To be a Christian is to be alive to these needs in ourselves and
        others and respond to them.
     C: WELL, LET'S GET BUSY!

+ + + + + + + +

*5. L: This has been a beautiful time together. But has it really made
        any difference?
     C: WE ARE THE ANSWERS TO THAT QUESTION. WE PLEDGE NOW
        TO LIVE OUR LIVES IN SUCH A WAY THAT WE DO MAKE A
        DIFFERENCE FOR GOOD. WE GO FORTH COMMISSIONED TO
        BE GOD'S AGENTS OF LOVE IN THE WORLD.

+ + + + + + + +

6. L: God is always on the side of the oppressed.
    C: WE ARE ONLY AS NEAR TO GOD AS WE ARE FAR FROM THE
      PERSON OR GROUP OR NATION WE LIKE THE LEAST.
    L: Our job is reconciliation with justice.
    C: IT IS NOT EASY.
    L: We will likely never see total victory in our lifetimes.
    C: BUT IT IS OUR JOB.
    L: Go with God's blessing knowing that no matter how rough the going,
      God's love and care is with you.
    C: AMEN.

+ + + + + + + +

7. R: God, we know that you will never forget us.
    L: Help us never to forget you.
    R: Help us to remember you in the midst of our busy routines.
    L: Help us to remember you in the bright moments of joy.
    R: Help us to remember you in the cloudy times of depression.
    ALL: HELP US TO LIVE SO THAT WE REFLECT THE HEALING JOY
       OF YOUR LOVE THROUGHOUT OUR LIVES. AMEN.

+ + + + + + + +

Make a niche for silence in your life or your life will be filled with noise rather than meaning

188

(Acts of Dedication cont.   L=Leader; C=Congregation)

8.   ALL: WE HAVE GIVEN SOME OF OUR MONEY, A LITTLE OF
              OUR TIME, A PART OF OUR SPIRITS IN THIS WORSHIP
              OF GOD.
      L: It all seems so partial, so little, so incomplete.
      C: WE ARE CREATURES OF LIMITS. THERE IS ONLY SO MUCH
         EACH OF US CAN DO AND DOING ONE MORE THING MAY
         UNHINGE SOMETHING ELSE.
      L: And what does that mean for our dedication?
      C: IT MEANS THAT WE CAN PLEDGE TO DO THE BEST WE CAN
         WHILE ACKNOWLEDGING OUR LIMITS. WE MAKE THIS
         DEDICATION IN COMMUNITY BECAUSE WE KNOW THAT WHAT
         ONE OF US CAN'T DO, MAYBE ANOTHER ONE CAN. AND WE
         DO IT BEFORE GOD KNOWING THAT FINALLY WE REST IN
         THIS CREATIVE POWER OF THE UNIVERSE THAT IS BRINGING
         THE WORLD TO UNITY IN LOVE.

                  + + + + + + + + +

9.   (Congregation holds hands)
      L: As we touch one another we are reminded of the loving touches of
         Jesus in his ministry here on earth.
      C: THE BLIND WERE MADE TO SEE, THE LAME TO WALK.
      L: If we are Christ's agents of love in the world, we are called to share
         this same touch. Extend all the power of your love through your hands
         to the persons touching you. God's love is the greatest power of the
         universe. Feel it flow through you with healing.
      C: WE GO FORTH TO SHARE THE LOVING TOUCH. ENERGIZED BY
         THE STRENGTH WE HAVE RECEIVED HERE. ALLELUIA! AMEN.

                  + + + + + + + + +

10.   L: Time is a fragment of eternity.
      C: IT IS THE MOST PRECIOUS GIFT WE CAN GIVE EACH OTHER.
      L: Time to listen.
      C: TIME TO COMFORT AND BE COMFORTED.
      L: Time to cultivate fragile relationships
      C: INTO DURABLE ETERNAL FRIENDSHIPS.
      L: Time to risk rejection..
      C: TIME FOR SILENCE.
      L: Time to share our faith.
      C. WE DEDICATE OURSELVES TO USE THE PRECIOUS GIFT OF TIME
         WITH THE CAREFULNESS WE HAVE JUST DESCRIBED. WE HAVE
         TIME, GOD. HELP US TO USE IT LOVINGLY. AMEN.
         (Based on a poem by Barbara A. Clayton, used by permission.)

                  + + + + + + + + +

(Acts of Dedication cont. L=Leader; C=Congregation; l=left; r=right)

*11. L: Who are you?
      l: WE ARE THE PEOPLE WHO ONCE WERE LOST BUT NOW
         HAVE BEEN FOUND.
      r: WE HAVE BEEN FOUND FOR A PURPOSE. WE HAVE BEEN
         GIVEN A JOB.
    C: IT IS FOR US TO LOVE AS WE HAVE BEEN LOVED, TO DIE AS
      OTHERS HAVE DIED FOR US.
    L: Then go forth to your task in the knowledge of your acceptance before
      God; be present to life as it is given to you; and remember your
      obligation to every creation; in the name of God the Creator, Redeemer
      and Sustainer. God be with you.
    C: AND WITH YOUR SPIRIT.
    L: Amen.
    C: AMEN.

+ + + + + + + +

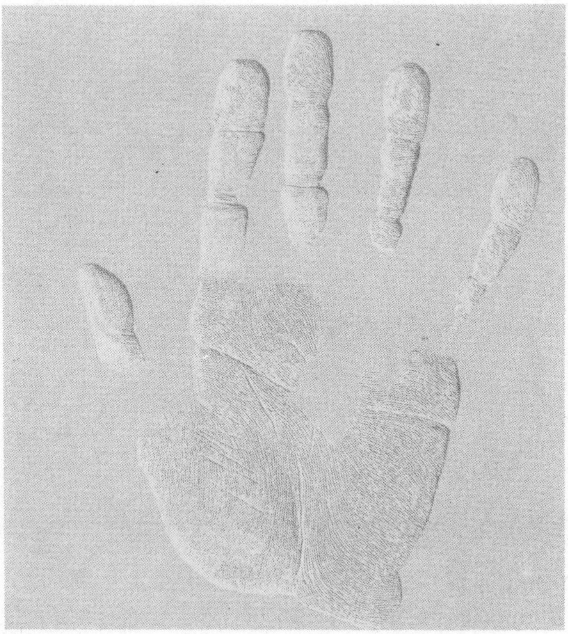

190

BENEDICTIONS

L=leader
C=congregation

*1. L: Go now, remembering what we have done here. Go, remembering
that you are a forgiven people, eternally loved, thoughtfully
instructed, gratefully obedient, responding, and responsible
wherever you are. You can never be the same again.
C: WE KNOW. WE GO TO BE GOD'S PEOPLE IN THE WORLD.
L: May God's peace and joy go with you. So be it.
C: SO BE IT!

+ + + + + + + +

*2. L: Go forth now into a world where apathy and halfheartedness are
dominant. Move the world a little. In the name of God the
Creator, Redeemer, and Sustainer. God be with you.
C: AND WITH YOU.
L: Amen.
C: AMEN.

+ + + + + + + +

*3. L: With your love deep in our hearts,
C: GOD, GO WITH US;
L: With your wisdom to know and understand,
C: GOD, GO WITH US;
L: With your Spirit stirring in our souls,
C: GOD, GO WITH US;
L: With your power to care and share in your world,
C: GOD, GO WITH US TO A NEW DAY. AMEN.

+ + + + + + + +

*4. (to be prayed together in unison)
God is before us.
God is behind us.
God is above us.
God is below us.
God's words shall come from our mouths
For we are God's essence, a sign of God's love.
All is finished in beauty
All is finished in beauty
All is finished in beauty
All is finished in beauty.

(adapted from an ancient Navajo benediction)

+ + + + + + + +

(Benedictions cont. L=Leader; C=Congregation)

5. L: God is a gentle God.
    C: WE ARE TO GO FORTH WITH THIS GENTLENESS IN OUR LIVES.
    L: God is a tender God.
    C: WE SHALL BE KNOWN AS PERSONS OF TENDERNESS.
    L: God is a forgiving God.
    C: WE ARE TO BESTOW THE GIFT OF FORGIVENESS IN OUR
       RELATIONSHIPS WITH OTHERS EACH DAY.
    L: We are made in God's image.
    C: WE ARE TO BE EMBODIERS OF GOD.
    L: God is with you in this joyous, awe-filled commission.
    C: AMEN.

                    + + + + + + + + +

6. AN AFRICAN BENEDICTION -- to be done in pairs following a demonstration
    by two people who are familiar with it.

    (The first person points to her/himself and says:
    THE POWER AND THE GLORY IS IN ME.
    (The second person then does the same.)
    (Hug each other and say together:)
    THE POWER AND THE GLORY IS IN WE.
    (Reach and look upward touching fingertips and say together:)
    THE POWER AND THE GLORY IS IN THEE.
    (Do this benediction with as many people as you wish.)

                    + + + + + + + +

*7. (To be said to one another as the congregation reads in unison)
    TODAY IS THE FIRST DAY OF THE REST OF YOUR LIFE AND
    THE LAST DAY OF THE FIRST OF YOUR LIFE.
    LIVE IT AS BOTH A BEGINNING AND AN END,
    WITH THE HOPE THAT NEW BEGINNINGS BRING,
    WITH THE COMMITMENT THAT ENDINGS DEMAND,
    KNOWING IN ALL YOU DO THAT GOD'S LOVE IS WITH YOU,
    SUSTAINING, SUPPORTING, ENCOURAGING. AMEN.

                    + + + + + + + +

192

(Benedictions cont.   L=leader; C=congregation)

*8. L: May God's grace, mercy, and strength be with you.
    C: AND MAY WE BE INSTRUMENTS OF GOD'S GRACE, MERCY,
        AND STRENGTH TO THE WORLD IN WHICH WE LIVE.
        AMEN.

+ + + + + + + +

9. C: IT IS TIME TO LEAVE, BUT HOW DO WE SAY GOOD-BYE?
    L: We can use the Biblical word shalom. It stands for all aspects
        of human life in its full and God-given maturity: righteousness,
        truth, community, peace, gentleness and love. It summarizes
        all the gifts of the messianic age; even the name of the Messiah
        can simply be shalom (Micah 5:5, Eph. 2:14). It is the best
        that we can wish each other. Shalom my friends.
    C: SHALOM!

+ + + + + + + +

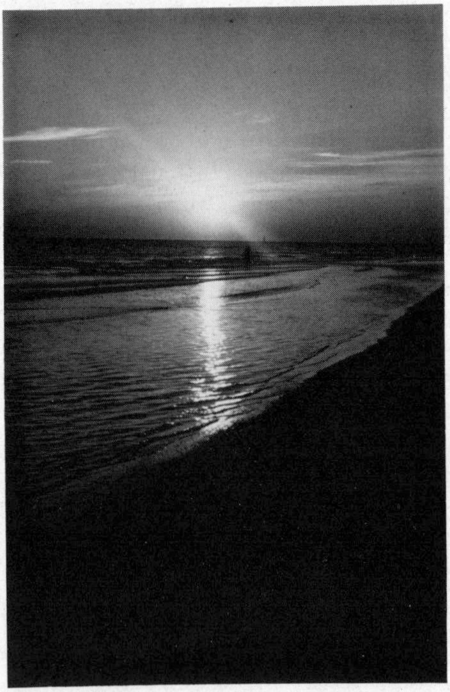

SHALOM

SHALOM

shalom

SHALOM

SHALOM

Cheryl Munn

FOR SPECIAL OCCASIONS

CHRISTMAS

L=Leader
C=Congregation

A CHRISTMAS CALL TO WORSHIP:

L: It was cold, and Mary and Joseph were fearful.
C: BUT THAT DID NOT STOP THE BIRTH.
L: They were poor and had no room waiting for them.
C: BUT THAT DID NOT STOP THE BIRTH.
L: They were uncertain what God wanted from them.
C: BUT THAT DID NOT STOP THE BIRTH.
L: And today we are still sometimes cold and fearful, certainly poor in so many ways and without the rooms we need, and unclear about what God wants of us.
L: BUT THAT NEED NOT STOP THE BIRTH. BE BORN IN US TODAY. AMEN.

+ + + + + + + + + +

CHRISTMAS GENERAL PRAYERS OF CONFESSION:

Forgive us, God, for what we too often do with Christmas. When the day is over we put away Christmas with the left-over wrappings, the tinsel and lights. The hope, the joy, the tenderness are packed off into the attics or the basements of our lives. Envy and suspicions come back, the old humdrum takes over. Don't let it happen this time, God. Remind us of the wonder of Christmas, of the glory of your gift. Keep us celebrating your great love, year around. Keep life gentle, hopeful, festive, always. For Jesus' sake. Amen.

***

God, we look upon our lives and are sorry for our many wrongdoings. We have approached Christ's birthday with selfishness and greed. Too often our concern has been to show off our fine taste through the cards we send and the gifts we give rather than to try to deliver your frightening and marvelous message of love and peace for our world. We have been guilty of being so anxious to please some people that we have treated others -- clerks, store managers, lonely people -- as less than human. Help us to see how your birth calls us to love all people, not just our friends. Help us to be open to the rebirth of your love in our lives this Christmas season. In Christ's name we pray. Amen.

***

194

A CHRISTMAS AFFIRMATION OF FAITH:

I believe in Jesus Christ, and the beauty of the gospel begun in Bethlehem.

I believe in the one whose spirit glorified a little town; and whose spirit still brings music to persons all over the world in towns both large and small.

I believe in the one for whom the crowded inn could find no room, and I confess that my heart still sometimes wants to exclude Christ from my life today.

I believe in the one who the rulers of the earth ignored and the proud could never understand: whose life was among common people, whose welcome came from persons of hungry hearts.

I believe in the one who proclaimed the love of God to be invincible: whose cradle was a mother's arms, whose modest home in Nazareth had love for its only wealth, who looked at persons and made them see what God's love saw in them, who by love brought sinners back to purity, and lifted human weakness up to meet the strength of God,

I confess our ever-lasting need of God: the need of forgiveness for our selfishness and greed, the need of life for empty souls, the need of love for hearts grown cold. Amen.

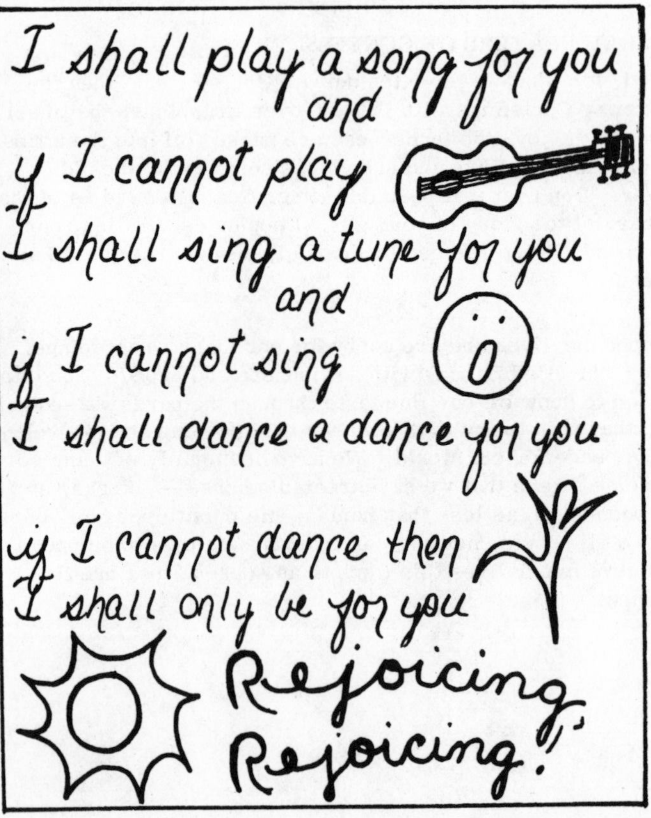

EASTER

AN EASTER CALL TO WORSHIP:
L: Easter began in darkness. It looked as if Christ was dead, love defeated.
C: ROLL THAT STONE AWAY!
L: We sometimes taste this same sense of defeat and despair.
C: ROLL THAT STONE AWAY!
L: But the message of Easter is that all is not lost. The victory has been won. Love has triumphed!
C: THE STONE HAS BEEN ROLLED AWAY AND CHRIST IS RISEN. ALLELUIA!

***

AN EASTER GENERAL PRAYER OF CONFESSION
Ever gentle and loving God, who has brought again from the dead our saviour Jesus Christ, we confess that too often we live as if this resurrection had never taken place. Forgive us for the way in which we allow discouragement and despair to sweep over us and prevent us from being effective agents of your love. Forgive us when we give up hope for anyone no matter who they are or what they have done. Help us to experience the beautiful power of your love that never gives up on any human being -- that power which responded to the dreadful onslaught of evil at the crucifixion with the wonder of the resurrection. Grant us so to die daily to sin that we may evermore live with Jesus Christ in the joy of the resurrection; through Jesus Christ our saviour. Amen.

***

AN EASTER AFFIRMATION OF FAITH:
We believe that resurrection is always possible.
We believe in resurrections because of what we know happened in Jesus.
We see a living faith as witness to Christ's resurrection.
We also affirm other resurrections which have happened.
We know persons who have been turned around in their lives and given a brand new start.
And because of the resurrections we have seen we affirm that
THERE IS NO SUCH THING AS
a hopeless situation
an unredeemable person
a death without eternal life
We look forward to the final resurrection when all the world will be one with God. Amen.

***

AN EASTER BENEDICTION:
L: It is now time for us to leave.
We are each on a journey, a journey homeward, a journey toward a new day.
C: MAY OUR WAY BE A ROAD TO EMMAUS, A ROAD ALONG WHICH WE FIND CHRIST MORE SURELY UNTIL OUR HEARTS GLOW WITH EASTER FAITH. AMEN.

***

Unless otherwise indicated, all items which have an asterisk by them first appeared in Women and Worship: A Guide to Non-Sexist Hymns, Prayers, and Liturgies (Harper and Row, 1974). They are used by permission of the publisher.

GUITAR HELPS

CAPOING: SIMPLIFICATION OF KEYS *

To simplify a key like:

C# : Capo up one fret, play chords in key of C, sounds key of C#
G# : Capo up one fret, play chords in key of G, sounds key of G#
D# : Capo up one fret, play chords in key of D, sounds key of D#
etc.

To simplify the key of:

F : Capo up 1 fret, play chords in key of E, sounds key of F
Capo up 3 frets, play chords in key of D, sounds key of F
Capo up 5 frets, play chords in key of C, sounds key of F

B^b: Capo up 1 fret, play chords in key of A, sounds key of B^b
Capo up 3 frets, play chords in key of G, sounds key of B^b

B : Capo up 2 frets, play chords in key of A, sounds key of B
Capo up 4 frets, play chords in key of G, sounds key of B

E : Capo up 2 frets, play chords in key of D, sounds key of E
Capo up 4 frets, play chords in key of C, sounds key of E

A : Capo up 2 frets, play chords in key of G, sounds key of A
Capo up 5 frets, play chords in key of E, sounds key of A
Capo up 7 frets, play chords in key of D, sounds key of A

F#: Capo up 2 frets, play chords in key of E, sounds key of F#
Capo up 4 frets, play chords in key of D, sounds key of F#
Capo up 6 frets, play chords in key of C, sounds key of F#

* Developed by J. Shepherd Crumrine

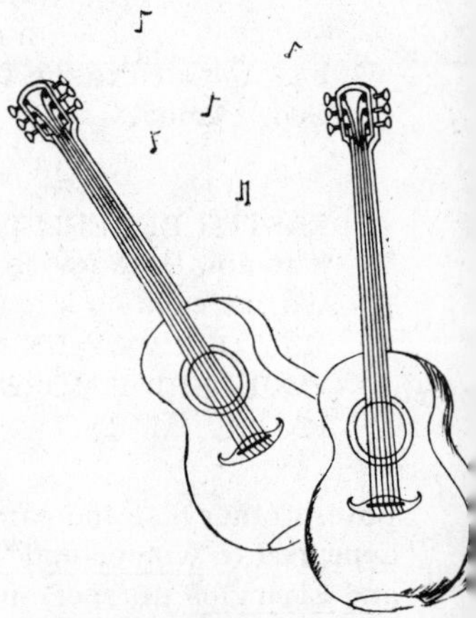

TRANSPOSITION CHART*

Key Signature	I(Key)	II	III	IV	V	VI	VII
	C	Dm	Em	F	G(7)	Am	Bm
##	D	Em	F#m	G	A(7)	Bm	C#m
###	E	F#m	G#m	A	B(7)	C#m	D#m
b	F	Gm	Am	B$\flat$	C(7)	Dm	Em
#	G	Am	Bm	C	D(7)	Em	F#m
##	A	Bm	C#m	D	E(7)	F#m	G#m
####	B	C#m	D#m	E	F#(7)	G#m	A#m
bb	B$\flat$(A#)	Cm	Dm	E$\flat$	F(7)	Gm	Am
bbb	E$\flat$(D#)	Fm	Gm	A$\flat$	B$\flat$(7)	Cm	Dm
bbbb	A$\flat$(G#)	B$\flat$m	Cm	D$\flat$	E$\flat$(7)	Fm	Gm
bbbbb	D$\flat$(C#)	E$\flat$m	Fm	G$\flat$	A$\flat$(7)	B$\flat$m	Cm
bbbbbb	G$\flat$(F#)	A$\flat$m	B$\flat$m	C$\flat$	D$\flat$(7)	E$\flat$m	F
b	Dm	Em/dim F/aug	Gm	A^7	B$\flat$/dim	C dim/C
	Am	Bm/dim C/aug	Dm	E^7	F/dim	G dim/G
#	Em	F#m/dim G/aug	Am	B^7	C /dim	D dim/D

* Developed by J. Shepherd Crumrine

INDEX OF AUTHORS